JOHN DIEBOLD
BREAKING THE CONFINES OF THE POSSIBLE

THE FUTURE MAKERS tells the history of our times through the men of our times.

THE FUTURE MAKERS is a series of books on dynamic younger men who have already contributed to the progress and development of many fields, and whose current achievements hold even greater promise for the future. Each book is biographical in structure, yet at the same time weaves into the man's life story the broader implications of what his attainments and goals are contributing, and will contribute, to our way of life. The individual achievements and pioneering of each man in the series decisively affects current events and movements. As a maker of the future, he is a contributor to history.

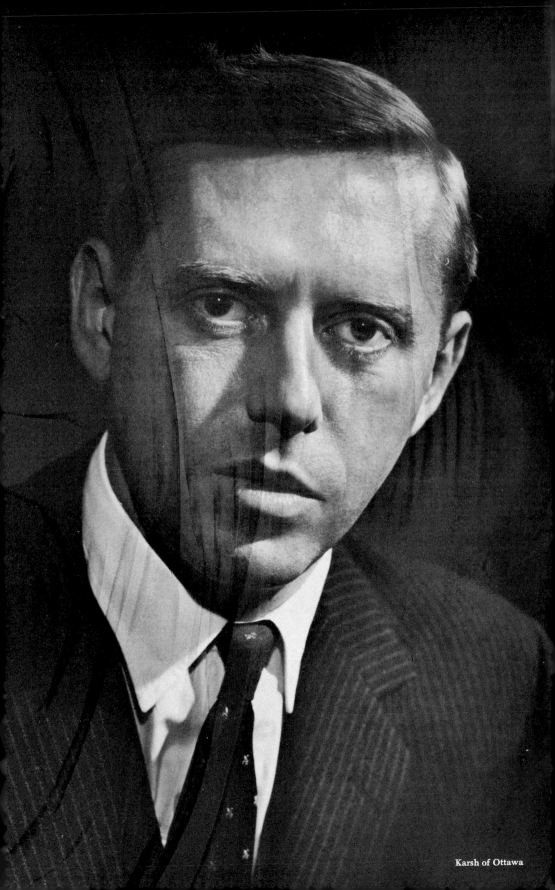

Karsh of Ottawa

The Future Makers

JOHN DIEBOLD
BREAKING THE CONFINES OF THE POSSIBLE

BY WILBUR CROSS
Introduction by Karl A. Hill

JAMES H. HEINEMAN, INC., NEW YORK H

OTHER BOOKS IN THE SERIES:

SAMUEL S. STRATTON: A Story of Political Gumption
by Wilbur Cross

EUGENE H. NICKERSON: Statesman of a New Society
by Arturo Gonzalez

STIG VON BAYER: International Troubleshooter for Peace
by Edward Hymoff

FIRST PRINTING 1965

HD
45
C69

FOR *my daughters, Candy, Melissa, Alison and Jennifer, who will grow up in an automated world*

and especially for my wife, Sunny, who with countless other mothers, could have used a little more automation all along.

Preface

WHEN publisher James Heineman approached me on the matter of authoring a book on automation, my initial reaction was that of a student who has just been asked to prepare a term paper in a subject that he has passed by the skin of his teeth and then dropped from his curriculum forever. I had never done well in scientific subjects. I thought of "automation" as perhaps the most formidable of all technical subjects, dealing with the most advanced electronic and mathematical principles—a subject which would be so far beyond the comprehension of a general author that he might as well try to reduce the Einstein theory to a limerick as to expect to communicate any part of the whole idea.

However, at Heineman's insistence, I did agree at least to meet and talk with the man he had selected as the lens through which the reader would focus on the whole broad subject of automation: John Diebold. From the time of that meeting on, I was totally, and voluntarily, committed to the project. Not only that, but automation increasingly became deeply fascinating as a subject involving not just scientific wonders and thinking machines, but the whole broad sweep of human experience and achievement. The sociological impact of automation is, if anything, more significant than the technological, the moral and spiritual implications more meaningful than even the economic and industrial.

I am utterly convinced, however, that my viewpoint and my interpretation of automation would have been technologically lopsided and almost meaningless had I not met John Diebold and gradually come to see the subject through his eyes. That is why I eventually came to write the book, and why I think that most readers will understand automation far better through this broad perspective than they ever could by approaching it as a study unto itself.

The publisher wanted to select a "future maker," through whom automation, at once one of the most discussed yet least understood subjects in the world today, would come alive. It was after several weeks of evaluating that he decided on John Diebold. There is no doubt that Diebold is in the top echelon of the incredibly few entrepreneurs who really understand automation. But, like all pioneers, he is often surrounded by controversy, wrenched apart from certain authorities who hold different views, or a thorn in the side of many who do not want to depart from the traditional ways of doing things.

As a result, this book is a unique product of a unique age. It brings together two dynamic subjects to dramatize forces that will have the profoundest effect on our lives and our future, and that are already chaining the world.

Referred to as "Mr. Automation," as "a prophet in his own time," as a "creative thinker" and "one of the more powerful men in the country," John Diebold is perhaps more fully immersed in the new phenomenon than any man alive. His personal story alone is an astonishing saga of success, involving the creation of a world-renowned, multimillion-dollar enterprise from nothing but an idea on paper, and in a matter of a few brief years. More significantly, John Diebold's career, in its upward swing, represents a driving force behind the whole far-ranging sweep of automation.

Not all readers will like this book. Some will be shocked by it. Many will take issue with it. Among the more frequent barbs of critics will be the comment that it is "repetitive." Indeed it is! It has the elements of a fugue, utilizing variations on a constant and persistent theme. But that is the *man.* John Diebold is dedicated, determined, persistent, constantly returning to his theme, his interpretation and repeating it at all levels and in a thousand ways. That, too is *automation,* a tremendous force that is adaptable and changeable, that keeps coming back in an alarming number of ways, but that cannot be thrust aside, though it may frighten some, irritate others and intoxicate mankind all at the same time.

The one thing that all experts will agree upon is that automation is here to stay. Whatever you may think of it, however you react to it, you have to face it. I hope that this book will help you to understand why.

WILBUR CROSS

Bronxville, New York
November, 1965

Introduction

I N 1957, John Diebold came to Dartmouth to present one of the
lectures of the *Great Issues Series.* He was 30 years old. He
spoke of the challenge to management inherent in the barely dis-
cerned revolution in information technology. It was an exciting
speech that carried the audience of youthful, intelligent people
with him as he shared with them the challenging vistas of a new
society and a new leadership in the making. They understood
him.

He can still do that with an audience, especially one of youthful people. Perhaps it is because his ideas are young, probing the
future. But it is more than that. It is because he thinks and expresses his thoughts with such remarkable clarity.

His book, *Automation, The Advent of the Automatic Factory,*
(Princeton, N.J., D. Van Nostrand Company, Inc., 1952, 181
pages) was his first major effort to acquaint leaders in business
and government with the emergence of a new technology and
with the probable impact of this technology on social, economic,
and political institutions. From this point forward, Diebold's ideas
have had an increasingly important impact on the thinking of key
groups in our society. His frequent testimony before Congress, his
addresses at Columbia University and other institutions of higher
education, and his appearances both in the United States and
abroad before groups such as the National Industrial Conference
Board, The American Management Association, and the European Community Conference have brought to widening leader-

ship audiences the concepts hammered out of the experience he developed in the course of his management consulting business.

The success of his effort to create awareness and understanding of automation may be verified in many ways. The one which gives me the greatest satisfaction is based on a recent conversation with a New Hampshire friend. I happened to mention John Diebold's name, and the response immediately was, "Isn't he the automation expert?" The significance of the comment rests on the fact that this man had no professional reason—business, education, or government—to be aware of Diebold's work. His response clearly indicates the degree to which Diebold's name has become linked with the term "automation" in the general public's mind.

The success of his mission in developing awareness and understanding of the basic concepts and technology involving automation, undoubtedly rests on the solid foundation of his unusually successful career as a consultant to business and government. What John Diebold communicates is based on experience and how he communicates is tempered by the constant need to get across his findings and recommendations to the leaders of enterprise who are his clients. Today his firm, The Diebold Group, Inc., has extensive operations in this country, Western Europe, South America, and the British Commonwealth. The growth and development of this firm from its modest start as John Diebold and Associates, Inc., in 1954, three years after he graduated from Harvard Business School, to its present scale of operations is a model for students of constructive entrepreneurship.

In recent years, Diebold has had continuing interest in the challenge of adjusting higher education to the needs of our highly developed technology and economic system. His views on these matters have provided stimulation for many in the academic community, particularly for those serving on business school faculties.

Within his own firm, Diebold has launched two projects that demonstrate in still another way his overriding concern with the need for continuing educational efforts to aid in developing competence in dealing with modern technology and its impact on existing institutions and people.

The Diebold Research Program is an imaginative operation designed to help participating corporations keep abreast and ahead of technological developments and to provide these companies with an effective device for preparing plans and programs to adjust effectively to these developments. It is a continuing study in depth of developments in industry, universities, and government. From its conferences and publications can come the awareness of significant trends and innovations necessary for effective corporate long range planning.

Since the ability of organizations to adjust effectively to the consequences of rapidly accelerating technological change have long been of concern to Diebold, he has initiated within his firm the Diebold Organizational Research Program. This Program is designed to draw on the experiences of groups not usually considered in current organizational studies, in order to learn more about the fundamentals of organization itself. The Program is looking at organizations ranging from the Catholic Church to the Rand Corporation, and from the Mafia to the Medici Bank. It is considering issues such as the role of organization structure in communications, the role of the leader in large, complex organizations, the maintenance of creativity in decision making, and the relation of the organization to the larger community of which it is a part.

At this time, one cannot readily assess the full impact of John Diebold and his ideas. A recent book by Mary Stephens-Caldwell Henderson (*Managerial Innovations of John Diebold*, Washington, D.C., The LeBaron Foundation, 1965, 138 pages) was the first systematic effort to review his writings, speeches, and addresses and to assess the impact of his ideas on management thought. The present book by Wilbur Cross is another source for those who wish to study the man and his contributions. Too often, books are written about people *after* they have reached their zenith and are either on the way down or retired from their field of activity. This book is about a man who is striking out in new directions from a very solid base of past achievement, but who is really only on the threshhold of what may be his most exciting contributions to business and public affairs.

I suspect that any final evaluation of his contributions should be deferred for many years. We are now on the edge of technological breakthroughs that go far beyond anything visualized by Diebold in the earlier periods of his career. In a very real sense, his greatest contributions to society and to management should be in the difficult years ahead. I have confidence that he will meet this challenge successfully.

For those of us who have been fortunate enough to know John Diebold during the past fourteen years, the scope of his activities and the range of his accomplishments to date present both a challenge and an inspiration. He is a living example of the continued relevance of intellect, energy, integrity, and dedication to goals larger than oneself in winning recognition and success in our society. It is heartening to know that his years of greatest productivity and accomplishment should lie ahead.

SEPTEMBER, 1965
KARL A. HILL
Dean, Amos Tuck School of
Business Administration
Dartmouth College

Table of Contents

JOHN DIEBOLD

BREAKING THE CONFINES OF THE POSSIBLE

1

A new dimension

*"In 38 years, you have shown management new
vistas, industry new ways to solve problems; and
you have added excitement and drama to the
world of business.
Change, feared and resisted by so many, is to
you not only a part of life, but a welcome part."*

CITATION, UPON BEING AWARDED AN HONORARY
DOCTOR OF LAWS DEGREE, ROLLINS COLLEGE

IN JANUARY OF 1962, the late President John F. Kennedy sat at
the center of his Cabinet table for a meeting with the "ten distinguished Americans" his Secretary of State, Dean Rusk, had
chosen to head a large American delegation to the United Nations
Conference on the Application of Science and Technology for the
Benefit of the Less Developed Areas to be held the following
month in Geneva. One of their number, a Nobel laureate, was
briefing the President on the position of the U.S. with regard to the
sweeping changes that would come about in developing societies
as a result of scientific innovations.

As the briefing continued, President Kennedy's alert eyes wan-
dered around the table, contemplating the seated men. Suddenly,
as he looked directly across the table at the chair usually occupied
by the then Vice President Lyndon B. Johnson, he reacted with a
surprised smile. He had not noticed in his concentration on the
briefing, but the man in that chair was some twenty years
younger than any one other than himself in the room that day. In
fact, he looked, if anything, like a university graduate student.
How often had President Kennedy himself been in similar cir-

cumstances—the youngest by far in a gathering of those engaged in forming our society.

The man sitting in the Vice President's chair was John Diebold, then only thirty-five, and looking some ten years younger. There was good reason for him to be there, in the presence of the President of the United States and of senior representatives of the scientific world. For a decade he had been pioneering in the field of automation, leading the leaders in government, business and labor towards the meaning of a technology that stretched far beyond concepts of automation itself. His stature was such that as early as the mid-1950's he was called to Washington as the first witness at the first joint Congressional hearing on the problems of automation.

In the words of the New York *Times*, "John Diebold has become a prophet in his own time. He is known as the man who coined the word automation, but his influence in the world of modern technology goes far beyond that of being a phrase maker. . . . In 1954, when few people realized the importance of the computer or other new technical developments, Mr. Diebold saw that these were the raw material of the future and based his entrepreneurial efforts upon them."

In perhaps more human terms, Diebold is an energetic and dynamic young man, ever impatient to get at the future, yet restraining himself with infinite discipline, not only examining problems of the present, but often dipping far back into the past to seek out answers. Like all entrepreneurs, his character is a complex pattern of personal strengths and weaknesses, many of which are interesting, even fascinating, from a biographical point of view. He is at one moment naively candid about the significance of his accomplishments and objectives, and at the next the very soul of humility as he listens to what someone else has been doing and achieving. He is the sedate, perfectly tailored chairman presiding over the conference table—and also the image of playfulness sliding down a banister with coattails flying. He can be gentle and charming in the most difficult social situation, or a bear for perfectionism in the most minute detail.

Yet no matter what he is or how he works or what impression he gives to a variety of people in a variety of situations, his personal nature and characteristics are always reflected off the glass

4

through which he sees the world: the broad pane of information technology, or what we know more commonly as "automation."

The story of automation—its implications for the present and the future—provides the fabric for this book. But the story cannot be told through a history of the subject. For this history is but an immediate yesterday in the span of man's accomplishment. The story cannot be told through pure case histories of what is being done. For case histories are as limited as the history. Nor can the story be told through a discussion of scientific progress. For scientific progress concerns itself here too much with physical and technical developments and not enough with human concepts and consequences.

There is only one way to tell the story of automation, and that is through the eyes of a man whose vision is sharp enough to focus on meaningful details, yet broad enough to encompass the entire tapestry. There are only half a dozen men in the world who even begin to qualify as candidates, and among them only one whose own personal destiny has been the pioneering destiny of automation itself. "John Diebold," said the New York *Times*, "has often been described as the high priest of automation. He is closer, however, to being the chief evangelist. His is the voice of the new technology crying in what he calls the wilderness of ignorance and inaction. He does not threaten fire and brimstone, but rather that nations as well as companies that do not come to grips with the full meaning of modern technology will crumble."

In John Diebold we have the symbol of our age reflecting all that is automation, and far more. Known and respected in the corridors of power on both sides of the Atlantic—actually he is better known in Britain and Europe than in this country—he occupies a unique position.

In that Cabinet room on that early winter day of 1962 the late President saw a man who, as himself, was conditioned for a station in life that steadily demanded more vigor and endurance and alertness. The youthful Diebold was attuned to serving as pioneer and interpreter of one of the most demanding social revolutions in the history of man.

Later, in writing of automation, President Kennedy said: "It is not enough to say that the benefits of technological progress outweigh the bad effects. Rather, it is necessary to face all the implications of a highly complex and constantly evolving technology. This means accepting scientific and technological progress as beneficial to the entire human community, while at the same time, devising and putting into action programs which will reduce to a minimum the cost in human values that inevitably are generated by technological change."

Yet even President Kennedy, aware as he was of the problems of automation, would have been astonished by the full implication of a technology which generates increases in its own potential as we move into the future. Indeed, it is this very pace which makes the potential difficult for many otherwise astute labor, business and government leaders to grasp. The self-imposed objective of John Diebold has been, since the late 1940's, to evaluate automation and its related developments, to impress upon people the magnitude of the technological revolution, and to show why the concepts he originated are basic to the field and not just matters of personal theory.

John Diebold expresses a simple yet highly effective image of progress. He refers to it as the "flat corner" concept. "One of the characteristics of our time and the future is that we are turning corners, around which we cannot see, faster and faster. Once the corners are turned, they become *flat*. That is, we not only can look ahead, having passed the critical point, but we can look back. The landscape behind us is flattening out increasingly, so that we are able to look back, farther and farther, into history and pre-history."

The turning process quickens because of, among other things, the interaction of science and technology. Scientific break-throughs bring about technological advancements and these in turn help to speed up the technological process and bring about more breakthroughs, and at constantly increasing rates of speed. This reenforcement process has achieved its greatest, most astounding, most exciting results through the process we know as "automation," which, as a concept, is really more far-reaching than the technological manifestations of the term themselves imply.

The computer itself is, indeed, the most powerful instrument devised by man—actually more powerful than even nuclear fission because it is profoundly involved in controlling that source of power or destruction, as an extension of man's intellect. Yet, the computer is but one component—albeit a currently symbolic one —of the broad field of automation. Automation and its related developments will have a greater effect on mankind in the coming decades than all of the wars that have taken place on earth since the first crude weapon was invented. Its influence will be more far-reaching and in fact, far more revolutionary than the Industrial Revolution. The ways in which its many elements are accepted or rejected, understood or misunderstood, developed or ignored, will determine the rise and fall of great corporations, the destinies of nations and the progress of man himself, as he reaches out towards the moon, towards Mars—and beyond.

These are strong statements to make about a subject which many people associate only with a large, highly complex and frighteningly costly business machine. They are strong statements to make about a subject that other people, somewhat more knowledgeable, relate to problems of unemployment. They are even strong statements to present to professional technologists who live in a world of circuits and transistors and electronics and supermachines.

Automation and its related fields are not subjects solely for the professional concern of the technologist, the industrialist, the businessman. Their impact will be felt by the community, the family, the individual as well.

"I used to worry most about nuclear war," said the Very Reverend Francis B. Sayre, Dean of the Washington Cathedral, when interviewed recently by *Life* magazine, "but atomic wipe-out isn't the big threat today . . . Neither this country nor Russia is going to let that happen. Our primary concern is cybernation —the application of computers to human life. Scientists say that if they construct machines to run society, they must have theologians to tell them what kind of society we want, and what man should be like in it. Computers may so totally change society that man will no longer recognize what he is in charge of. If the church doesn't have anything to say on the problem, then there is no reason for the church to survive, and it won't. If we don't solve the problem, history will walk right over us. The church must be in discussion with those who propose to play God!"

Dean Sayre's concept is alarming, and while there is truth in it, there is also so much left unsaid—which could not possibly be said within the scope of a single interview or even a single article. What then, is this twentieth-century technological Jekyll and Hyde that all mankind must face and live with from now on? That is the question to which this book addresses itself. That is the question which it tries to answer through an examination of the career of John Diebold.

One reason John Diebold appropriately serves as the lens through which this new age can be brought into focus was defined by President Hugh F. McKean, of Rollins College, at the eightieth anniversary convocation of that institution. Rollins College was honoring John Diebold with the degree of doctor of laws. The pertinent part of the citation read:

> Change, feared and resisted by so many, is to you not only a part of life, but a welcome part.
> . . . You have lived out the dream of so many American boys . . . and this American dream must be lived out again and again to keep it our heritage.

"The American dream"—that is the element which has for almost two centuries intrigued young men. The phrase does not have a connotation of nationality, however, but expresses a search for high achievement. More and more, it is becoming the human dream, one whose horizons are becoming limitless.

A perceptive friend of Diebold's long ago inscribed a photograph: "To John . . . whose dreams come true."

2

The house at number 62

"Automation begins here."

—FROM THE BIOGRAPHICAL LISTING OF JOHN DIE-
BOLD IN CLEVELAND AMORY'S *Celebrity Register.*

THE HOUSE AT Number 62 Columbia Terrace in Weehawken, New Jersey, is not in the slightest degree outstanding in appearance. It is what the newspapers might refer to as "a modest home on a tree-lined street in a middle-class American community." Except for its unique location, high on the Palisades rock outcropping, with its eastern fringe overlooking the Hudson River and New York harbor and with a dramatic view of the Manhattan skyline, this particular section of Weehawken is not impressive either. Many of the houses show signs of wear and tear, and the older inhabitants are aware that the metropolitan sprawl, from New York City outward in all directions, has brought with it occasional inroads of juvenile gangs and outrageous vandalism. Yet, by and large, the community has maintained its original small-town identity and quiet conservatism.

The story really begins around the summer of 1931. At that time, the house at Number 62 looked much the same as it does today from the outside, except that the present owner has added some siding and changed the color. Inside, however, the house was the stage setting for a most unbelievable and astonishing real-life drama—a revolution, in fact, that was just beginning and that is today having far-reaching effects from New York to Los Angeles, from the outlands of South America to the wastes of the Arctic, from Berlin to Tokyo and beyond.

The story is even more astounding when it is realized that the instigator of the seedling revolution was himself but a child of five. But what a child!

John Theurer Diebold had been born in that same house on Tuesday, June 8, 1926, the son of William Diebold, a moderately successful lawyer and his wife, Rose. As the second son, arriving eight years after his older brother, young John lived pretty much in a highly imaginative world of his own. He was christened at the Good Shepherd Lutheran Church at 98 Columbia Terrace, where he later was to be confirmed. At the age of four and a half, having earned a total of two dollars doing jobs, he asked to be taken down to the local bank, where he personally requested that a savings account be opened in his name. By the time he was five, he was well on his way to starting a collection— not the usual childish collection of miscellaneous shells or gum wrappers or stamps, but what was to swell during his boyhood into an entire museum of such proportions that it was later to require some eighty packing cases to store it.

Diebold had an avid desire, not just to collect things, but to catalogue them and relate them to one another as symbols of the whole encompassing civilization of man, insofar as he could see it from his youthful viewpoint and limited environment. Although he himself would probably be the first to protest the simile, he was in a sense "programing himself for the future," storing information the way a computer might do, in a logical and calculated fashion. Since the young collector could not travel far afield, he began, from the age when he could first write coherently, to correspond with museum curators and other learned people around the country, telling them about his collections and inquiring about theirs in a highly professional manner. The response was so good that he not infrequently received small donations from these busy people, including a piece of ancient armor from the collection of the late William Randolph Hearst. He also acquired a whale oil lamp from the Admiral Bryson Collection, a rare, early autographed edition of *The Man Without a Country,* by Edward Everett Hale, and a rifle from Gettysburg.

One of the fascinating early donations to his museum was a collection of fragments of the famous dinosaur eggs that Roy Chapman Andrews, the noted explorer and naturalist, had found in the Gobi Desert. They were of great historical significance, for through this discovery Dr. Andrews established the fact that dinosaurs did, indeed, grow from eggs. "There was also," recalls John Diebold, "a contribution from one of my brother's college roommates at Swarthmore. He was a Mexican boy who later became a skilled economist in the service of his country, and the donation he made was that of a shrunken human head obtained from the tribe that had collected it from the original source!"

Among the interesting letters he still keeps (in large, superbly bound scrapbooks), is one that might be called typical. It is dated July 25, 1932, and says in reply to an inquiry by the youthful curator:

> I received your letter and request for a chestnut from the historical "Friendship Tree." It is very interesting to know there are some boys who are taking such an interest in the historical things worthwhile.
>
> As soon as the tree bears, I shall be glad to send you one of the chestnuts.
>
> Asa K. McIlhaney

What had all of this to do with the age of automation that would come into being some two decades later?

John Diebold's early concepts of organization in fields of boyish interest were later to prove themselves as having been significant steps towards his overall outlook on the world of the future. This outlook, coupled with his participation, was to win him numerous awards for achievement and, in a narrower and somewhat deflected way, see him described as "The Elder Statesman of Automation," "The Crown Prince of Automation" and "one of automation's high priests."

To take first things first, Diebold's collections expanded so rapidly that within a short time there was no longer room enough for them in the basement space allotted to him by his indulgent parents, and he was permitted to take over a room in the attic, and later a bedroom on the second floor. The museum was implemented by a growing menagerie of snakes, turtles, fish ("I had more than 30 tanks"), white mice, rabbits, chickens and other animals, all properly caged and carefully labelled. Part of the zoo eventually spilled over onto an enclosed back porch and then into the yard, starting with a small rabbit hutch built against the garage and expanded with the growing population.

"All of the cages were built in sections," recalls Diebold, "using bolts and fitted parts, so that they could be dismounted in case we ever sold the house. Throughout my boyhood, animals—both live and stuffed—continued to be a major interest. In fact, the American Museum of Natural History came to be my second home."

Occasionally animals escaped, as happened one day when a delivery boy was almost frightened out of his wits to see a snake slithering across the kitchen floor. On another occasion a policeman wounded himself in the foot when he tried to shoot an escaped groundhog that had been reported by a startled neighbor. Diebold liked to let groundhogs have the run of the backyard, where they felt right at home, even to the point of hibernating in one of the many holes that pockmarked the terrain. One of these won the young zoologist recognition when he came up out of the hole precisely as he was supposed to on Groundhog Day and was written up in the local newspaper.

Long before he had reached his tenth birthday, John Diebold was acquiring and developing one of his most notable characteristics: the ability to crowd about two hours of activity into each single waking hour, as well as to get by with a minimum amount of sleep. While building his museum and menagerie, he was also in the process of acquiring, arranging and displaying what was to become a valuable collection of more than four thousand toy soldiers; and he was becoming proficient as an amateur magician ("at every opportunity, I used to catch the ferry and go across to Max Holden's magic shop on 42nd Street to learn more tricks and get more equipment"). Not content with sleight of hand work and various manufactured gadgets for the art of prestidigitation, he studied the works of Houdini and other magicians and created his own elaborate occult devices. One of these was the familiar sword box trick, for which he designed and made twenty trick swords, to give the illusion of piercing the body of an assistant who "volunteered" to climb into the contraption. Before he had finished with this pastime, he had devised and staged for the neighborhood a complete magic show that required three and a half hours to perform.

The sets for the magic act, all elements of which he designed, laid out and constructed himself, occupied a small moving van. On a smaller, but no less complex, scale, he put a great amount of creative effort into the construction of three painstakingly authentic miniature theatres, along with the design and modelling of sets for them. This interest continued on into his first year of graduate work at Harvard, where, he admits, "I spent more time designing a model stage set during the first semester than I actually spent in class."

At an early age he developed a marked propensity for organizing and leading other boys in a rapid round of activities. "People would do anything for John," said his aunt Marie. "He would come up with some wild idea, but pretty soon we would all be involved in helping him carry it out. The other boys around the block were attracted to him and to his activities like flies to sugar. They would be down in the cellar for hours on end, hammering and building and carrying out instructions or out in the yard digging enormous holes to make underground caves."

His brother, William, recalls this talent with great admiration. "Throughout John's entire juvenile life," he says, "he was always able to get others to work for him, not by bribery or tricks or dictation, or even by just stirring their enthusiasm. It was something much more to do with leadership and imagination and knowing what he wanted done and having an instinctive sense of planning a campaign to accomplish the job. This was a durable characteristic of his, even when the personnel changed, although it might be noted that a number of these participants went right on being friends and helpers of his through college and afterwards."

When he was ten, he founded "The Black Arrow Society," which attracted a large following of members and would-be members because it had rigorous entrance requirements. Several preserved copies of the typed membership application list ten tests:

1) Archery Test
2) Arrow Pulling Test
3) Archery Release Test
4) Archery Climbing Test
5) Bow Stringing Test
6) Rifle Shooting Test
7) Rifle Cleaning Test
8) Shock Test
9) Sword Test
10) Fencing Test

The forms were neatly mimeographed, with space for the participant's name and qualifications and a statement at the bottom that had to be "witnessed" by an officer of the club, attesting to the satisfactory completion of the tests. It was characteristic of Diebold that, although he insists he has never been much of an athlete, he qualified himself only after completing each of the tests to his own highly demanding satisfaction. Not content with the commercial models, he took to making and stringing his own bows and shaping his own arrows. He was a reasonably good shot with a rifle, qualifying for pro-marksman, marksman and marksman first class at the age of about eleven.

Whenever a special holiday arrived, Diebold was in the habit of organizing his friends, notably Kenneth Dudley, Ralph Risch, Tom Callery, Donald Blesse and William Klempt, along with a large neighborhood group, into a parade, complete with costumes and other equipment. They would then march down the street with banners flying, towing wagonloads of caged animals from the menagerie, each one suitably groomed and ribboned for the occasion.

During his quieter and lonelier hours, he read a great deal, particularly the Oz books ("they were of enormous importance in my early reading"), and he avidly pursued the study of nature, starting with the fictitious peripatetics of the remarkable Dr. Doolittle. The very same Doolittle and Oz books now stand on a shelf over the bed of his little daughter, Joan. (Occupying the same shelf, however, is an innovation, a toy "computer" with a series of lights that blink in random sequence for a period of a year or so before the mysterious elements within lose their power.)

Later, as his interests matured, John Diebold turned to more scientific works, such as Paul de Kruif's *The Microbe Hunters*, which had a great effect on him; Sarah Bolton's *Famous Men of Science*, and Francis Barry's *Pasteur, Knight of the Laboratory*. He enrolled as a member of the Junior Astonomy Club and was a member—certainly one of the youngest—of the American Society of Amateur Microscopists.

"Laboratory work was a deeply serious pursuit," he says, "and I used to keep at it until far into the night, often getting up early the next day to take up where I had left off."

On one occasion, the pursuit of science almost became too

serious. The young scientist, then eleven and already a member in good standing of the American Rocket Society, had decided to construct a rocket. One of the significant points in connection with the rocket engine was not the firing of the missile into the air but the test of a new batch of liquid fuel which he had formulated and prepared himself. While experimenting, he set off the fuel prematurely, burned a hole through part of the basement ceiling and another one through his shoe, received a face full of acid and burns in the white of one eye, and released so many fumes and clouds of smoke that the entire house had to be vacated temporarily. From the bed where he lay in pain during a long Easter weekend, "I promised my family after the incident that I would confine my research to non-explosive subjects."

His older brother, despite the difference in years, recalls that he first heard the name of Dr. Goddard, the rocket pioneer, from John when he was a small boy. "He knew all about this man, long before there were any articles in magazines and newspapers of the sort that I might read."

Again, organization became a necessary byproduct of his consuming interest and he founded the Diebold Research Laboratory. The firm was legally registered as a New Jersey proprietorship, with papers filed in the Hudson County Clerk's office on September 26, 1941, when John was fifteen years old. The nature of the business, which had its own stationery and letterhead, was listed as "general scientific research." By this time, he had already enjoyed something of a notable scientific career. It was his practice to spend as much time as possible with Dr. Louis Lange down the block, a noted surgeon who taught him a great deal about medicine and who used to invite the boy, then thirteen or fourteen, to the hospital to witness operations and autopsies. "I might have gone on into medicine," says Diebold, recalling the fascination it had for him, "if I had not become even more interested in the broader aspects of scientific research." As it was, he frequently performed minor surgery on injured animals, administered medicines to those that were sick, and once undertook an operation to prevent a young pet rooster from prematurely ending his own career by crowing. Young Diebold had worked out an understanding with the Weehawken police chief that although no chicken raising was allowed he would not be bothered if he raised no chickens that crowed.

15

On another occasion, he successfully performed an even more interesting operation, removing a tumor from the eye of one of his pet alligators. He was assisted in this by a remarkably non-squeamish young lady, who participated in many of the science and nature studies around the house and who provided the kind of active encouragement that meant a great deal to a young boy with deep and varied interests. She was Marietta Schweizer, a distant relative, who had come over from Germany to live with his aunt and who remained as an important member of the family and is today playing much the same role with his daughter Joan.

Diebold carried on extensive correspondence with scientists of note, who seemed eager to help cultivate such precocious interests. When Raymond Ditmars, one of the great naturalists of our time, was curator of reptiles at the Bronx Zoo, he answered an urgent request from Diebold regarding the "proper method of hatching some eggs that one of my turtles had laid."

"Another scientist with whom I had some contact," Diebold recalls, "was Peyton Rous, who is popularly known as the 'chicken tumor man,' one of the first men to produce positive results in cancer research and one of the senior scientists at the Rockefeller Institute." Rous later arranged for him to visit the Institute for an extensive tour of the laboratories. The event gave him immediate ideas about the development and improvement of his own laboratories at home.

Not long ago a lady approached Diebold's brother and said that she understood that William Diebold, Sr., had been a prominent scientist. When told that he had not been a scientist at all, but a lawyer, she looked extremely puzzled and replied: "Well, my grandson was visiting the people who had bought your house and said that never in his life had he seen such a laboratory and accumulation of chemical and scientific equipment."

Such was the Diebold Research Laboratory, under the directorship of its fifteen-year-old president. Academically, John Diebold was reared in the usual way. He attended Alexander Hamilton Grammar School, Theodore Roosevelt Grammar School, and later Weehawken High, entering the latter with the first class to use what was then a brand new building. "I hated school," said Diebold emphatically, then admitting, however, that he actually derived a great deal from public school life, "particularly from the special projects or assignments where we could use our own imagination."

He recalls two science teachers who particularly inspired him, George Becker and John Sarafian, along with Raymond Hopkins, a physical education instructor, who "taught me a great deal about introduction to the skeleton and muscles and things that I studied very hard because of my interest in medicine."

Although Diebold has always had great difficulty spelling ("I even used to spell my own name two or three different ways") he felt that his English teacher, Miss Margaret Jane MacArdle, exerted an "important influence," as did Miss Alice McFadden, and Richard Miller, his math teacher. For many years, he did little reading, preferring to have his mother read to him. But when he did start, he suddenly acquired a voracious appetite for books, ending up with an honor certificate for reading from the Weehawken Board of Education. A list that he still keeps in his scrapbooks, dated June, 1939, includes the following books, many of them misspelled:

The Jungle Book, Kipling
Robinson Crusoe, Defoe
The Wonder Book, Hawthorne
Wild Animals I Have Known, Ernest Thompson Seton
Adventures of Huckleberry Finn, Mark Twain
The Odyssey, Homer
The Bears of Blue River, Charles Major
The Adventures of Ulysses, Charles Lamb

When he was eleven, he won commendation for an essay, "The Constitution and What It Means to Me." Three years later, he stayed up all one night to finish an impressive project study on "The Ruffed Grouse," assisted by his mother, who saw nothing unusual in working with her son from dusk to dawn without letup. He had already spent many days working on the assignment, including hours devoted to writing to wildlife representatives in every one of the forty-eight states, for information on the bird.

His father, too, was concerned with education, serving for a time as head of the school board. "He was not socially minded," explains Diebold, "but he was greatly interested in civic affairs." He was active in what we would now call civic planning and consulting, studying and recommending methods of good gov-

17

ernment. He was elected president of the Weehawken Home Owners Association and once ran for the office of mayor, losing by only 170 votes, a surprisingly slim margin in light of the fact that he was trying to unseat one of the strongest political forces in the country, a satellite of the old Hague machine.

The senior Diebold was also active in the "Save-the-Palisades" movement, which tried, successfully, to prevent the building of apartments on the river side of the Boulevard. Recently, such apartments have been constructed in increasing numbers north of Weehawken, although for the most part John Diebold feels that they have been well designed, serving the growing problem of providing attractive living space in the metropolitan area.

The Diebolds believed in practical education, making it a point to take educational auto trips to various places. They visited museums and historical places throughout New York and New Jersey, saw Niagara Falls, covered the Bear Mountain area and toured Valley Forge. John Diebold remembers the Century of Progress Exposition in Chicago, although he was barely seven at the time. In 1937, came the climax of his boyhood travels, a three-month trip to Europe. He vividly recalls watching a Nazi pageant and parade in Munich. The family had purchased a movie camera before sailing abroad and with typical curiosity and enthusiasm over anything technical, the eleven-year-old boy had immediately learned how to operate it like a professional. The black-and-white films that resulted are clear and sharp, and commendable even in comparison with amateur footage taken with today's array of photographic gadgetry. Marching soldiers had always intrigued young Diebold. (At the age of four, seeing pictures of the Japanese invading part of China, he had attempted to run away—actually getting several blocks down the street—to join the Chinese soldiers and fight.) So, notwithstanding the fact that it was a criminal offense to photograph military subjects, he posted himself at an upstairs window overlooking a square and took the forbidden pictures.

One of the more interesting episodes of the occasion was observing Hitler, Goering, Goebbels, Hess and others in the Nazi hierarchy in their Mercedes convertibles, surrounded by SS and brown-shirt police. The last year of real peace in Europe, it was the first year of his boyhood that Diebold remembers with almost total recall. "I am perpetually thankful for having had understanding parents," he says, "who gave me an opportunity to walk through pre-war Europe—a world I saw once, but which exists no more."

Looking back over the trips, of both long and short duration, John Diebold feels that his parents contributed more to his early education than any formal schooling. His home environment was doubtless unique. How many adults, short of the fictional Dr. Doolittle, would have permitted subterranean diggings in the garden, a rabbitry annexed to the garage, a museum that all but overran the entire house, thirty-odd fish tanks scattered about, snakes in the cellar, a rooster in the attic and a sprawling scientific laboratory sandwiched in between everything else? It was certainly the kind of environment in which the boy thrived, developing into a pioneer of an extraordinary type.

3

A talent for listening

*"Since meeting you . . . I have puzzled over
your eminence. How . . . could a man of John's
age reach such international prominence?
. . . You are the best listener I've ever encountered. You not only ask perceptive questions,
you also listen to the answers. . . ."*

LETTER FROM A JOURNALIST, FEBRUARY 25, 1965

A YEAR AFTER GRADUATION from Weehawken High School, the
eighteen-year-old John Diebold entered Kings Point, the
U. S. Merchant Marine Academy. During the intervening time,
he had completed his freshman year at Swarthmore, academically
one of the finest small liberal arts colleges in the country. Although the transfer represented at the time a largely unplanned
step in his education, brought on by fortunes of war, Kings
Point was to play a strangely forceful part in drawing Diebold
into a leading role in the field of interpreting the future.

"Kings Point was really the most important period in my life.
I matured. Up until then, I really had not, but the experience suddenly threw me on my own and I had to mature."

For a time, he considered entering the field of industrial engineering, in connection with ship construction. But even long
after going into other fields of endeavor, he never regretted the
time spent at the Merchant Marine Academy. The lessons he
learned there and the inspiration of the officers he served under
gave him what he needed to go on to other achievements. Machinery had always intrigued him, so it was natural that he should
be attracted by ship's engines and the engineering aspects of
study at the Academy. Even today, he finds occasional excuses to

return to Kings Point to discuss common interests with Captain Tyson, who as a lieutenant had served as adviser to the Academy yearbook, *Midships,* for which Diebold was editorial manager. Or he visits Fulton Hall, the engineering building, to reexamine the complete ship's engine housed there and discuss technical matters with Captain McCreedy, head of the engineering department, whom he describes admiringly as "an individual enormously involved in his job and in building a first-class department."

In the engine room, Diebold was right at home. He took it apart piece by piece, put it together again, learned how to fabricate makeshift parts from scrap materials, to prepare for emergencies at sea under wartime conditions. He polished brass until his arms ached; marched in parade until he could hardly stand up; spent a night in an open boat in the bay in midwinter to learn survival tactics; lived aboard a sailing ship to see how the oldtimers put to sea; and graduated in December, 1946, as an ensign, USNR and USMS, licensed as a third assistant engineer for both steam- and diesel-driven vessels of unlimited tonnage. For a youth who considered himself immature on entering, he conducted himself with enough poise and application to earn a regimental academic award, serve as a cadet/midshipman officer on the Battalion Staff, receive a letter of commendation "for taking the highest possible grade on studies conducted under own initiative while on sea duty" and set something of a record for going through the entire course without once receiving a demerit. He graduated sixth in his class with a final grade of 86.75.

Courses in shipping management by Lieutenant Commander Walter von Gronau and Commander Lyle Bull, chairman of the ship management department, particularly interested John Diebold, for they were his first brush with formal management study. Coupled with the extensive engineering program, these studies provided Diebold with a solid technical and industrial engineering basis for his later studies.

During the course of his training, Diebold saw action in 1944 and 1945 North Atlantic convoy duty aboard the merchant marine ship, *S.S. Shooting Star,* for which he received two combat bars and the Merchant Marine Medal. His ship was the first to survive the one-day trip up the Scheldt River to Antwerp, where it was subjected to several weeks of continuous bombing by both buzz bombs and piloted planes at the time when the Germans still held the northern suburbs of the city. "The closest that I knowingly came to death," he says "was in Antwerp during the war. After dinner one evening, my shipmate George Jackman and I were walking down the main avenue looking for an American officer's club. We turned the wrong way, left instead of right, and had proceeded as far down the side street as where, as we later discovered, our destination was—but we walked in the opposite direction. Suddenly there was a whistle, the last-second warning sound of a V-2 and an explosion. We spent the rest of the night helping to get the bodies out of the ruins of the officer's club for which we had been searching."

Despite the first-hand glimpse of some of the grimmer aspects of war, Diebold thinks of those years as containing "memories of moments in history that I still feel privileged to have experienced. It was the interval between the Europe I had briefly seen as a child and the era in which we live today."

He recalls not only "the moment between flame-out and impact of a buzz bomb, when the subway roar of the already dead engine kept coming," but "the chalk cliffs of Dover with the vapor trails of bombers high above them . . . the entire sea covered as far as you could see by a huge convoy . . . the anger of the North Atlantic in deepest winter . . . the wake of a ship following a lonely zigzag course to shake off an enemy submarine . . . the hollow gauntness of a great frozen city, still gripped at one end by a retreating German Army, yet already being given a new life as the Allied liberation forces established pitiful little night clubs in the basements of once elegant mansions of another age . . ."

After the war, he was assigned briefly as an engineer aboard the *S.S. America*, where he had the dubious pleasure of serving under a legendary chief engineer named Pat Brennan, a huge man with steel gray hair, who was said to have once won a fight with Jimmy Braddock when the boxing-champion-to-be was a deck hand and persisted in running cargo over the engineer's water lines. Brennan insisted on keeping up the pressure so that the safety valves were always just about ready to pop. But let one of the safety valves blow off steam and the officer in charge would be in for trouble, a situation in which Diebold found himself barely twenty minutes after taking over his first watch while moving out of New York harbor.

It had become a legend from earlier days that Brennan's reaction was to hurl a heavy wrench at the offender, missing him by as little as possible, to put the fear of God into him. Thus it was that the young officer and his crew were startled *not* to have the expected wrench end up clattering at their feet. Instead, the immaculately white-uniformed Brennan gave them a tongue-lashing in a deep Irish brogue that seemed to shake the boiler room.

The chief engineer was also said to have had the legs of coal-carrying wheelbarrows sawed off, during the coal-burning days, so that no one could ever set them down to take a rest.

"I remember," said Diebold, "one time when a newly assigned officer appeared in the engine room. He had been known at Kings Point as one of the sternest disciplinarians, an administrative officer and member of the faculty. But on that particular day his uniform was not exactly in shape for a dress parade. Brennan looked him up and down coldly and shouted, '*What*, sir, are you?'"

The significance of the merchant marine training in the life of John Diebold was not wholly in the discipline he experienced or the lessons he learned. It was also in what he *observed*. He became fascinated with the remote control mechanisms—crude in 1943, but improving as the war progressed—used to fire naval guns. Radar-controlled automatic tracking and firing systems struck his imaginative mind as being wondrous inventions that must be suitable for other, non-military applications. He studied their operation carefully while training with naval gun crews and at every opportunity. Someday that knowledge was to be exceedingly valuable.

Many years later, he was again to have an intimate contact with Kings Point, this time in a somewhat different capacity. His firm became one of the joint sponsors, with the Academy and the Merchant Marine Institute, of the first conference ever held on the use of computers in the maritime industry. And today, the firm is actively completing project assignments in connection with the new breed of automated ships.

In addition, Diebold launched plans, with the Academy and the Institute for a broad international conference on the application of management science to ocean shipping. Thus, interestingly enough, the circle swung around again to Kings Point, to help fulfill critical objectives in the automation and replacement of the United States merchant fleet. And today, Diebold enjoys close friendships with Admiral McClintock, the superintendent of the Academy, and with his former instructor, Captain Tyson.

It is all a far cry from the time when he spent the better part of a year during midshipman days on a square rigger or when he helped to stoke a coal-burning ship with soft coal carried in a bag on his back, while he was stripped to his shorts in the middle of a hot summer.

Released from service, John Diebold returned in the winter of 1946 to Swarthmore, to complete the remaining three years of his college education. He had selected this small, but distinguished, Quaker college in Pennsylvania partly because his father and older brother had gone there before him, but mostly because it seemed to offer a real academic challenge. "I really was accepted because my brother, Billy, had such a brilliant record. He entered when he was fifteen, won a scholarship for all four years, earned a degree with highest honors and went on to graduate work at the age of nineteen. By contrast," admits John Diebold, "I had to major in economics because I could not pass the foreign requirements."

He has the greatest admiration for his brother, and was particularly impressed when he turned down the scholarship. "My father was able to send him, even though we were far from being well-off, and he and my brother felt, in those Depression years, that the scholarship should go to some one who could not otherwise have afforded to go at all."

Getting of to a slow start made John Diebold all the more determined to achieve a good record. ("I was encouraged, too, by my roommates, Gerry Pollack and John Foster.") During the following summer, as one instance, he set himself a goal of reading a book a day. "It was very arduous because I'm a slow reader." In high school, he had developed an interest that college allowed him to pursue in more depth, and which is still with him today: the study and collection of rare books, particularly examples of fine printing. For these he designed a bookplate in leather, imprinted with the coat of arms which a genealogical service had years before traced for the Diebold family. It contained a rampant lion and the legend *Fortitudo Magnanimitas Fidelitas.* Four

25

cases of his books were for some time on exhibit at the Swarthmore library, after having been painstakingly bargained for and assembled on a shoestring budget.

Always curious, he was not satisfied just with researching and finding out how illuminated manuscripts in the collection had been prepared. Once, in his teens, he spent four months of his spare time preparing an elaborate illuminated manuscript for his parents, as a gift for Christmas.

During his junior and senior years, he "read for honors." This was an ingredient of a unique Swarthmore institution. No lectures or grades were required for the final two years, but at the end of that period faculty members from other schools—top men in various fields—were brought in to administer an ordeal of eight four-hour written exams, followed by eight oral exams.

He majored in economics, with a split minor in political science and in psychology, but an odd situation developed. Awarded high honors by the outside examiners, he found that he nonetheless could not receive his degree because he had not completed the language requirements. "It was an awkward situation. But the college let me take a summer course at a Swarthmore-Colby language school, where I passed German by the skin of my teeth and received an official graduation certificate backdated to the sixth of June, 1949."

For those who like to read yearbook entries, the one in the Swarthmore *Halcyon 1949* reads as follows under John Theurer Diebold:

> most perfect gentleman on campus . . . sombre, nonchalant, an emotional rock of gibralter [sic] . . . but has his spurts . . . an unsuccessful policy of austerity toward women . . . sophisticated interests: gilbert and sullivan, broadway shows . . . expert on european royalty, despite an earnest endeavor to be a liberal economist . . . wonderful knack of making you feel terribly important . . . wonderful friend, even when you need him . . . if it's about horses, big john knows all

From early boyhood years, Diebold had always loved horses, even more than some of the other animals he saw more frequently. Entering his first horse show at the age of thirteen, he had won first prize. "I went at it very seriously," he says, "I did a lot of riding at college. We had an old Prussian instructor who had a tremendous sense of horsemanship. But I hardly do any riding any more. I just don't have the time."

Underneath the "sombre" surface, there was another John Diebold not quite brought out in the yearbook. Despite his ability to apply himself successfully and determinedly to his studies, he could not conquer the restless curiosity that was—and is—constantly with him. He bought a Buick sports convertible. "We weren't supposed to have cars, but I garaged it off campus in a home where sixteen elderly ladies lived. I used to enjoy going up there and talking to them, and they seemed to like me." In this—always with the top down, whether in warm weather or freezing cold— he toured the Pennsylvania countryside. Everlastingly interested in mansions and large estates, he used to visit two that were not far away, Turnermere and Longwood, to wander around the formal gardens and study the architecture and the furnishings.

Austere though he may have seemed, he enjoyed frequent dates with co-eds who shared similar interests, and he was not averse to occasional displays of sheer undergraduate foolery. On one occasion, he risked his neck to climb to the top of the clock tower, simply because the time was off and he wanted to see if he could reset the hands. "No one had ever done this before." On another occasion, he and a friend, Richard Cressey, whose great grandfather had been master of the famous clipper ship, *Flying Cloud*, decided to startle their classmates over a football weekend. At midnight, the night before the game, they went to a small pond on the campus of the rival college, Haverford, and dyed it blood-red. It was a disappointing attempt, however, for by morning most of the color had flowed away. Yet even this practical joke had a meaning.

"We thought this would be a good idea, and a kind of example," he explains. "So many college kids were going around painting things before football games, and it was horribly destructive. But painting water—that was different."

On the more constructive side, Diebold says that he gained great benefit from his studies at Swarthmore. He particularly remembers Professor Frank Pierson who was then chairman of the department of economics. "Frank Pierson was very important to me in planning that I go into honors work, and then in guiding me while I was in the honors program."

He cites Paul Ylvisaker, a young instructor in political science, who "was important in introducing me to case study and through that introduction to a sense of the real drama involved in administrative situations," and Professor Roland Pennock, chairman of the political science department, whom he respected greatly.

From Swarthmore, the next step was Harvard. "Harvard Business School had seemed to me for some time—I guess first consciously while at Kings Point—to be a fine complement to the liberal education of Swarthmore. I considered it the finest business education available. Most of the graduate schools of business at that time—and in most parts of the U.S.—could be classed as little more than vocational training schools. Harvard seemed to me to be at the opposite pole from this, and to provide the kind of atmosphere that would be one in which I could thrive. The concern with policy matters, the planning of strategy, the ability to study on one's own and develop at Harvard—these qualities were perfectly compatible with Swarthmore and with the values I had learned to respect."

It was at the Harvard Graduate School of Business Administration, which he entered in September, 1949, that John Diebold really came into his own—academically and professionally. He worked closely with General Georges F. Doriot, professor at the Business School, president of the American Research and Development Corporation in Boston, and today a good friend and advisor. They get together on occasions to discuss Europe, the Business School, trends in automation and other subjects of common interest. "I would say that 'perceptive' is the best word for John," says General Doriot thoughtfully, trying in his Gallic, continental, somewhat formal manner, to describe an individual with such unique characteristics. "He looked exactly the same then as he does now. You see those great big eyes looking at you alertly, with great perception and judgment. He is very courageous. He knows what he wants and is not afraid to venture. Yet you may catch that deep, pained expression as he contemplates an idea and is not quite sure about it."

The general himself gives a slightly pained look as he tries to capture the man in words. He is a slim, tight little man with gold-rimmed glasses, sharp, gray-blue eyes, a trim mustache and thinning gray hair. Very much the epitome of the European academician, yet at the same time a senior business director, he speaks with crisp words and a distinctive accent. "John did not have an early maturity. He has matured constantly though, at the same time keeping his youth—his youthful, constructive attitude—and not becoming pompous. He is an excellent *listener*." The general emphasizes the word. "At times he is quiet and hardly talks. He knows how to hear people, to handle them, to take a sympathetic attitude towards their viewpoint. He also has the ability to take advice, to understand things and people. John is a very wonderful person. I have real affection for him."

At the Business School, Diebold entered into the thick of activities. Among other things, he became a member of the Marketing Club and the Century Club, which required academic distinction. And he served as editor of the 1951 yearbook, *Annual Report*. Apparently, he did not get off to a fast start scholastically. "During the first semester," he recalls, "I convinced my faculty advisor and friend, Jim Healy, that I was going to fail. But he started devising arguments for giving me another chance." The approach was unquestionably successful, for Diebold ended up fourteenth in a graduating class of 532. As had been true in his past education, he really came into his own when working with special projects. Under Professor John Lintner, he participated as the only student member of a seminar on economic theory during the last part of his second year and engaged in some searching studies of the subject. Under Professor Charles Bliss, who guided his studies in productivity analysis, he embarked on a treatise on the subject. This was so successful that it was later published in the *Harvard Business Review* (July-August 1952), under the title "The Significance of Productivity Data," one of the first of many articles he was to write.

"Mr. Diebold," said a highly favorable review of this early article, in the business section of *The New York Times*, "a management consultant with an impressive grasp of, and perspective on, his subject, apparently was almost literally driven to do his expository piece for the *Harvard Business Review* by a mounting consternation at the widespread belief among business men 'that the productivity of their workers will increase at the rate of two per cent each year.' But this article is a great deal more than a job of debunking. It is personally conducted sightseeing in the sphere of education at its best."

For the first time, in a business way, at the age of twenty-six,

Diebold was coming to grips with the little understood subject of automation. He had a threefold purpose in presenting the material: (1) to clear up misunderstandings about the meaning and measurement of productivity (2) to underline new variations in productivity that were frequently overlooked or ignored (3) to point up several ways in which productivity concepts could be of use to business management. As one example, he presented the case of a baker who had a choice of increasing his output of doughnuts by working harder, or by using a doughnut-making machine. In the latter case, he would produce more with the same amount of effort—or even with less effort. What the author successfully attempted to do was to get across the idea that productivity is "more of a measure of the efficiency of labor and of the efficiency with which labor is used than a measure of the efforts of labor."

Perhaps one of John Diebold's significant contributions to the study of automation in those early days was his concentration on the human relations aspects. The very first article that he published, for example, was a treatise on the human relations aspects of the work of Frederick Taylor, a pioneer in the field of management and the study of more effective systems of labor. "I think it is significant," says Diebold, "that my first article was in connection with human problems. Too many people try to characterize anyone working in this technological field as being an automaton."

In the fall of 1950, General Georges Doriot announced, as was customary, that the students were to start on special projects. "I told them to pick a project that would have a future," he says, "I don't remember who actually suggested the subjects. I tried never to arrange the subjects, although I could veto any that were, to my mind, not significant." At any rate, it finally evolved that John Diebold was assigned as group leader of a "manufacturing research team in automatic control mechanisms." The group's assignment was to write a report, subsequently titled "Making the Automatic Factory A Reality." Dr. Curtis Tarr, now president of Lawrence College and at the time General Doriot's assistant, was the faculty advisor.

The group was largely on its own, however, from the moment the project was initiated and approved. Working with group leader Diebold were Carlin Englert, his roommate during the second year and also a Kings Point graduate; Jeffrey L. Lazarus, Jr. of the Federated Department Stores family; Irvin M. Yanowitz, who is now one of the officers of the Sharon Steel Company in Pennsylvania; Melvin A. Saslow, now an executive with Airborne Instruments on Long Island; John Wright, a student from England; Harry M. Gage; and Nicholas C. Siropolis.

The first responsibility of the group was to talk to people in the subject field and determine whether the research could really be classed as significant, and whether it would be increasingly important in the future.

Looking back on the project thirteen years later, General Doriot termed it an outstanding piece of work, adding that it was "remarkable that men in their early twenties were able to look so far ahead." The timing of the report was of considerable importance historically, for it marked one of the first times that concentrated attention had been given to a subject that was little known and that would, within a decade, become as significant as anything that had appeared in the business world since the Industrial Revolution.

While heading the research team at Harvard, John Diebold developed a growing curiosity and respect for the work of the Hungarian mathematician, John Von Neumann, who was then at the Center for Advanced Studies at Princeton. "I wrote to him and made an appointment to visit him during my Christmas holidays," says Diebold. "On the day of the appointment, there had been a heavy snowfall just before. I remember the scene vividly because while conversing with Von Neumann, I looked out the window and across a broad snow-covered field, bordered by two long lines of trees. Only one figure could be seen gradually approaching the building, between the trees. It seemed to me then to be the subject for a perfect photograph. As the figure moved closer, it became apparent that it was Albert Einstein." Pausing, Diebold cannot refrain from adding with a smile: "—whom I later encountered, to the amusement of us both, in the men's room!"

Diebold explained to Von Neumann that he was fascinated by the possibilities of applying computers and control mechanisms to the factory. He was interested in the great man's reaction, for it was Von Neumann who in the early 1930's had described what subsequently was to become the electronic computer. "In a very real sense," explains Diebold, "and in a way that is today forgotten because of all of the attention paid to pioneer Norbert Wiener, it was Von Neumann who in those years specified the logic of the machine. Every computer we have today is a Von Neumann machine."

John Diebold, having known both men and their work, feels that Von Neumann was "an even more basic thinker, and if you can discern grades of brilliance at that high level, more brilliant than Wiener." When Diebold discussed the idea of using computers to control process plants, such as oil refineries and chemical works, Von Neumann did some calculations on the blackboard and said that he felt convinced that the types of equations that would have to be solved and the nature of the control problem were things that the computer would be used for.

"I said, 'What are you going to do with this?'

"He replied, 'I have done everything I am going to do. I am convinced that the problems are purely those of application.'"

Regarding that other great thinker in this new technology, Dr. Norbert Wiener, Diebold first became interested in the man when he read his classic book, *Cybernetics*. It was not long thereafter that he arranged to see the noted scientist, at M.I.T.

"When I opened the door to Wiener's office," said Diebold, "several workmen were making a frightful noise in one part of the room, doing some construction. Wiener, standing in the center of the room, simply said, 'Well?' and asked whether we could not start talking. I began to describe my project (the group study) with him, with this overpowering din going on a bare three feet away. Despite the commotion, Wiener was oblivious to it. Fortunately, his secretary, who was working at a desk in the same room, became conscious of the frustration I was experiencing and said, 'No, no. You must go into a quiet room,' At this point, Wiener stopped talking and obediently followed as she led. We came to an empty classroom and went in and Wiener asked his secretary, 'Is this all right?' She said that it was, and we then sat down and began talking as though nothing had happened.

"Wiener said that it was a most important project that we were engaged in, and that I should go and talk with a variety of people. He mentioned Dr. Vannevar Bush, and then ran through a list of the greatest names in American science."

At a later encounter with Wiener, says Diebold, "I was particularly impressed by the fact that he carried with him a little card on which his secretary had typed instructions, saying what he must do at each point along the way. I then thought this a great joke. I now find that I carry such a card myself!"

During the remainder of the academic year, and after he had received his Master's degree, with distinction, in business administration in 1951, John Diebold continued to compile information on automation. He began to organize an outline and piece subject areas together in chapter form. During the second semester of his second year, and then while working on his first job, he began to write a book which really started where the Harvard report had ended. Although he has steadfastly asserted that he is not a writer, he managed to capture the full essence of a difficult and little understood subject and commit it to paper, page after page.

"I went over the manuscript draft of his book," recalls his older brother William, himself an internationally recognized author and the director of economic studies for the Council of Foreign Relations. "It was so thoughtfully and carefully prepared that it needed very little revising or editing."

The book, *Automation: The Advent of the Automatic Factory* which was published by D. Van Nostrand Company in 1952, represents Diebold's dedication to perfectionism when it comes to dealing with facts at hand, and his genius for looking at subjects through long-range glasses. Although the author was only twenty-six at the time of publication, he spoke with so much authority that the book is still a recognized reference work in its field and has been printed in six languages. More than simply an enlargement of the Harvard Business School report, it represented a considerable amount of original thinking, and the individual development of many of the ideas touched on to a limited degree by the group. As the jacket described the scope of the work, it was "a provocative study of the possibilities, limitations and social and economic consequences of the revolutionary new machines of the electronic age and what they will mean in terms of jobs, cost of goods and services, standards of living and increased leisure time."

There is an interesting story about the title and the word *automation* itself.

"Automation" writes Diebold in a prefatory note, "is a new word denoting both automatic operation and the process of making things automatic." But he admits that he began using the word because, poor speller that he has always been, he could not successfully cope with the already accepted term, "automatization."

From that moment on, John Diebold had been credited with coining the word *automation*. But, as he thoughtfully pointed out in the book, and as he has emphasized numerous times since, it had already existed, used by D. S. Harder, then vice president in charge of manufacturing for the Ford Motor Company, specifically to describe the automatic handling of parts by machines.

Ever since that day, a strange tempest has raged in various editorial teacups, mainly in the form of letters to the editor. "Mr. Harder has been shortchanged," say these communications in effect, referring to the coinage of the term. Although Diebold himself gave full credit to his predecessor, he himself deserves recognition for the *concept* of the word as we know it today. Mr. Harder used the word to describe the use of machines for the automatic processing of parts, whereas the Diebold interpretation relates to the broad application of communications technology, ranging far afield from the factory and the assembly line.

It was tragic that the person who had shared most in the development of John Diebold's many projects throughout the past two decades could not have enjoyed this new accomplishment. Before the book went to press, and even before the Harvard project was completed, his mother, Rose Theurer Diebold, died of cancer on July 21, 1950.

4

Automation as an historical development

"It is critically important that we develop a capacity and talent for leadership in this new era of technology. If we do not establish the momentum to lead society into tomorrow's world of automation, we will have no choice but to fight a retreating, defensive action that will ultimately cost us our political and economic freedoms."

JOHN DIEBOLD, ADDRESS BEFORE THE COUNCIL OF THE INTERNATIONAL CHAMBER OF COMMERCE, PARIS.

THE FLOUR MILL outside Philadelphia was operating smoothly and efficiently. Grain was fed into the automatic machinery at one end, but from that moment on as it moved through a continuous process, using three basic types of powered conveyors, no human labor was required until after the grain had been milled into finished flour at the other end. Automation was proving itself.

Although the description might sound like something from recent times, this prototype of the automated factory functioned in 1784, before the Industrial Revolution had even begun. It was conceived, developed and built by Oliver Evans, a Pennsylvania inventor who is also credited with having perfected various kinds of steam devices, including what is believed to have been the first automobile in the world. As John Diebold points out in *Automation: The Advent of the Automatic Factory,* we therefore can say that automation is not new at all, but something that has been around for almost two centuries. As a matter of fact, if we want to think about information processing as a step, we can logically go right back to the dawn of history.

"Information processing," said Dr. Ulric Neiser, "is not something done only by modern machines; it is as old as man, and much older."

As he goes on to explain, the earth in itself is a kind of gigantic computer, in which is stored vast information beyond belief—information which science is steadily learning to seek out and interpret. Consider the tracks of the glaciers, and the infinite scratchings and tracings and configurations on rocks. Through study of these, man can compute the size, rate of movement and even the temperature of frozen masses during the Ice Age. In another way, carbon 14 tests help science to determine more exactly than ever before, how long ago certain men and animals lived, though only minute remains of them may be found.

"Information about still earlier ages," says Dr. Neisser, "is probably stored on the moon; that is one reason we are eager to go there."

Dr. Margaret Mead, curator of ethnology for the American Museum of Natural History, describes how man himself began information processing in the most rudimentary way with records scratched on rock and bark, later with cumbersome forms of script. This eventually led to "the embryo library classification systems with their reliance upon the systematizing potentials of an alphabet traditionally set in a fixed order. . . ."

As far as machines themselves are concerned, however, we would do well to consider Archimedes who in the third century B.C. invented an automatic windlass, a water device used by the Romans to control the opening and closing of temple doors, or what was probably the first coin-operated machine in history, invented by Hero Xtebus in ancient times. The weight of a five-drachma piece deposited in a slot forced down a flat valve inside a large water container. The control lever opened another valve, which dispensed an instant stream of holy water through a spigot at the bottom. In the course of action, the top valve tilted, the drachma-piece slid off into a money container and the sudden loss of weight caused the water valve to close, thus shutting off the flow until another coin was inserted.

These devices, however, hardly deserve recognition as being automated. They were followed, during the Middle Ages, by more sophisticated inventions, and, around 1680, by a steam safety regulator, invented by a Frenchman, Denis Papin. In 1671, Gottfried Leibnitz failed in an attempt to invent a mechanical calculating machine. "It is unworthy of excellent men," he said, "to lose hours like slaves in the labor of calculation." But it was not until the time of the first Industrial Revolution that man began to devise what are the real prototypes of today's automation. One of the outstanding entrepreneurs was Joseph Marie Jacquard of France. The son of a weaver, he read an English journal which in 1800 announced a prize for a simple loom that could weave patterns. His invention won an industrial medal in 1801 and was so successful during the next few years that by 1812 there were some eleven thousand Jacquard looms operating in France alone. They were controlled by punched cards, similar in certain respects to those used in automated office equipment today. Producing intricate patterns as quickly and easily as older looms made plain cloth, the new invention gave rise to the term "Jacquard" as it is applied to elaborate weaves found in table damask, brocades and bedspreads.

We can look back a little farther than Jacquard and Evans and see other developments that were really laying the ground work. As early as 1741, Jacques de Vaucanson had contrived a mechanical loom for manufacturing figured silks, and by the 1760's James Hargreaves in England was well on the way to perfecting his spinning jenny, the first machine to spin more than one thread at a time. At about the same time, James Watt was developing the condensing steam engine, to put power behind the coming Industrial Revolution. Not so well known, popularly, but of perhaps even greater significance than the steam engine as far as automation is concerned was Watt's centrifugal governor. This device made it possible for a condensing steam engine to maintain a constant speed, no matter how much work was required of it. Whenever the machine tried to slow down, the governor, which was nothing more than two metal balls at the end of a lever, permitted more steam to flow into the machine, thus bringing the speed up to normal. Conversely, if the engine had light work and tried to speed up, the governor would cut down on the flow of steam, thus keeping output and input in proper balance.

The Industrial Revolution produced so many pioneers—Dr. Edward Cartwright, Eli Whitney, Samuel Crompton, to add three more names—and so many inventions that we are inclined to think of the revolution in terms of the technological and the mechanical. However, as John Diebold has pointed out, it was much more than that. "The industrial revolution was revolutionary," he said in an address entitled "Automation as a Historical Development," because "it created a whole new environment for mankind—a whole new way of life. What it gave to history was much more than the steam engine and the cotton gin, the railway and the power loom. It gave society a whole new tempo, a whole new outlook.

"It took men off the fields and out of small shops and put them for the first time into factory life. Hence it gave us mass production, and through mass production the first civilization in history in which luxury was not confined to a few. It gave us as well a sense of hurry, of time, which is still unknown in countries that have not gone through an industrial revolution. It gave us a sense of material progress, an itch to get ahead, which is also unknown in those parts of the world which are still pre-industrial."

As John Diebold pointed out in an article for the National Planning Association in May, 1959, technical innovations have, throughout history, stirred up widespread controversy. "By 1813," he said, citing the Oliver Evans invention, "millers were pleading before Congress for 'relief from the oppressive operations' of Evans' patent, and Thomas Jefferson was called on for advice. Jefferson dismissed the whole thing as an old story. 'The elevator,' he said, after inspecting the mill, 'is nothing more than the old Persian wheel of Egypt, and the conveyor is the same thing as the screw of Archmidedes.'"

"This is one of the few cases," said Diebold more recently, "in which I think I would disagree with Jefferson—as has history!"

So the very prototypes of automation provided warnings of the social upheavals and protests that would follow each technological step forward—even two centuries ago.

It is all well and good to go back two hundred years and look at some of the prototoypes of modern automation, but it would seem almost impossible to the layman to go back more than a couple of decades to find the origins of that fantastic machine, the modern computer. Not without really stretching the subject and pointing to the old abacus, used by the Egyptians in the fifth century B.C., as an ancestor. Yet the computer was already 124 years old when, in 1946, the first of the new type of all-electronic digital (using digits to key electrical impulses) computers was completed.

It was in 1822 that Charles Babbage, described as "one of the most inventive and surely the most irritable of nineteenth-century British geniuses," devised and demonstrated his difference engine. Sheer annoyance as well as necessity might well be said to have been the mother of the invention. Forever damning the "wretchedly inaccurate" output of human calculations, Babbage resolved to produce a machine that would have none of the dismal human fallibilities. The principles of the difference engine have astonishing similarities to those of modern-day computers. The big difference was really in the limitation imposed by the mechanical operation, as compared with today's use of electronics. Babbage was actually too far ahead of his day to devise a machine that would see much practical application. He went on to design another form of computer called the analytical engine, this time a machine that would actually follow instructions. It was to be made up of a brain, or memory, an arithmetical unit, a punch-card input system and a method for transferring to the operator data stored within the machine's memory.

Babbage was never able to complete the computer because he did not have the available resources. His difference engine had been financed by the British Government but Babbage's temper was so acute that his original backers shied off rapidly when they saw him coming again. As one contemporary described the irascible Britisher; "He spoke as if he hated mankind in general, Englishmen in particular, and the English Government and organ grinders most of all." The last reference was to a group of men he tried to prosecute for disturbing his thoughts; they retaliated by blowing bugles outside his window all night long.

There was one person Babbage did like, and who was strangely drawn to him: Augusta Ada, Countess of Lovelace and daughter of the poet Lord Byron. A beautiful young lady, she had a unique grasp of mathematics and was one of the few people on earth who could either understand, or sympathize with, the irritable inventor. In a rare moment, she helped him devise a system for beating the horse races. Although it may have been mathematically sound, the system had serious flaws. As history records it, the outcome was that the Countess had to pawn her jewels to remain solvent.

In 1939, Howard Aiken, at the time a Harvard graduate student in physics, and now head of Howard Aiken Industries, Inc., undertook to develop a large-scale computer with the backing of International Business Machines. At the time he did not know about Babbage and his work, but when he finally did read what the British inventor had written, and saw what he had accomplished, he was amazed to learn how close the difference engine and the analytical engine came to incorporating some of the very principles he was working on during the 1940's. "Automation," he said recently, "came much quicker than I expected and it has reached out into a broader field than I ever expected."

In between the two men, considerable groundwork had been laid for the modern computer. William Thomson, Lord Kelvin, had followed Babbage's work later in the nineteenth century by devising methods whereby machines could solve mathematical problems. In 1872, he constructed the first machine for predicting tides. It was described as a "magnificent assembly of cams, pulleys, cables, gears and tapes which did, in fact, predict the tides in a crude sense." He was so far ahead of his time, though, that it was not until 1919 that an analog computer perfected in Germany was able to be put to practical use. Given some twelve working hours, it could prepare annual tide tables for any harbor in the world.

In 1878, Lord Kelvin prepared plans for a computer which he called the harmonic analyzer. He failed in putting his theories to work because there was no technological means in his day to build machines with the precision required for actual performance. It was not until the mid-1930's that Dr. Vannevar Bush and colleagues at M.I.T., using fine machine tools, were able to build— after some five years of effort—the first differential analyzer that really worked. Like Babbage's difference engine, however, it had to work on a purely mechanical principle, although it did have electric motors to drive the various components.

The 1940's gave birth to the modern-day computer because,

for the first time, the mechanical drawbacks could be tossed into the wings and the new field of electronics brought in to play a leading part. "The electronic developments of the 1940's made it possible to perform by means of electronics what the differential analyzers did mechanically," wrote John Diebold in his first book on automation. "With the completion of the IBM *Automatic Sequence-Controlled Calculator* (Mark I) at the Harvard Computation Laboratory in September, 1945, and the Electronic Numerical Integrator and Calculator (ENIAC) at the Moore School of Electrical Engineering, Pennsylvania University, in February, 1946, a new family of modern high-speed digital computers came into being."

In effect, electronic computers were made possible by the invention of the vacuum tube by Dr. J. A. Fleming of England, and by Lee De Forest's introduction of a third element, the grid, into the original two-element tube. But the vacuum tube itself imposed limitations, because of its very size and the vast number of tubes that had to be used in any single computer system. With the coming of the transistor, able to do the same job as the vacuum tube in an infinitely smaller space and with greater longevity, much of the problem of space was solved.

The 1940's saw another outstanding milestone in the history of automation: the development of systems of control. In the early part of the twentieth century, considerable inventive experimentation went into a field known as "remote position control" (RPC). Great liners and other ships required mechanisms attached to the rudders to make it possible for the helmsman to retain proper control over the vessel under changing conditions of sea, wind and weather. In 1922, an engineer named Minorsky published a theoretical analysis of remote position controls, but it was not until the early 1930's when two men, Hazen and Wyquiest, developed the real concept of automatic controls that paved the way for full automation to come.

The early control systems of the 1920's and 1930's were to play an important part in World War II when military demands called for an endless number of solutions to the problems of controlling not only steering, but the maneuvers of high-speed aircraft and the action of rapid-fire weapons of many types and sizes. The result of the emergency applications of hundreds of scientists was the servomechanism, an automatic refinement of the old remote position

41

control. Through the use of servomechanisms (or closed-loop systems), such weapons as anti-aircraft guns could be fired at extremely high speed, with good accuracy and from remote positions. The closed-loop system, in which errors are automatically corrected by the machines themselves, made it possible for weapons to zero in quickly on fast-moving targets—far more quickly than the ablest artillery men had ever been able to do computing by instruments and mathematics.

The development of servomechanisms during the war has thus led to the perfecting of similar systems for the internal control of all kinds of peacetime automated equipment. It was the potential application of these wartime technologies to industrial uses which strongly attracted John Diebold's interest when he first served on convoy duty in the Atlantic. In them he saw the beginnings of modern automation concepts. The industrial descendant of the unit which once helped naval gunners find aerial targets when under bombardment may now be controlling the precision shaping, drilling and milling of metal parts, helping to navigate aircraft during low visibility, or operating high-speed equipment under constantly changing conditions.

Another milestone in the development of the machines of automation was the invention and perfection of printed electric circuits, so designed that they could fit into small spaces and function far longer than the old types. In the 1920's various electrical engineers and research scientists conceived the idea of taking the complex networks of soldered, fragile wires that made up radio circuits and forming spider webs of conductors held solidly together on a flat plane of insulated board. In 1927, F. W. Seymour designed and patented a plated circuit, which was followed two years later by a stamped-wire circuit devised by H. H. Wermine. The initial models were crude and not easy to manufacture in the mass production style desired. By the end of the thirties, however, the printed circuit as we know it was beginning to evolve. Fundamentally it is a simple process: printing or etching conductive metal on plastic or other insulating material and then treating the unit so that all elements are rigidly fused in place, able to withstand mechanical shock and vibration to an extreme degree. The most complex patterns, or networks of circuits, can be printed almost as easily as a publisher might print a line drawing of the same circuit in a book.

While these circuits were suitable for radios, and later for television sets, they had not reached the maturity necessary for fully effective use in computers and other machines of the automation age. A breakthrough came shortly after World War II when a British engineer, John A. Sargrove, created a system for producing the old flat plates in molded plastic forms of almost any size and shape required. He thus eliminated the need for splicing flat printed circuits together to form the more complex circuited structure. He also made it possible for entire units to be processed and produced by automated methods. Sargrove's first efforts were practical only for simple radio circuits, but later developments increased the complexity of the units so that they could be built for other automated equipment.

During the late forties and early fifties, as the tools of the Automation Age multiplied and became more efficient, it became increasingly apparent that the new breed of machines was going to be able to do far more than simply make computations and give directions. A great deal of imagination was needed, nevertheless, to comprehend how best this new automation could be harnessed. One roadblock was that the designers could not grasp the developing *philosophy* of the new technology. They saw fundamentally a need for better tools with which to turn out the same old products. But John Diebold, along with a very few others, kept pounding away at the traditional outlook, often to the great irritation of his elders. As early as 1952, when he was only twenty-six, he had asserted that manufacturers should consider changes not only in machines and methods, but also in *products*.

"It is often necessary to redesign the product as well as the process," wrote Diebold, "for fully automatic production. Sometimes the changes are small. For example, the addition of a reference point on a casting may permit automatic positioning of the piece on a machine tool. Even with consumer goods, minor changes rarely affect consumer acceptance. The small glass nipple (or lug) on the side of a liquor bottle—which permits automatic positioning under the labeling machine—does not reduce product acceptance. . . . An ice cube designed with a hole in the middle allows fully automatic production and by providing a larger cooling surface is a better product."

One of the outstanding pioneers as automation began feeling its growing pains in the middle and late 1940's was the late Dr.

Norbert Wiener, the father of the whole broad concept of cybernetics. Wiener coined the word *cybernetics,* defining it as a theory of communication, the process of control in both man and machines. In its academic application, it is a comparative study of various systems of control and communications, including those of living things, entire societies, organizations and machines.

Wiener felt that "it is degrading to a human being to chain him to an oar and use him as a source of power; but it is an almost equal degradation to assign him to a purely repetitive task in a factory which demands less than a millionth of his brain capacity."

The man described as "one of the most original and significant —yet idiosyncratic—of contemporary scientists" was first exposed to his subject matter when he was assigned some mathematical problems regarding target-tracking radar and weapons systems that used the radar. He began to see that he was not dealing with an isolated set of problems, but with the entire theory and concept of control. Moreover, the problems dealt with a combination of elements, including human communication, an overall control system and machines. What resulted logically, therefore, was an investigation of the entire field now known as cybernetics.

"Cybernetics," wrote Stephen Toulmin, in an article on Wiener in *The New York Review* in September, 1964, "is a subject with many ramifications. Its concepts lie behind the design of all those self-monitoring factory assemblies that we refer to collectively by the term 'automation'; it has important connections with the operation of electronic computers; it has made significant inroads into physiology, notably in explaining the failures of muscular control occurring in ataxia, and in permitting the construction of artificial limbs controlled by the actual nerves of the amputated stump; and it is widely hoped—indeed, expected—to throw much light on brain functioning, and on the operations of sensory perception and discrimination."

In 1948, Wiener wrote a book, *Cybernetics,** which—although unintelligible to most laymen—represents a milestone in the whole subject field of automation. "What Norbert Wiener did," concluded Toulmin, "was not to banish the Ghost from the Ma-

---

* *Cybernetics, or Control and Communication in the Animal and the Machine,* M.I.T. Press, 1948 (revised edition, 1961).

chine. Rather, he demonstrated that, in the formal pattern of their activities, the Ghost and the Machine are one."

Starting with the middle and the late 1950's, the rush to automation was on—even though many manufacturers who were automating or readying production lines to produce fully automatic products really did not understand the overall concept of cybernetics, or even the real implications of specific types of automation. Perhaps technological development was impelled so much faster than sociological understanding that man simply could not keep up with what he had invented. The transistor, for one, came at a time when automation needed it badly (at least from the technological standpoint) to decrease the size of equipment and increase the efficiency. Other inventions such as tiny semiconductors the size of a pinhead, magnetic inks, and new kinds of recording tape have speeded up and improved the capabilities of hundreds of types of machines.

One of the latest innovations is the silicon-controlled rectifier, originally developed in 1957, but just gaining wide acceptance. Despite its fancy name and extremely technical background, this device, commonly referred to as the SCR, is quite simple in makeup and operation. It acts as an automatic switch, sometimes operating long after the original impulses have ceased. A typical use would be in an electric kitchen mixer, which requires a wide variation in speeds under different, and ever-changing loads. The old way of slowing the mixer was to add resistance to the electrical circuit, at the same time keeping the current on. This wasted energy, in much the same way you would waste energy if you kept your foot on the accelerator of your car and at the same time used your brake to slow down, instead of simply lifting your foot the desired amount. The SCR in effect "chops the power on and off many times a second," thus actually cutting down on the flow of electricity.

In an electric golf cart, which uses widely varying amounts of power while navigating a course, an SCR can conserve power to a remarkable degree. One golf cart operator reported that instead of getting only 36 holes to each battery charge, he could get 100 or more. Home power tools are also taking advantage of SCR. Saws, drills, sanders and other tools can tackle heavy-duty jobs without burning themselves out, yet always receiving enough power at crucial moments.

The late sixties and early seventies will see some astonishing developments in this kind of control for consumer products, as well as throughout industry and business. Thermostatic controls will not only take care of heating homes and regulating cooking temperatures, but will have some sensors more acute than any human sense, to detect dangers or any form of problem-developing situations. It will become almost impossible to overload motors, burn toast, scorch the beans or run out of hot water.

These things do not come easily. Pioneers in the field of automation are constantly struggling to try to maintain a realistic balance between the practical and impractical, to focus understanding on the sociological implications of automation and away from the yen for gadgetry. "We have to be dragged screaming and shouting that there really was nothing new," said John Diebold, "—or at least not both new and 'practical'—every step of the way. Each development in turn is first described as visionary, blue sky or cloud 9; next it becomes 'practical' because some one tried it properly and finds it economically justified: When it becomes generally accepted, it is described as nothing new after all.

". . . All great ideas are simple and never 'new' in the sense of being created in a vacuum, or first exemplified; but the self-conscious realization of the possible use and ramification of an idea is. . . . The theory of interchangeable parts was revolutionary regardless of whether any particular factory previously used it, because after Whitney this society became aware of its implications in the production of goods. . . . So with the feedback principle, the historians do not have to search for particular mechanical devices to show its prior existence, for we are all aware of the interaction of our sense perceptions and brain—true feedback circuitry."

The history of automation goes far back, to the dimmest recesses of ancient civilization. That we can fully understand. But what is more difficult—sometimes impossible—to grasp is the realization of the fantastic rate at which automation is snowballing. At a conference at the Harvard Business School, Professor James Bright said, "Do you realize that the amount of physical knowledge is doubling every fifteen years? The life of a weapons system back in the Christian Era was four hundred years. The life of a weapons system today is around three to seven years. Do you realize that the speed of the B-58 (bomber) is further ahead of the B-52 than the B-52 is ahead of the Wright Brothers plane? And there are new systems coming along that are going to wipe that out."

Within just four years, Professor Bright's statement about the B-58 was disastrously right.

Consider, too, what is happening to the computer. Since computer memories contain millions of cores, or individual repositories for bits of information, size has always been a factor in design, installation and practical use. ENIAC, the first true electronic computer, hogged some fifteen hundred square feet of office space, weighed thirty tons and used about eighteen thousand vacuum tubes. Twenty years later, the same capabilities could be squeezed into a cabinet the size of a kitchen refrigerator— and operate far more effectively and reliably at that.

"The process has not stopped," wrote Dr. Jan A. Rajchman of RCA, in a professional article on "The Shrinking Computer," for today "we have already made it practical to make complete computer circuits on single chips of silicon so small that you could fit a thousand over this sentence."

Put another way, a thin silicon wafer the size of a quarter could be cut into more than two hundred integrated circuits. And each of those circuits, one-twentieth of an inch square, contains the equivalent of fifteen vacuum tubes or transistors, plus thirteen other elements, used in the components of early-day computers.

Power is another astonishing factor, along with tremendous increase in speed. As Dr. Rajchman explains, noting that internal computer speeds have increased by a factor of ten thousand in less than two decades, "We can now switch electronic signals in a billionth of a second. This time is so short that light, which travels at 186,300 miles per second, only moves one foot in that time . . . !"

Yet two decades from now, this kind of speed will be classed as downright lethargic.

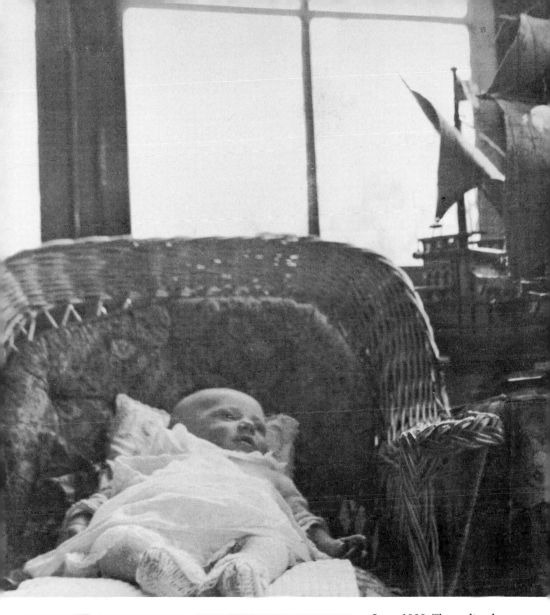

June, 1926. The earliest known photo of John Diebold, taken on the sunporch of the house at No. 62 Columbia Terrace.

Rose Theurer Diebold, 1884-1950.

William Diebold, 1881-1962.

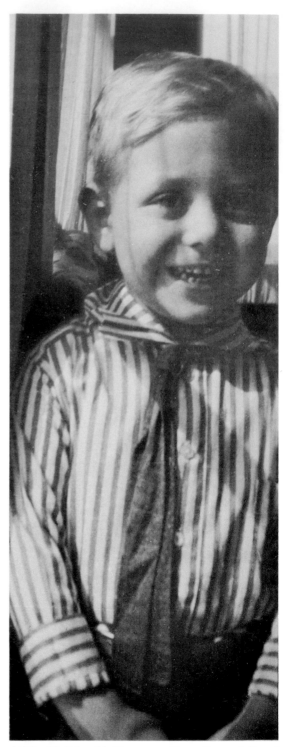

At No. 62 Columbia Terrace: with mother and Grand-mother Theurer *(upper left)*; brother 'Billy' *(lower left)*.

In front of the house at No. 62 in 1929, a unique event typical of his childhood — a 'parade' of his friends and animals *(top)*. *(above)* Jumping a horse during the summer of 1942.

The 1937 trip to Europe, during what proved to be the last year of real peace, provided John Diebold with memories of a world which for better or worse would never again exist. The center photograph he took illegally from a balcony in Munich as he watched one of the great prewar Nazi spectacles: *Zweitausend Jahre Deutsche Kultur* — which also afforded an unphotographed but memorable view of Hitler and his lieutenants.

The house at No. 62 Columbia Terrace changed only slightly during his childhood. A series of photos record him growing up in the stability of the same rooms. *(above left)* With his brother William in 1930 and *(right)* in 1947, during his 'one book per day' summer.

As a Cadet-Midshipman Officer at Kings Point, 1948; a junior engineering officer aboard the S.S. America, 1947; on a climbing expedition atop Mt. Katahdin, Maine, 1949, with two of his German language instructors from the Swarthmore-Colby summer school of languages.

John Diebold spent as much as possible of his time at college out of doors — at Swarthmore, studying each day in the rolling Pennsylvania countryside, as well as on the campus itself; at Harvard, going for long, daily walks.

With Doris, during the first year of their marriage in the Cedar Street apartment in which they lived while in Chicago.

Making the announcement that his firm would mount ten one-week courses on the management use of computers in as many European cities in 1958 *(upper left);* posting a project marker on master map and talking with colleagues, both at The Diebold Group's headquarters office; inspecting the computer installation of a client firm.

Discussion of a problem with colleagues in his headquarters office conference room.

Walter Hallstein, President of the European Common Market *(above),* and Professor Enrico Medi, Vice Chairman of EURATOM (Atomic Energy Commission for the Common Market) *(below),* extend congratulations to Diebold upon his address to the High

Commission of the European Economic Community, Brussels, December, 1960.
(above) With Assistant Secretary of State, Harlan Cleveland, 1963. Talking with Governor Nelson Rockefeller *(below)* during a three-day briefing, arranged by Rockefeller, of key State officials by Diebold staff. Albany, 1960.

The Ten Outstanding Young Men of 1961 at conclusion of ceremonies. From left to right: Theodore Sorensen, Special Counsel to President Kennedy; Dr. Edward Lilley, Director of the Harvard Space Radio Project; Newton Minow, Chairman of the Federal Communications Commission; Dr. David Rogers, Chairman of Vanderbilt University Department of Medicine; Ray Keyser, Governor of Vermont; John Diebold; Major Virgil Grissom, Astronaut; Peter Peterson, President of Bell & Howell; Dr. Harold Brown, Chief Scientist of the Defense Department; and Dr. Stanley Sturges, Director of the Himalayan Medical Mission in Nepal.

Fielding questions at Santa Monica press conference, January, 1962, with President Kennedy's Special Counsel Theodore Sorensen and Newton Minow, Chairman of the F.C.C.

Richard Nixon (in a rare juxtaposition with Ted Sorensen), extending congratulations to Diebold, Dr. Brown, and Dr. Lilley on Ten Young Men Award, Santa Barbara, California, 1962.

A plenary session of the UNICEF Conference at Palais des Nations, Geneva, Switzerland, in February, 1963. The U. S. delegation heads *(reading from aisle);* Walsh McDermott, Cornell University (delegation leader); J. Herbert Holloman, Assistant Secretary of Commerce for Science and Technology; Jerome B. Wiesner, President Kennedy's Science Advisor; John Diebold; Isidor I. Rabi, Columbia University; Isador Lubin, Economic Consultant to The Twentieth Century Fund.

With President John F. Kennedy's Science Advisor, Dr. Jerome B. Wiesner, and Chief Nigerian delegate, Professor J. C. Edozien, Dean of Abadan University Medical School, at Geneva, February 5, 1963. UPI photo.

At the Presidential briefing of the heads of U.S. delegation to the U.N. Science Conference, together with Dr. Walsh McDermott, leader of the U.S. delegation, January, 1963.

(Right) With the late Secretary of Labor, James P. Mitchell, and C.I.O.'s Walter Reuther at The White House Economic Conference, Washington, D.C., June, 1962.

Honorary Doctor of Laws degree is bestowed by President Hugh McKean at the 80th Anniversary Convocation of Rollins College, February, 1965.

Lunching with British Minister of Science and Technology, Frank Cousins, at British Institute of Management Conference, "John Diebold—View of the Future," January 27, 1965. (Diebold sustained a temporary eye injury prior to the conference.)

House of Rothschild Gets a Role in Automation

Banking Group Purchases
Interest in Diebold Unit

John Diebold Urges a Coming to Grips With Technology

By WILLIAM D. SMITH

John Diebold has often been described as ...

Friendly visit at the Ritz Hotel in Paris with New York's Senior Senator, Jacob K. Javits, November, 1964, during the NATO meetings.

August, 1964—President Lyndon B. Johnson signing the Automation Commission Bill into Public Law.

Weekly staff luncheon in the Park Avenue, New York, headquarters office of The Diebold Group, Inc., 1964.

With daughter Joan, in the drawing room of his home.

5

"Such a young American!"

*". . . you are an enterprising and brilliant man
. . . you have lived out the dream of so many
American boys who hope to rise in the world
by courageous thinking and effective hard
work. . . ."*

CITATION, UPON BEING AWARDED AN HONORARY
DOCTOR OF LAWS DEGREE, ROLLINS COLLEGE.

FOR A YOUNG MAN who had shown a remarkable grasp of the widest possible variety of subjects, from economics to medicine, magic, natural history, stage design, industry and engineering, John Diebold was faced with a somewhat perplexing question: What to select for a lifetime career?

Besides these and other interests previously mentioned, he had long had a considerable interest in international affairs. He was attracted to foreign students at Swarthmore and Harvard, with whom he discussed the economy of Europe—notably Ladislas Rice, a British subject of Czechoslovakian birth; Peter Gorb, an English student; Chris Platou, a Norwegian; Pedro Castillo, whom he later visited in Cuba, and Olivier Giscard d'Estaing, later to found and head the *Institut Européen d'Administration des Affaires,* the first venture in Europe of an American-type graduate

49

school of business (on whose U. S. Advisory Committee Diebold now serves).

In the summer of 1950, he had worked as a student-intern for the United Kingdom Branch of the Economic Cooperation Administration in Washington, D. C., at a salary of $50 a week (an improvement over his $65 per month while in the merchant marine). While there, he was engaged in writing a series of analyses of European-sterling area trade patterns; he did original statistical work; and he helped in constructing European rearmament models.

It was perhaps natural, then, that he should have turned to the consulting field, where he could test his imagination on a broad range of challenging assignments. Upon graduation from Harvard, he accepted a job as a junior consultant with Griffenhagen & Associates in the New York office. Although his starting salary was the lowest of any Harvard Business School graduate that year ($300 a month), he proved so valuable to the firm that the founder, E. O. Griffenhagen, a highly demanding individual, broke a precedent of forty years standing and asked him to go to Chicago and serve as his personal assistant. He was an important influence on Diebold, since it was the first time he had encountered and worked closely with any one in a real business situation.

Also significant to the fledgling consultant were James G. Robinson, an elderly Irishman wise in organizational matters, who was Griffenhagen's partner, and Hugh J. Reber, who served as the first controller of the United Nations and who had a distinguished career in international finance.

Mr. Griffenhagen was a pronounced individualist, characteristically close-mouthed, but occasionally unleashing a bit of venom if he felt it necessary to accomplish something, or if he thought that an employee had fallen down on a job. Diebold had not been in Chicago long when he began to receive an unbelievable flow of paper from the boss's office. Griffenhagen was a great one for communicating on paper rather than by word of mouth and had devised a system of sending out memoranda to his personnel, using initials and various abbreviations, rather than names. (It saved typing time.) John Diebold kept receiving instructions, some of them rather odd, with his initials "JTD" at the top. After all but going out of his mind trying to keep up with the parade of paper and the endless instructions, he and Griffenhagen's secretary finally figured out what was wrong. Griffenhagen was simply communicating to *himself* on paper and "JTD" stood for "*Jobs To Do.*"

Diebold had met and been greatly attracted to a good-looking and brilliant young girl, Doris V. Hackett, of Pittsfield, Massachusetts. After they had decided to become engaged, Diebold announced to his employer that he was to be married to Doris in Pittsfield on November 22, 1951, which was Thanksgiving Day. At the time, Diebold had been working for the firm for several months. "I was working seven days a week and pretty long days at that," he recalls, "primarily on my own initiative because I was very interested in what I was doing."

Griffenhagen digested this news reflectively for a few moments, then looked up and said, "Why don't you take *Friday* off, too?"

Doris Hackett Diebold had grown up in New England, in Cranston, Rhode Island, on the outskirts of Providence. While of modest means, she came from old New England stock, numbering at least one hero of Bunker Hill among her ancestors. She attended Pembroke, graduated with honors and then went to work as engineering assistant at General Electric in Pittsfield, where she did analytical work in the design of induction voltage regulators. "She is an enormously conscientious person," says her husband, "who works, and always has worked, very hard indeed. She aspires to, and practices, the personality characteristics associated with the New Englander—the loyalties, the abilities and considerable reserve. She is shy by nature, and considerably more reserved by desire."

An example of her strength of will and character is the fact that Doris is a confirmed vegetarian, a practice she adopted in her late teens when she took great exception to the slaughtering of animals. She applies her philosophy with great vigor, completely abstaining from meat or fish and most of the products derived from them, and working quietly to introduce more humane slaughtering methods, since she realizes not many are likely to follow her example of abstinence.

"Doris," says John Diebold, "is an enormously self-effacing person and a retiring one. A great deal in the development of the business has occurred where she has had to do things she has not enjoyed. Many things such as the extensive European travel, the involvement with leaders in fields of journalism and business and international affairs, which to many people would be the sustenance on which they would thrive—these to some extent have been things that she has not enjoyed because of her retiring nature, but has endured because it was necessary to me in achieving the goals that I have been driving toward.

"By her own desire she remained in the background, partly because of her own nature, and partly because she felt it was better that she not appear to be playing a role in the business, since we were striving to build a company in a competitive profession that dealt with the highest questions of business policy and anything that gave the business an appearance of amateurishness, which businessmen still read into the part of a wife working with a husband (despite the notable exceptions of the Gilbreths and the Wallace Clarks) would hurt it."

In Chicago, the couple lived in a two-room basement apartment, which they decorated themselves, with considerable night and weekend labor, turning it into attractive modern living quarters. They even made much of the furniture themselves. The house was owned by Mr. Griffenhagen, and stood on East Cedar Street, directly next to a small, red brick house which was an early Frank Lloyd Wright design with a studio on the second floor. John Diebold was intrigued by a characteristic Wright invention, a turntable for turning cars in the exceedingly narrow garage space.

Since Doris started working for the Griffenhagen firm herself shortly after the marriage, the two used to walk together to 333 North Michigan Avenue along what was called by Chicagoans, the magnificent mile. Yet "even in winter," says Diebold, "when you had to hang onto guide ropes on the portion going from Cedar Street by the Lake, it made a wonderful walk. It was a nice long walk, and provided the chance to get some exercise, some fresh air, and also a very real feeling for this portion of Chicago. The view from the office was a superb one of the Lake. We used to drive some around Chicago to such places as the Indiana Dunes and also visited the Art Institute, the Museum of Science and Industry, and other parts of the city environment."

Diebold cannot remember a time when he was not in the Griffenhagen office on Sundays as well as Saturdays. This was, however, all of his own doing, since he was rarely asked by his employer to devote this extra time to the job.

Diebold early began putting his ideas on automation to work in his consulting assignments. An example of this approach to his work is a paper that he prepared, Management Report No. 151, issued by the Griffenhagen firm in 1952 and entitled, "The Automatic Factory." As an address presented by Diebold, it discussed mechanization vs. work effort, the automatic factory and its future, the history of automatic controls (going back to Joseph Marie Jacquard's punch-card system in 1801) and machines which are self-correcting. He emphasized his belief that it was an error to think of automation in terms of hardware and gadgetry, which could result only in peripheral benefits: "Full promise of the new technology cannot be realized as long as we think solely in terms of control." The analysis of processes in terms of function was what was significant.

During this period of his career, Diebold began to meet people who were important in shaping business, industrial and international affairs, all of whom influenced him profoundly and many of whom became close personal friends. There was Harold Smiddy, a vice president of General Electric and a pioneer in management, who assisted him in the publication of his manuscript on Frederick Taylor and human relations. Another was Lillian Gilbreth (the Mother in *Cheaper by the Dozen*), who recognized the significance of some of Diebold's ideas and went out of her way to inform some of her notable associates about the work he was doing. "All this meant far more to me," says Diebold, "than I realized at the time."

One of the most influential of his senior friends was an Englishman with whom he was to be closely associated later on in business, Lt. Col. Lyndall Urwick, who is recognized as one of the great men in the management movement. Shortly after the time of their first meeting, Urwick invited the young consultant to go to England to teach in the Urwick Orr School of Management. Diebold was interested, but the plan fell through. When Urwick returned to England, his partners rejected the proposal, aghast at "the idea of bringing such a young American over —and to teach managers!" Some ten years later, after the two men had started a joint company in England, Urwick, addressing the annual meeting of some two hundred members of his firm, said that if the original plan had not been rejected, perhaps the American would not now own half of Urwick Diebold, Ltd.!

Diebold feels that he owes much of his current success to the interest, friendship and advice of many outstanding men in many places, including noted economist and management thinker Peter F. Drucker, who is an important source of advice ("I think I've read everything he has ever written"); Sir Leon Bagrit, the "Mr. Automation" of Great Britain; Louis Armand, one of the most advanced and imaginative thinkers in France; and Roberto Olivetti and his late father, Adriano, who built Olivetti into the remarkable company it is today. After visiting Ivrea, the North Italian hill town in which Olivetti makes its headquarters, Diebold came away, greatly influenced by the example Adriano set in the character and the spirit, as well as in the more obvious attributes, such as the design and social consciousness and concern with city planning, for which this great Italian industrialist was justly famous.

Diebold has never shied away from association with controversial figures, if he feels that there are areas of mutual interest and understanding. One such man was the late Axel Leonard Wenner-Gren, the adventuresome Swedish tycoon, who started as a fifteen-cents-an-hour factory hand in New Jersey and went on to amass one of the largest personal fortunes in the world. He made a hundred million dollars by founding the Electrolux Company and foreseeing the rapidly expanding demand for household appliances of all kinds.

Many businessmen avoided Wenner-Gren or any negotiations with him. During World War II, he was blacklisted by the United States and Great Britain, presumably for dealing with the Nazis. Some said that he was using his island paradise in the Caribbean as the site of a U-boat base. (It later turned out that he was cutting a channel through coral so that guests could bring their yachts right up to their palatial guest houses.) Later, after the war, his name was cleared and he was subsequently presented with an honorary degree by the Weizmann Institute of Science in Israel, and was further honored by having the computing laboratory named after him. Interestingly, he had served as an intermediary between Goering and Chamberlain, trying to prevent the outbreak of World War II. At the time of his death, Wenner-Gren, one of the last of the prewar international mystery men, was said to be worth upwards of $200 million, with successful enterprises all over the world, including the U.S., Sweden, Mexico, Germany and Venezuela.

At the time Diebold met the colorful Swedish financier in the early 1950's, Wenner-Gren had taken a fancy to computers—awkward and sprawling though they were at the time—and needed advice from a consultant in the field. The association between the two men began when Diebold visited Wenner-Gren at one of his five great homes, Shangri-La, the above-mentioned tropical retreat, later sold to Huntington Hartford, who turned it into the resort community known as Paradise Island.

Shangri-La was a world in itself. It required hundreds of workers to maintain the place and since the island was largely coral, Wenner-Gren had set many men to work importing trees of all sizes and planting them in pots scooped out of the coral. For a young man from a modest home, it was a profound experience to sit at a dinner table in the most rarefied of atmospheres on an isolated Caribbean island estate, opposite a man who was used to doing business directly with kings and heads of state (he had personally financed Mannerheim's Finnish campaign against the Russians), whose wife at this family dinner was wearing half a million dollars or so in precious jewelry, including a heart formed of uncut rubies and diamonds and a sapphire arrow.

When she asked the visitor if he liked her pin, Diebold replied shyly, "It's very nice."

When Mrs. Wenner-Gren took this as damnation with faint praise, she blurted out to her husband, "Axel, he says it is *very nice.*"

Not understanding that she was miffed, Wenner-Gren mentioned what he thought was most important about the jewelry, "It is red, white and blue."

Someone seemed to be giving Wenner-Gren poor advice on the business of computers, and the newborn firm was undergoing staggering losses. For awhile Diebold stepped in and managed to cut down some of the losses, but from the very start he repeatedly advised Wenner-Gren to sell the computer company. All during this time, the busy tycoon was charging around over the globe, from one venture to another, leaving behind a trail of overseas phone calls, lengthy cablegrams, controversial remarks and frayed nerves. But Diebold enjoyed his initial brush with this world. He was intrigued by such matters as Wenner-Gren's 4:00 A.M. phone calls from Stockholm asking him to try to sell the telephone company building in Mexico City to provide scarce U.S. dollars to pay for a shipload of Volvo autos arriving two days later—all while he was struggling to set right a badly conceived California computer company.

Marguerite Wenner-Gren, an American from Kansas City, Missouri, was a talented and perceptive woman of many interests. At one time she had sung the lead in the *Opera Comique* in Paris. She later became a very good friend of John and Doris Diebold, a friendship that has continued long after the death of her husband.

What attracted John Diebold most about this first visit, however, was not the atmosphere of wealth so much as the sense of being right in the middle an an international spider web. "There was indeed throughout all my dealings with Dr. Wenner-Gren," says Diebold, "a great sense of adventure. The association with this fascinating personality gave me the vicarious opportunity of living a kind of spy thriller, with taut little men in big overcoats arriving for secret conferences at his Stockholm country estate, Häringe, an eight-hundred-year-old castle with huge drawing rooms, great halls, and magnificent ballrooms."

As the year went by Diebold became more and more a part of the childless Wenner-Gren's family. The magnificent eighteenth-century Sheraton table in his present apartment dining room was a gift of Marguerite Wenner-Gren when she closed Shangri-La. Birger Strid, whom Axel Wenner-Gren called his finance minister, and Madame Brita Procopé, a Swedish noble lady, widow of the Finnish foreign minister, who occupied herself as Axel Wenner-Gren's secretary, playing a key role in business and family matters, both became fast friends of John Diebold. All three visit frequently in New York; at Madame Procopé's own house on the Häringe castle grounds, in Stockholm, and in other parts of the world at any of which places they feel entirely at home. Thus, what started as an interesting exposure to another world, has become very much Diebold's own world.

In 1954, John Diebold took the step that has, more than any other single move, made him a pioneer in the field of information technology, and eventually a remarkably successful businessman in his own right. He returned to that unique world in which he had been brought up, the house at Number 62 Columbia Terrace, in Weehawken, N. J., and founded John Diebold & Associates, Inc. He had no capital. He had no employees. He borrowed no money. And for a full year and a half, he did not even have any clients.

He did have several other ingredients, however, which were to be extremely valuable in the battle: courage, resourcefulness, imagination and determination. While he read everything he could lay hands on regarding the subject of automation (and there was precious little to come by), productivity and related subjects, his wife, Doris, first of the "associates" in the firm's name, more realistically, went out and secured a job to provide income.

"I find it very hard," says Diebold, "to convey to people the many, many simple and humble tasks that we both performed in the early days of the business. Most people that are in our firm today—or in any other substantial professional management firm —would not have put up with either living in an attic or doing the hundreds of chores that were necessary in making the business come into existence, with no capital whatever."

Yet no one should be misled into thinking that the fledgling firm of John Diebold & Associates, Inc. was an amateurish affair or a youthful "mama-papa" operation, even in those early days. The two Diebolds knew more about automation than did the combined staffs of many of the largest consulting firms in New York City. Doris Diebold kept pace with her husband in learning about the concepts and tools of automation. One of the functions they both were concerned with in those early days of the business was setting up a sound method for comparing computing equipment. Doris devised a structure for comparisons. She attended several of the earliest computer schools conducted by the manufacturers and learned about the machines themselves.

In a process rather remarkable for the day, she learned through her own studies and applied do-it-yourself methods on how to program a computer. At the same time, she filled several volumes with comparisons of early equipment, even while she was devising financial and administrative procedures for use in the business.

For many months, Diebold faced outright discouragement time after time as he made contacts and tried to sign up at least one client. With blond, often windblown, hair, and an exceptionally youthful face and a bubbling enthusiasm, he gave (and still does) the impression of being a bright college graduate student with a constant well of imaginative ideas. So even when he did manage to get in to see top executives of companies that he considered good prospects, he was not able to turn them into actual clients.

"People would listen to what I had to say," he recalled to *Esquire* editor Clay Felker in an interview, "and if they didn't say it outright, I knew exactly what they were thinking: 'What does this *boy* know about business?' And they were right. I had a degree from Harvard Business School, but I didn't really know how to run a business. All I knew was that I wanted to build my own firm in the management consulting field."

The best entrance proved to be the back door. Although John Diebold & Associates, Inc. did not put up a very convincing front, the young entrepreneur was attracting attention with his published works. His book slowly gathered a considerable following, both here and in Europe, where it appeared in translation. He had his *Harvard Business Review* articles to show, along with a number of Griffenhagen speeches and reports that had been reprinted. He had also written a series of three authoritative and stimulating articles for *The Nation* in 1953, including "Factories Without Men" and "Atoms and Automation."

In 1954 John Diebold took steps toward fulfilling a need he had for some time seen in his field, a magazine that would discuss automatic controls. He discussed the idea with Gerard Piel and Dennis Flanagan, the publisher and editor respectively of *Scientific American*, who not only gave freely of their editorial advice, but suggested that he consult J. K. Lasser, long known as a tax expert, but also one of the outstanding authorities in the trade publishing field. With Lasser and the partners of a new law firm, Richard Kilcullen and Gayle McGuigan, he established a company, Automation Publications, Inc., and conceived a new magazine, *Automatic Control*. However, since his main energies were channelled into getting his young consulting firm rolling, and because he did not envision publishing as the center of his life, he effected a merger with Reinhold Publishing Company, of which he became a stockholder. Diebold held the position of associate publisher and editor, and Fred Peters, an executive of Reinhold—one of the few "bosses" Diebold has ever had—served as publisher.

After doing everything necessary to launch the new magazine, including recruiting a staff, selling some ads and lining up such untypical trade book writers as Harry Schwartz of the New York *Times* for an early piece on Russian computers, Diebold's active participation in the editing focused on the preparation and writing of a monthly column entitled "Feedback." In the first article of the series, Diebold referred to the publication as "the first business magazine of the second industrial revolution," and predicted that automatic control would indeed enjoy a bright future in our economy. In the second piece, he pleaded with the new industry to establish standard terminology, badly needed at both technical and management levels to assure full growth potential in the field of automatic controls. He attracted considerable professional attention by challenging the experts to define, and distinguish between, terms like cybernetics, fleximation, robotization, and automatic operations, as well as automation itself.

In the meantime, after some eighteen months of trying to inject life into John Diebold & Associates, Inc., using the family home for his office, he brought in his first client, Stromberg-Carlson, to provide guidance for developing products, in the field of automation. Another early client was Crowell-Collier, whose president, Paul Smith, commissioned a large and significant assignment in the management information systems field. After that, other companies fell in line, and Diebold moved into a single room on Park Avenue, in order to have a New York City address and be more accessible to his new clients. In the process of expanding, one room then another was also leased at the Park Avenue address. Later, the firm moved down to Wall Street, where it leased space from one of its clients, Bache & Company. Diebold described Harold Bache as "a man who took a keen interest in our work when we were a very tiny firm and few believed in us." Mark Millard, a partner in the investment banking firm of Carl M. Loeb, Rhoades & Co., also retained Diebold in the very early days of his professional growth.

The next move was back to the original location in New York, 430 Park Avenue, where what is now The Diebold Group, Inc., takes up a full, city-block-long floor. In 1957, Diebold bought the business of his old firm, Griffenhagen & Associates, and two years later merged L. J. Kroeger & Associates with it to form Griffenhagen-Kroeger, Inc. That year, too, he purchased Alderson Associates, Inc., a Philadelphia management consulting firm that specialized in marketing. He also established the Management Science Training Institute as an organization to provide training courses in automation, marketing and public administration.

At the beginning of the firm, Doris Diebold gave up her cherished career in mathematics and took up what an associate described as "what every mathematician hates more than anything in the world, namely, accounting." She taught herself, largely, about accounting, as well as about office methods and management and taxation. "I think it significant," says her husband, "to note that in the entire period that she has been treasurer of the company we have, of course, had many tax examinations. Yet she has a record that I have never before encountered: namely, not one dollar has ever been disallowed in any tax examination. Some people say that this means we have not taken advantage of some of the provisions in the tax law. I know that not to be the case. Rather, Doris is an enormously honest person, and a very thorough one, and the results have come through the extremely restrained and careful application of good business principles."

After ten years, Doris Diebold relinquished the position of treasurer to occupy herself with a wider range of management activities and to devote herself to their daughter, Joan, who was born in the summer of 1962. "She has," says John Diebold, "borne a very great burden of loneliness during the endless amounts of time I have been away. During the years of setting up the European organization, something she felt we were attempting at much too early a point in the growth of our firm—and she was correct—I was in Europe a part of every month for several years. This was before the jets, and it meant unbelievable amounts of travel."

John Diebold was determined from the very beginning to build an international organization. He formed two partnerships abroad in 1958: one as Urwick-Diebold, Ltd., in England and the other as Berenschot-Diebold, N.V., in The Netherlands. The late Prof. I. B. W. Berenschot had heard of Diebold through his work with the Urwick group, and because of the association was interested in effecting a joint venture that would be to their mutual interest. In 1959, Diebold established a European company with operating subsidiaries in Paris, Frankfurt and Milan.

The Diebold Group, Inc., was well along in its marvelous metamorphosis from a bedroom office in Weehawken to a position as one of the leading international management consulting firms in existence, with offices in fourteen cities on three continents, and more than three hundred professional assignments on its calendar each year.

Yet the head of all this still does not look any older than he did in the days when prospective clients dismissed him as a mere boy.

"While I was sitting at my desk working early one morning," said John Diebold recently, "the scaffolding that is used for cleaning the windows at 430 Park Avenue was in motion, with two window cleaners being hoisted up to begin their job. I was bending down over my own work, catching a glimpse of this out of the corner of my eye and paying no attention until I clearly heard one man call attention to my office as they passed on the way upward.

"'A twenty-six-year-old kid,' he said, 'and they give him an office like that!'"

6

Concepts and innovation

"This development is of such fundamental importance that it would be difficult indeed to overstate the magnitude of change that will take place in the lives of all of us, and in human history, as a result of the information revolution that has so unobtrusively taken place in our own day. One would be hard put to find the least evidence of popular understanding of what it means."

JOHN DIEBOLD, ADDRESS AT THE XI INTERNATIONAL MANAGEMENT CONGRESS, PARIS, JUNE 26, 1957.

JOHN DIEBOLD has not only produced, from the seed of an idea, a many-branched and multimillion-dollar business, but he has made major substantive contributions to the entire concept of automation. These conceptual innovations are, in fact, of far greater meaning than the astonishing business success story of the man, a story that is likely to impress people far more than the intangible philosophies that have made it possible.

It is significant that Diebold is already the subject of a scholarly study, "The Managerial Innovations of John Diebold," by Mary Stephens-Caldwell Henderson, published by the Le Baron Foundation and based upon a master's thesis submitted to the School of Government, Business and International Affairs at

George Washington University. Referring to the fact that her subject had been called "Mr. Automation" by the London *Times* and "the world's expert on the subject" by author Andrew Bluemle in his book, *Automation,* Miss Henderson writes, "Automation is not, however, the only area in which he has had fresh insights. His innovations have ranged from a new way of looking at the meaning of productivity figures to ideas for revamping the theories of organization which have been accepted since the beginning of the Industrial Revolution. . . ."

When Diebold wrote "The Significance of Productivity Data" for the *Harvard Business Review* in 1952, many people were operating under the erroneous belief that the productivity of workers increased at a steady two per cent per year, the same rate as had been the national average of the previous fifty years. It was left to Diebold, an industrial neophyte of only twenty-six at the time, to try to convince his supposedly sophisticated audience that not only could this average *not* be counted on in any given year for any given industry, but that the output of specified groups of workers might actually be on the decline while the national rate was rising.

Diebold's viewpoint was so constructive that the U. S. Commissioner of Labor Statistics personally began to look into the questions which the young author raised. The net result of Diebold's study of the situation was that he laid the basis for a new and different concept to serve as a guide to management, an approach that he called *output per man-hour analysis.* Briefly, this was a theory developed to show how *productivity accounting* could provide management with a system comparable, in the financial structure of business, to cost accounting and profit-and-loss data.

Another area of innovation can be seen, according to Miss Henderson, in Diebold's study of the automatic factory. Although this was based on what sounded like a discussion of largely mechanical procedures, "Making the Automatic Factory a Reality," it went far beyond physical concepts. Businessmen and industrialists, said Diebold in the early 1950's, were concentrating far too much on gadgetry and the fascinating new control mechanisms that were being made available by manufacturers. To develop commercial applications properly, he said, the would-be users would have to devote far more time to studying the problems and implications than simply to think, say, in terms of engineering specifications and equipment comparisons.

"A Diebold innovation of major importance," writes Miss Henderson, "which dates from the very early 1950's is his concept of 'rethinking.'" He was disturbed by the prevalent attitude that industrial improvement was a matter of examining existing processes and machines and then simply improving certain components or extending their capabilities. As he pointed out, managers who tried to reproduce human motions mechanically were ending up with technological monstrosities—"Rube Goldberg devices of stupendous proportions" that could be added to *ad absurdum*. Diebold suggested that the production processes should be analyzed in terms of *functions* that had to be performed, instead of looking at the steps that already existed, all the while rethinking the entire operation.

By 1956, owning or at least having access to a computer was regarded in many industries as a kind of fashionable status symbol. Unfortunately, the eager acquisition of machines did not always justify their extremely high cost. For a period of two or three years, management blissfully accepted the latest in the supermachine world without critically assessing the real needs.

Consequently, it came as a painful shock to many a manufacturer to find out that the new technology, instead of making his dreams come true, had brought him to the precipice of financial disaster. One highly skilled producer of auto body frames—to cite an example—lost nearly $10,000,000 in the attempt to convert a single plant to automation. In another case, a major utilities company was forced to return its large-scale computer to the manufacturer. Despite two years of advance planning, those responsible for the installation had greatly underestimated the running time of the daily billing cycle. Hence the machine, through no fault of its own, was in no way adequate to the assignment.

Manufacturers, too, were having their headaches. One lost $7,000,000 in a relatively short period of time, trying to break into what it thought was going to be a technological gold mine. That was some ten years ago, and today the stakes are almost twenty times as large!

In 1957, Diebold and his associates made a study of some two hundred installations. About 34 per cent of the firms using large-

scale computers, 44 per cent of the middle-scale users and more
than 50 per cent of the small-scale users were distinctly unhappy,
feeling that the results had failed to match their original antici-
pations. The reason these firms were experiencing such problems
was, as Diebold saw it, that they were viewing computer applications as purely technical problems instead of as managerial
ones. They were permitting—even encouraging—technicians to
make decisions that should have come from management. In the
middle and late fifties, Diebold was beginning to make some
managers aware of their responsibility to *manage*. But the job was
not an easy one.

Looking at the situation almost ten years later, Miss Henderson
found that the problem was still greatly unresolved in many areas
and that business was still failing to grasp a real understanding of
the new information technology. "As of the spring of 1965," she
wrote, "there are three major conceptions with which John Diebold is concerned and which he is starting to make known in the
way he did earlier with some of the other innovations. . . . One
is that a major obstacle to the effective use of technology is the lack
of a methodology of systems analysis. Another is that businessmen
are not comprehending the impact of technology." The third one
noted in the thesis is that "organizational theory is not keeping
pace with the changed conditions of today's world."

The single greatest need, says Diebold, is that of a methodology. Put into simplified form, what he is actually saying is that,
while industry has the new technological tools, it has not yet
devised any consistent, uniform method for putting the tools to
work. Systems are lacking, and without the systems and the related objectives, the tools cannot be put to coordinated use.

In the area of business planning, the need is for a dynamic
system of total preparation, making use of today's technological
change, rather than planning merely to adjust to the buffeting
of such forces.

As for organizational theory, Diebold feels that our entire structure is badly ready for an overhaul, that it is, in fact, fertile. There
is a need for a new theoretical base. In the spring of 1965, he
took the first of a number of major steps, a ten-year organizational
research program with two main objectives: (1) to examine
present concepts in light of their applicability to today's world
and empirical experiences and (2) to explore neglected fields,

such as the application of useful human experience of the past in training administrators of the future.

One of the most interesting Diebold innovations is his interpretation of information technology as an entrepreneurial opportunity. Many businessmen can grasp the idea of using the new machines as a means for reaching present and future goals more quickly and effectively. Yet few think of it as a vehicle for seeking out entirely new types of goals. Diebold and others who are aware of the potential see the new technology as a development which will determine not only *how* a goal is reached, but actually what new and different goals should be sought to begin with.

The manufacturer of computers may well understand the breadth of the horizons that he can explore, because he is developing the machines themselves and the concepts of what they can do are limitless. But the manufacturer of consumer products and the provider of services is likely to be short-sighted, seeking at most new ways to make his product better and more attractive to buyers, and not deliberately looking for undeveloped fields to enter. Diebold believes that technology creates its own markets, and that the entrepreneurs who can anticipate these new markets are the ones who will reap the ultimate benefits.

Probably the best example of technological invention creating demand, is the case of computers themselves. Originally, it was thought that perhaps a dozen computers could meet the information needs of an entire country. Yet, within little more than a decade after the first real commercial models were on the market, there were more than twenty-two thousand in use, and the market was expanding at an astonishing rate. Similar examples are Xerox and Polaroid, spectacular success stories which came about through technological pioneering. The innovations on which these companies were based not only brought about great changes in existing procedures, but also changed the very types of needs that arose. There was, for example, no real consumer need (or even desire) for instant pictures until Polaroid proved that it could be done at reasonable cost. Today, there is an overwhelming need (and desire) for this kind of photographic reproduction.

And how many people—even businessmen—were greatly concerned over efficient copying machines for office use until Xerox and other companies in this field took pioneering steps to show what could be accomplished?

As Miss Henderson puts it, "By means of the process of the innovation interacting with its environment, the products created their own markets."

The creation of new products, new services and new markets are in themselves of great importance to our civilization. Yet they are only specific elements which collectively represent far-reaching sociological changes. Diebold says that people are not sufficiently aware of the social implications of the new technology. They tend to focus on individual elements (unemployment is a familiar example) and cannot see the forest for the trees. Diebold does not claim that his interpretations of the social effects of automation are "new," for in fact he has been writing and talking about this subject from the very beginning of his career. Yet it is safe to say that his ideas on social change are innovations to most people and in most areas of endeavor.

Many people interpret recent changes as the results of a kind of technological spurt, following World War II, and something that will taper off. Quite the opposite is true. The phenomenon will continue at an increasing rate—a rate directly affected by four dynamics which Diebold points out are now at work. The first of these is the steady population increase, which in itself increases the probability of major innovations. The second is the educational process, now moving at a pace greater than anything known, or even anticipated, in the past. Thirdly, the expansion and perfection of various systems of communication foster an environment receptive to change and conducive to innovations and pioneering. Lastly, vast changes are made possible through research and development programs sponsored by private and government organizations alike. The $280,000,000 spent on research and development through all sources in 1940 was less than three per cent of the sum spent in 1959. And, according to Diebold, an estimated $20,000,000,000 will be spent annually for this purpose by 1970.

With these four factors, and others, at work, new technologies will change our entire approach to work, to society and to life itself. Perspectives will be vastly broadened. Only since the end of World War II has peacetime industry in general really begun to think internationally instead of just domestically. Today, even small companies are hustling to establish links overseas. This metamorphosis has come about to a great extent through improved communications. No longer is it too soon for great corporations to think in terms of what may happen when communities are established in outer space. And already considerable thought has been given to the legal implications of who is entitled to what.

In a more immediate way, entrepreneurs are giving thought to that vast unknown world that is closer at hand: inner space. Who can lay claim to the deep recesses of the seas, and what are the commercial and sociological implications?

One example of what is being done may be seen in the current work of the Westinghouse Electric Corporation, which created an Underseas Division of the company's Defense and Space Center to explore the mysterious realm that lies beneath more than 70 per cent of the earth's surface. Westinghouse is one of a growing list of pioneering corporations trying to anticipate the tremendous sociological changes that will be taking place as technology leads man further and further away from the mores and habitats now familiar to him.

"We will need to explore and develop systems of education not yet known, in order to prepare people to live and get along in these new environments," says John Diebold, thinking of the new worlds being created on earth and beyond.

The worlds are not always physical and as graphically definable as a futuristic space house perched on a crater of the moon or an underwater domed apartment anchored in a five-thousand-foot-deep underwater trench. "We must think," says Diebold "of what information technology is doing to change in a very basic way the conditions and future of mankind. It is making possible the production of materials and the perfection of formulas that will affect the evolutionary process itself. It will shortly enable us to alter the molecular structure of DNA, the template of the genetic code. It has already made possible the development of 'artificial intelligences,' machines which improve their performance as a result of encountering a certain environment or set of situations. Man must make a monumental effort to evolve psychological, spiritual and philosophical systems capable of dealing with changes which are so overwhelming and so totally unprecedented."

7

Broadening the concepts of mankind

"Automation, and other technological advances as well, demands an ability to adapt to rapid change. Change in our frame of reference, change in the perimeters of our everyday world, is continual and increasing rapidly. Training in specific skills, greater and greater specialization, is a desperate and misguided reaction to such change. It is self-defeating, for today's specialty is replaced by tomorrow's new need."

JOHN DIEBOLD, GREAT ISSUES LECTURE, DELIVERED AT DARTMOUTH COLLEGE, HANOVER, NEW HAMPSHIRE, 1957.

QUITE APART from his recognized accomplishments as an innovator, John Diebold is something of a gourmet, who recognizes and appreciates both traditional and creative products of the culinary art. It was with some astonishment then that a friend reacted to a minor incident that took place in one of New York's finest French restaurants during a luncheon.

When the waiter took the drink order, Diebold, instead of asking for the expected aperitif, said, "I don't know what you call it, but I'll have a glass filled half with tomato juice and half with beer."

The waiter blinked noticeably, but a few minutes later returned with the concoction, as requested. Diebold hesitantly took a sip and announced to his friends, "It isn't really bad at all."

Replied the waiter, "It looks like a Bloody Mary, but I call it a Bloody Shame."

Asked how he had come to make such a selection in the first place, Diebold said that the president of one of his client companies had described the drink. "So I decided to try it, just for a change. It's hardly traditional, but I like to try things. I find—and I think many of us find—that we go along in some accepted manner, or using a familiar system without ever breaking out of it, to see what's on the other side.

"I don't mean to use beer and tomato juice as an excuse for launching into an academic lecture, but more and more we are finding that the reluctance to change is one of the big problems roadblocking automation and technological change today."

There are any number of examples of this reluctance to change, not only on the part of, say, manufacturers or businessmen who might use automation, but on the part of consumers and honest citizens who have mental blocks when it comes to accepting some of the changes that are instituted. A case in point might be that of the New York City Transit Authority.

When the City of New York a few years ago publicized the news that it was about to operate a fully automated subway train on the short shuttle run between Times Square and Grand Central Station, not a few strap hangers of long standing shuddered with a reaction approaching sheer terror. It was bad enough to experience the daily frustrations and hazards of having pincer-like doors closing on one's feet and being jammed in during the rush hours like herds of cattle off to the slaughter. But what would happen with no motorman to prevent the whole rolling package of humanity from slamming at full speed into the buttress at the end of the line? Who would calm the panic-stricken mob inside if the doors failed to open and there was no official on hand to work emergency releases?

And what if a breakdown occurred somewhere in the middle and everyone was stranded in limbo, at the mercy of cantankerous electronic devices that perhaps were just smart enough to want to annihilate mankind and take over the world?

In short, although a goodly crowd of the curious, the adventuresome or the just plain ignorant, who didn't know they were on an automated train, began using the regular run, it was evident that many an old hand did not trust the city's new wizardry and preferred to stick with the unautomated trains that still continued the run under human guidance.

Automated elevators have become accepted in the larger cities, but only after a considerable amount of anguish on the part of the unwilling users who, because of moves to new buildings or modernization of old ones, found themselves at the mercy of the new contraptions. A few people, upon hearing that the buildings they lived or worked in were to be automated, announced that they would climb the stairs rather than succumb to mechanical integration. Eventually of course, most of them gave in—after seeing that fellow human beings were surviving the revolution without loss of life or limb.

You can reason with people that an operator is not—despite tradition—necessary to safe, efficient and speedy rail transportation. You can demonstrate that operatorless automatic elevators are actually safer and many times more convenient than the old type, but you cannot break down the resistance of a certain percentage of the population until the innovation has been in use for so long that it finally becomes old hat.

The doubts continue to persist as vague, underlying fears, rising sharply to the surface whenever old, familiar methods or things give way to machines. All of which indicates that mankind, sociologically, is not entirely ready for automation. During the two decades since World War II, we have trended in the direction of specialization, as far as jobs are concerned. Engineers, technicians, doctors, business executives, educators and others have found their fields broadening so fast that they must limit themselves to smaller and smaller areas, just to keep abreast of new developments. In doing so, many specialists have unwittingly left themselves wide open for exploitation and uprooting by machines, because machines can be crammed with everything there is to know about one narrow subject field, so that they can provide the optimum in service within that limited scope. Night and day—for 24 hours a day, 168 hours a week if necessary—they can concentrate on specialized problems. The noted inventor and innovator R. Buckminster ("Bucky") Fuller put it this way recently: ". . . The machine is about to make man obsolete as a specialist because the machine can differentiate and seek out much more accurately, swiftly and persistently than man can."

John Diebold, however, approaches the matter as a positive challenge, to be met by a reorientation of attitudes towards education. "The easiest mistake one can make," he says, "and certainly the most common, is to assume that scientific training must be the root of all education in the future, and that only those trained as scientists will play important roles. This is a mistake not because technology is unimportant, but because what is truly important, both for technology and for society as a whole, is orderly thinking, and orderly thinking is neither necessarily nor exclusively developed by studying science."

Thus, in a broadly educational sense, as well as in a strictly occupational sense, man is going to have to broaden his concepts, whether he likes it or not. Automation is a culmination of social and scientific change. Yet it has come about not through any sudden technological advance, but through a cumulative process over the years. Even the great breakthroughs that have made automation possible are—like a volcanic eruption—simply the dramatic, visible signs of upheavals that have been in progress for a long time. Too frequently, the sudden breakthroughs are directly associated with inventions, or some kind of physical evidence of progress. Thus, the computer has come to symbolize automation. But the computer itself is not nearly as significant to the broad concept of automation as is the sociological pattern that developed over many years and made possible the revolutionary changes in man's ability to communicate.

The philosopher Alfred North Whitehead described the Industrial Revolution of the late eighteenth and early nineteenth centuries as a time of great upheaval, suffering and calamity. The problems, however, as he explained, were not caused so much by the mechanical innovations—the steam engine or power-operated looms—as by social and economic deficiencies. No rational, properly planned moves were made to achieve a social breakthrough comparable to the ones being made in the mechanical field. The new world of automation—whether you want to call it the Second Industrial Revolution or any other name—faces a crisis of the same kind, and in overwhelmingly greater proportions.

Speaking at the time as Secretary of Commerce Luther H. Hodges said in a speech on the theme, "Automation: the Challenge of Change," that we can forge ahead in the new technology "only as fast as we meet our social and economic responsibilities to those workers and families whose livelihood is affected by change. Regrettably, we are not—we are moving much too slowly in these areas." He went on to point out that technological capabilities must be used to stimulate economic growth, to raise our standard of living and to preserve America's position in the world. But, he cautioned, it cannot be done without imagination and long-range sociological and economic planning. "Massive steps must be taken and they must be taken now," he concluded. "Answers to our automation problems will not come automatically. They will require hard thought and hard work and we don't have much time left to find them."

Part of the "hard thought" is the matter of education, and in this respect the social change and the cultural changeover are almost overwhelming. Traditional concepts no longer hold. It used to be that we thought of education as a chronological process —up to a point. We went to grammar school and high school, and, if reasonably fortunate, to college. After that, for a limited number of people there were graduate schools and law schools, medical schools and other professional courses. By and large, however, education came to a sudden shuddering halt with the award of high school or college diploma. Even on-the-job training courses and other types of specialized programs within the business and industrial fields were rather spotty affairs, often amateurish and usually tacked on, or compressed into, a full schedule of work and normal employment responsibilities.

That concept is changing. Education may become even more important *after* high school and college than it was during the bright student years. Education will be a never-ending process, as important to job-holders at almost all levels as continuation of good health is to their ability to perform well.

Consider the comments made by a Westinghouse executive, A. C. Monteith, who said that a graduate engineer today has a "half-life" of about ten years. What he meant was that half of everything learned and known by an engineer in 1965 would be obsolete by 1975. In addition, about half of what that engineer will need to know in 1975 is *not yet available* for learning today.

The same situation applies in any of the sciences, in the professions generally and in almost any field of endeavor—right on down to clerical and labor ranks which will need to know about systems not yet in acceptance.

Man is not yet accustomed to becoming educationally obsolescent. The realization comes—and will come—as a shock to the Old College Grad, who points with pride to the Ivy League diploma on his wall and says, "I've been educated in the right manner."

"It takes no special insight to spotlight our educational process and philosophy as the major cause of the sputter in our social engine," says Neil W. Chamberlain, professor of economics at Yale. "We are still operating as though a person can acquire in the first twenty years or so of his life all the formal education he needs to keep him on an ascending career through the remaining forty years or so of his working life. But the fact is that the clock starts running down the moment a young man or woman steps from the commencement platform, be it college or high school."

It is a lack of knowledge and understanding that has often put men in embarrassing situations and made them seem like fools in the face of automation. This leads frequently to the criticism that automation is degrading to mankind. John Diebold likes to point to a typical case reported by a newspaper, in which the failure to indoctrinate a man sufficiently led to a touchy situation. A worker who for twenty-seven years had been a job setter at an automobile factory, was shifted to the new automated engine plant, where he sadly discovered that he could not cope with the assignment.

"The machine had about eighty drills and twenty-two blocks going through," the worker told a reporter from New York, "You had to watch all the time. Every few minutes you had to watch to see everything was all right. And the machines had so many lights and switches—about ninety lights. It sure is hard on your mind. If there's a break in the machine the whole line breaks down. But sometimes you make a little mistake, and it's no good for you, no good for the foreman, no good for the company and no good for the union."

The worker lost out to the revolution. He was shifted to a lower job at less pay. He was not ready for automation.

In April, 1965, the Communications Workers of America

published a report, "Automation, Impact and Implications," which had been prepared by The Diebold Group, Inc. It aptly summarized the reasons behind the plight of this kind of "skilled" worker:

"The very meaning of 'skill' is undergoing a transformation from something linked to manual dexterity to something in the realm of responsibility—of being able to handle oneself while in ultimate control of many consequences. . . . The worker's arms get less tired, but he sleeps less well at night.

"This change in the content of 'skill' is why employers with increasing frequency require a worker who, rather than doing one thing well, has the judgment to determine how a number of things are done. Such 'skill' is the result of education—as compared with mere training."

The popular reaction is to suggest that the social change is really only affecting the older people in our society, and that the younger people have no socio-economic problem here in making the adjustment. This attitude has been dramatically, though not openly, demonstrated in the case of a company which has instituted a policy that there are to be no major promotions for men over forty. *Age*, however, is not the problem. Michigan State University has conducted extensive research on the economic and social effects of office automation and has found no relation between age and readiness to change. According to Dr. Einar Hardin, conducting research at MSU, the factors that determine the attitudes and results are a person's economic, social and educational status and background. People with higher status tend to welcome the change as a form of challenge, while those with lower status resist the changes. ". . . Those of higher education are more ready for change than those with a lower education," reported Dr. Hardin. "Those who think of themselves as being more capable than others in organizations are readier for change. Those who are supervisors are readier for change than those who are non-supervisors, and so on."

An interesting fact about attitudes relating to automation has been disclosed by studies of groups whose work has gradually been affected by the installation of computers or other devices that come within the scope of the subject. Often people questioned will say that there has been "no change" or "little change" in their jobs, when in fact there may have been a considerable variation over a period of eight or ten months. Surprisingly, what people *perceive* in their jobs often has nothing whatever to do with what actually has happened in those jobs over a relatively small period of time.

One reason why people do not sense the nature and extent of the great changes taking place is that they think of automation as the introduction of a great amount of machinery, much of it large, dramatic looking and conspicuous. While complex devices are a necessary part of automation, there is a great deal that is not visible, not tangible, not evident. "We must remember," says Dr. Arvid W. Jacobson, one of the nation's leading authorities on data processing, "that the computer is a system. It is an organism on which a business operates ultimately. It becomes the vital organ and line of communication . . . our society is becoming less of a production society and more of a service-industry society."

Many of the misconceptions about automation and its increasing significance in the socio-economic pattern derive from a failure to study the subject in depth and to the degree that is really required. In the fall of 1955, when John Diebold presented the opening testimony at the first Congressional hearing on automation, he proposed that an unbiased and objective study be undertaken, to analyze the real social effects of automation. He said at the time, in part:

> The problem in assessing the economic and social impact of automation is that we do not have the facts. If there is concern over the effects of automation, it seems to me highly desirable that we get these facts in the most expeditious way possible: through a thorough analysis of automation based upon a complete, factual, industry-wide investigation. Such a study would provide for the first time, a realistic basis for planning on both a national and a private scale. With the broader perspective such a study would provide, industry could plan automation policy with a finer regard for the consequences. National policy concerning education and training programs, retirement benefits and unemployment compensation must be based on factual and intimate understanding of the subject.

Despite Diebold's farsighted plea, the Congressional hearings did little to stimulate real study.

Some three years later, a translation from the German of a book by Frederick Pollock on the social consequences of automation repeatedly emphasized the fact that no serious studies had been made, or were even contemplated. "No one," he wrote, "has given a detailed account of the extent to which automation has actually taken place in the United States. . . . And no information was available concerning plans for automation in the immediate future."

As Diebold remarked not long ago, Mr. Pollock—despite his emphasis on the point that there was no real information on the subject—did not hesitate "to portray a technocratic society with a small ruling class of engineers as something to expect as a result of automation. Until the facts are known, unfounded prophecies and unsubstantiated courses of action will continue to dominate the picture given to the public. The results can be disastrous to our nation and to our way of life, and it becomes more and more vital each day to find out the truth."

Well, as in the case of everything else unknown, said the commentators, no one was really dying to jump in and till the land until a few predecessors had broken their ploughs against the hidden rocks. Studies would come along soon enough. Yet at the end of one full decade from the time Diebold testified before the first Congressional hearing on automation, except for his own firm's 182-page report to the Communications Workers of America in 1965, few studies had been launched, and most of them were isolated, limited or highly academic.

It is contradictory and ironic that a word which has captured attention as forcefully as "automation" has captured it should, in itself, be socially misunderstood. It is a word that usually produces an extreme reaction rather than an objective appraisal. The alarmists at one end of the scale see a destructive social upheaval in which machines take over and every one is out of work, while the faddists at the other end voice contentions that computers are going to solve all the problems of humanity.

In a monograph prepared for the National Planning Association, John Diebold lists a series of arguments for and against automation, pointing out that "it should be remembered that these points of view are argued with a vehemence that varies in inverse

79

proportion to the facts available." And he adds, "What we must avoid is a state of affairs in which national policy will be set by the group that shouts the loudest."

Among the arguments circulated by those who fear destructive social upheaval are:

1) Job opportunities cannot grow as fast as necessary.
2) Markets will become saturated. There will be fewer workers turning out the same amount of products, because there is a certain point beyond which additional units are not absorbed.
3) Mass unemployment will result because there will never be enough purchasing power to buy all the excess goods.
4) Automation means the subjugation of man by the machine.

The optimists, on the other hand, say that:

1) Automation automatically creates just as many jobs as it eliminates.
2) Automation is nothing new, so there is no reason for concern. Technological changes have occurred throughout history without dire results, and automation is just another technological change.
3) Unlimited demand for goods and services will prevent unemployment from automation. Since human wants are unlimited, increased productivity and production through automation will find a market in satisfying these wants.

The reason for the weakness of these arguments, Diebold states, is that as they now stand there are no facts to back them up. There are no data on which to base an evaluation of their worth. The truth may lie somewhere in between, but it may be years before society finds out exactly what the facts are.

One of the dangers to our society lies in a factor which the companies and industries that use automation heavily are most vociferous in condemning: government intervention. Since neither private industry nor local governments have initiated comprehensive studies of automation, it is evident that sooner or later the federal government will step in to play a dominant role.

Although we do not know one-tenth of what we should about the social implications of automation, we do know from history that machines have played a formidable part in transforming civilization. Automation, on a comparative basis, is so significant in its current and future role that it stands about as far above other advances in technology as the first atomic bomb did over conventional bombs of World War II. Automation represents tremendous social impact because it is not a single remarkable invention, but an entire way of life: it is communications and control, labor, manufacture, transportation, research and development and a thousand other things. It can translate from one language to another; perform intricate mathematical computations within split seconds; control satellites in outer space; design technical structures; beat man at his own clever games.

Automation is being used experimentally to study juvenile delinquency and the patterns of criminal behavior. It has assisted in psychoanalysis, by computing the number of times a patient used certain words over and over again. It is taking inventories and keeping track of finances and educating students.

Not only will mankind's physical and metaphysical concepts undergo a revolution, but our entire science of psychology will be affected. International outlooks and developments will evolve as language barriers become broken down and communication between nations and peoples is strengthened. Political and economic philosophies will require intensive reevaluation. And even our art and other aspects of culture will be deeply affected.

In any discussion of social revolution, there is always a conspicuous group of pessimists ready to point out the evils of change and the sure destruction of the human race that is likely to come about as a result. These critics repeatedly point to the examples of failures, the people who go downhill rather than up because the innovations have been too much for their sensitive souls. Then too, as one of technology's outstanding spokesmen, Dr. Vannevar Bush, expressed it: "A certain very small percentage of humans will abuse the new society which will come forth: slackers, malingerers, free-loaders, bums—whatever you wish to call them. But such drones have always been with us. They constitute a very small (and essentially sick) fraction of humanity. A fairly constant activity of mind and body characterizes the overwhelming majority of human beings. Indeed, society's severest punishment, next to execution itself, is deprivation of normal, free activity—to wit, imprisonment."

In an address before the New School for Social Research, the late Ambassador Adlai E. Stevenson pointed out that more than two thousand years ago Aristotle predicted that when looms could weave by themselves man's slavery would end. "At long last," said Stevenson, "looms *are* weaving by themselves today and we are fast approaching the time when machines will perform pretty much every other form of drudgery.

"It's no longer a question of whether this is bad or good for the world. The inescapable fact is that it's happening and the process can't be reversed—not even if we react as did the people of Samuel Butler's Erewhon or the working men of England more than a century ago. Destroying the machine will not halt the march. It never has, not since Adam discovered the advantages of putting a rib to work for him. . . .

"I am sure, however, that we in this country must alter our entire thinking about machines—a thinking that has changed little since the days of the Industrial Revolution. As with the nuclear bomb, we will have to learn to live with automation. And somehow we will have to develop a philosophy and control unique to it alone. Only thus can we avert a disaster of massive unemployment and discontent; only thus can we realize the opportunity of abundance for all, not only in material things, but in better health, education and cultural attainment."

There are no confines where automation is concerned. Today, IBM is successfully pioneering with the use of computers in Africa and Asia, applying new forms of communication to developing nations. How soon, asks IBM, can a few well educated people obtain enough skills to manage a modern economy? There is no answer—yet.

"At least," said one African government official, "we have this advantage. We can leapfrog the trial-and-error stages, and begin fresh with your newest tools and guidance."

That is why, in some of the most unlikely backwaters in the world, the latest computers are beginning to muster a kind of technological peace corps. In Nigeria, IBM equipment is helping to manage the nation's railroads. In Morocco, a computer is the heart of the country's first social security system. Elsewhere, the tools of automation are analyzing statistics to determine the best locations for roadbeds, to harness water power, and even to tell which crops would be most profitable to grow.

The social revolution is upon us, whether we like it or not.

8

The new profession

> "We are professionals in this field and we must
> do all that we can in guiding this profession.
> But we also have to understand that we are
> riding in the center of a hurricane which is
> changing society and we have as individuals
> and professionals a much wider responsibility."
>
> JOHN DIEBOLD, ADDRESS BEFORE THE DATA PROC-
> ESSING MANAGEMENT ASSOCIATION, SAN FRAN-
> CISCO, 1964.

ALTHOUGH THE SOCIAL revolution is here, as has just been demonstrated, many do not realize it, and among those who realize the fact, many do not comprehend it.

"It is easy to understand why non-business people might not
see the implications," says John Diebold, "why they would have
persistent fears about automation, or misconceptions of what it
is and what it can do. Yet this same naivete persists even among
the more sophisticated companies. We have found that some users
of the new tools of information technology will invest five or six
years of effort into developing systems, only to find them obsolete when finally completed."

The situation is alarming, not just because it will affect great
corporations and their millions of employees, but because consumers themselves are going to feel the ultimate effects as business and industry pass along to them higher costs for products

and services to help pay for the initial corporate misdirection. "In order to avoid both economic and social disaster," says Diebold, "we need to ascertain the shape of the future."

Diebold and his associates study information systems in an effort to avoid the disasters he speaks of and, more positively, to assist clients in achieving certain specific goals. As an example, the Group recently developed a method for using data processing equipment to help a company meet competition, where technology was improving products almost faster than manufacturers could adapt to the changes. It advised a computer manufacturer about new uses that would open up in the publishing field. And it helped another client, an office-equipment maker, to open Federal research and development markets that would effectively utilize its capabilities.

Diebold utilizes management information systems, not only to anticipate future technological developments, but to open up the new dimensions of the mind he spoke of. Such studies suggest simulation techniques by which it is possible to approximate different kinds of situations without the expense of actually installing the systems and testing costly equipment.

One of the most remarkable uses of simulation, for example, is the analysis now being made by Pan American World Airways of supersonic aircraft. Although many of the aircraft models being tested will not be available—even in prototype form—until 1972 or later, the study can be conducted through simulation. Pan Am engineers program supersonic jet specification figures into the company's Panamac computer system. By adding other pertinent data, such as weather statistics and operations information on existing, or proposed, airfields around the world, Pan Am comes up with basic indications as to how different types of supersonic jets—still on the drawing boards—would perform.

In a completely different situation, yet oddly enough in a somewhat parallel manner, The Diebold Group recently used mathematical models and data processing to aid in the selection of advertising media. By feeding cost factors, statistics on population shifts, and facts about competing media into the machine, the Group was able to advise a large metropolitan newspaper in the matter of readjusting advertising rates. Without this approach, the newspaper would have had to run expensive and time-consuming tests in the areas under consideration.

During the short life span of the computer on the international scene, as has already been pointed out, countless mistakes have been made and unknown millions of dollars wasted because of misguided concepts of automation. As a result of these costly errors, the growing field of automation has steadily attracted a brand new breed of enterpreneurs, many of them young, like John Diebold, whose aim is to explore the problems of automation, seek out answers and serve as counselors to clients in need. While quite a few firms, already in existence in the mid-1950's, ultimately moved into the automation field from broader bases of consulting, The Diebold Group is unique in that it started in automation and has steadily broadened its horizons as automation itself has broadened. Diebold, in fact, was regularly under attack during the early days by far larger competitors, who had lagged in evaluating the coming impact of automation.

Within a few years, however, the vindictiveness had largely vanished from the competitive scene and Diebold was recognized as one of the top international entrepreneurs in the consulting field.

In the eyes of many people—even business executives—an entrepreneur, a professional in the field of automation, is a man who holds a scientific degree and spends most of his time advising clients about computers and other data processing machines. While this is a big, and growing business, men like John Diebold will seldom be found at the controls of a machine—or even looking at one. They deal in *ideas*. They work with problems, many of them intangible, to develop systems and approaches and policies. They are not competing with nuts and bolts, or even microseconds and nanoseconds and picoseconds, but with conceptual problems.

When John Diebold & Associates, Inc., was changed in 1961 to The Diebold Group, Inc., the conversion represented the acceptance of the group concept of organization as it is practiced in Europe. It was one of the first such reorganizations on the part of an American company, thus providing a range of management services for clients through the concept of functionally specialized companies (all either wholly or largely owned subsidiaries of the holding company) which together complete the Group.

"One of the principal reasons for organizing as a group," explains Diebold, "was that I felt strongly that in the future, the old concept of the management consulting firm is going to run into increasing difficulty. Strong technical capability will be a necessary attribute, in order to understand and appreciate the more global aspects of any of the problems facing business. In a sense, firms are faced with the alternative of being generalists or being specialists. My feeling has always been that the generalist is going to be less and less capable of coping with the global problems unless there is a solid foundation of technical and specialized knowledge.

"The 'group' concept is that of maintaining a generalist organization to deal with business and technical planning at the top level, but supported by specialized legs. Each leg, in turn, is organized as a separate entity, so that it thrives or atrophies depending upon its proven capability in its own field."

Clients of the Group come to it, not so much for correcting existing inadequacies as for planning for the future. They include many of the top blue-chip corporations, such as Xerox, General Electric, IBM, Sperry-Rand, Westinghouse, IT&T, Phillips, Ford and Boeing.

The Diebold Group tackles some 300 assignments each year. While these projects deal with a wide variety of problems, the element common to nearly all of them is a concern with the business and management problems arising when science, technology and advanced techniques are put to work. The new tools of science and technology raise new managerial problems. It is a concern with these problems—the task of putting to work the tools of science and management—that characterizes the great bulk of the professional practice of the firm.

One such area of major creative activity is that in which the Diebold research program operates. The basic program, under Diebold leadership, is sponsored by upwards of eighty companies, not only in computer manufacturing and electronics, but in such diverse fields as petroleum, insurance, light manufacturing and railroading. A complementary program has also been established in the publishing industry. The focal point of the whole program, which involves expenditures of almost a million dollars a year, is on the problems faced by companies which require medium-to-large information processing systems.

One reason why Diebold had conceived and launched the

program in the first place was his belief that a troublesome gap existed between the kinds of systems that companies were planning for and the actual equipment that was available, or soon to become available. The purpose, then, was to bring together computer manufacturing companies and using companies, to facilitate a better understanding of managerial and technological objectives. A major aspect of the effort has been the evaluation of outstanding developments in military and space technology, in order to forecast which of these might carry over into the commercial field, and within what period of time. In anticipating the future, the Diebold staff has discovered that there is a fairly direct lead-lag relationship between military and commercial systems, of from three to five years.

There are, within the Group, several functional areas of professional activity.

The area of business planning includes the development of corporate and marketing strategies, not only within advanced technological areas, but within the whole broad field of management concern, which is being changed radically by developments in information and other technologies.

The Diebold Group applies programed learning to problems of business and professional training. It does not confine this, or other programs to business and industry, however. Many assignments have centered on improving the effectiveness of welfare and institutional operations. One example of this type of activity was a computerized survey of hospitals in the Philadelphia area, to determine the most suitable location of beds and facilities in line with current and expected population shifts. A major purpose of the study was to make more effective use of hospitals, and thus cut down the increasingly heavy demands on donors for funds to support new construction.

The Group is also heavily engaged in developing marketing information and planning, covering analyses of distribution and profit, measuring the market for new products and services, improving the positions of companies in defense markets and studying buying motivations abroad.

Diebold has long encouraged a large, and ever-growing publishing program for his staff, and for outside subscribers. The goal of this program is to "disseminate information on new techniques and technologies for management on which other sources of information appear inadequate."

Among these are:

Professional Paper Series, with monographs by staff members on "The Editor and Automation," "Mechanical Aids to Legal Research," "A New Look at the Machine Tool Industry," "Program Generators," and other subjects relating to automation in many fields.

Reprint Series, with reprints of articles or speeches presented by staff members or those associated with the firm. Some representative titles are "Electronic Data Processing for Hospitals," "Trade Policies Since World War II," "What Should Bank Management Expect from Automation?" and "How to Improve Defense Marketing Intelligence."

ADP Newsletter, a bi-weekly news publication, edited by the Group, which provides practical information and guidance on the latest applications and market developments in commercial and scientific information systems.

"The farther afield we reach," says Diebold, "and the more we cover broad bases, the greater becomes our responsibility to learn, to disseminate information, to communicate with each other. You can see what happens when we project what is going on in and around 430 Park Avenue to the far borders of the United States, and then overseas."

The Diebold Group is now involved, for example, with applying new techniques and technology to help upgrade geographic regions, or even entire nations. Through the use of programed learning in developing literacy and basic skills, largely illiterate population sectors are enabled to participate in programs designed to raise levels of educational activity. Through the application of modern management science techniques, methods are being perfected for improving fiscal and administrative procedures and overall systems designs for governmental operations. A recent project has been the Group's participation in a four-year program to improve the administrative procedures used in the Venezuelan government, including thirteen government ministries, the office of the president and the city of Caracas, through application of automatic data processing (ADP) techniques and the orientation of government officials.

Another activity has been the development of product specifications for U.S. and foreign markets, studying ways whereby clients could penetrate markets abroad, recommending data processing systems for European firms and exploring joint-venture programs abroad.

Diebold, who employs many foreigners, both at home and abroad, for his staff, has long been conscious of the international aspects of automation. Although he says that "in the practical application of automation concepts and techniques to industry, the United States leads the world at the present time," he adds a cautionary note. He warns against underestimating the progress of the Soviet Union and says, "It would also be a mistake to take a complacent attitude toward European business. Though we 'out-automate' Europe by sheer volume alone, their level of sophistication in automatic techniques is high, especially in factory automation."

Perhaps more than any other American in his field, John Diebold has a first-hand familiarity with the international scene. His Group numbers among its clients such major European firms as Agfa, Ciba, Lancia, Necchi, Olivetti, Roger et Gallet, Swiss Bank Corporation, and Union Industrielles des Pétroles. Diebold himself constantly attends, and often addresses, outstanding international conferences, like the International Management Congress in Paris, the European Community Conference in Brussels and the British Institute of Management. Reactions abroad have been highly favorable. After a Diebold speech to the latter Institute, for example, London's *Financial Times* headlined him as an "elder statesman" of automation and went on to say that someone should tell the President of the United States "to make him an ambassador. He could do more to make Americans popular abroad in half an hour than most of the career diplomats could in a year."

As early as 1956, John Diebold was planning ways of communicating his ideas and theories abroad. In 1957, he instituted a course on computer use that was attended by more than a hundred businessmen in Milan, Italy. By 1958, he had initiated the first of a series of ten one-week seminars to be given in different European cities, starting in London and covering the Continent. These programs were the first of their type ever to be presented abroad.

It is an interesting—perhaps significant—fact that, at the start of his career, Diebold found a much greater acceptance in Europe, of himself and of his ideas, than he had found in the United States. In part, it was a personal acceptance, for any number of European friends and business associates have commented that in his manner and in his approach, he was "not like an American." Others have commented that his reserve and his very wide interest in subjects beyond obvious business were attractive to Europeans.

The story is told that not long ago when Diebold was in Germany, the president of the major computer manufacturing company there beckoned him over to the window of his office, pointed out across acres of factory and said, "Mr. Diebold, I would like to thank you for this."

When Diebold, looking puzzled, asked him what he meant, the reply came back, "When you came to this country in 1958 on a visit, there were three computers in Germany. You awoke German managment to the computer through your many training courses and your talks, and this is what grew from it."

The Diebold research program was quick to catch hold in Europe, largely because Europeans readily became aware of the time lag in matters of technology and the urgent need for advanced information. Since there was not nearly so much of an aerospace industry in Western Europe as in the United States, and not much space effort in general, the very advanced information technology tended not to filter through to European industry for a long time after discoveries were made. The European section of the Diebold research program now includes, in addition to IBM, such top corporations as ITT, English Electric-Leo, Olivetti, Shell, Netherlands PTT, Imperial Chemical, St. Gobain, Siemens & Halske, Progil and Netherlands Government Mines.

Some indication of the growing activity in Europe may be seen in the findings of a 1965 census of European computers by The Diebold Group. In the key computer-using nations of continental Europe, there were 71 per cent more computers installed by the end of 1964 than there were by the end of 1963. The greatest developments were in Germany where computer installation rose from 996 at the end of 1963, to 1,657 a year later, and in France where the percentage advance was almost 90 per cent.

Yet, although Diebold is directly concerned with the most far-reaching aspects of automation at home and abroad, he is also steadily attentive to his own immediate housekeeping. At one of the many luncheon discussions he regularly holds in the convertible dining-conference room in the firm's New York offices, he recently focused the discussion on problems of communication within the Group, and possible solutions to them. "We need better methods of briefing," he said, "on such internal matters as the nature of the firm, how to familiarize ourselves with different arms of business, comparisons of procedures in the United States and Europe."

There are so many activities for staff members to keep in mind that the company publishes a 32-page "Group Calendar," which may list upwards of 40 important events in any one month. A sampling one month includes G-K Staff Planning Conference, Professional Development Meeting, Management Council Meeting, Group Executive Committee Meeting, Programed Learning Meeting, Mathematical Services N. meeting, Fifth U.S. and Third European Research Project Joint Meeting, Seminar-Diebold-Deutschland, MSTI Course, Chicago, National Automation Conference and Research Project Planning Meeting.

As the company expanded, an individual's knowledge of it tended to thin out. "We find that in past relationships," said Diebold, "a lot of information was in the head. People began to *assume* that every one knew certain facts, when in reality they did not."

Diebold has come to insist that his staff members keep meticulous records, especially when talking with new, or prospective, clients.

"*Who* are the people you have just met? *What* are their positions and problems? *What* are they doing?" He maintains long lists of people, to whom he and several of his staff members conscientiously send newspaper clippings, books, magazine articles, technical documents and other material they feel might be of interest or value.

"We are a graduate school," says Diebold to his executives, "Look at it this way. We are following a process of continuing education. Our business depends upon intelligence and knowledge. As you encounter things and facts and situations in the field, get them back to us by communication. Let every one know. Read professional reports constantly. Browse in the library. Keep learning. Read, read, read."

Diebold himself is a good example of the type of reader so frequently termed voracious. Not being satisfied with his pace, however, he completed a course in speed reading, in order to cover more ground. There are books in every available shelf and recess of his elegant Manhattan apartment. Next to his bed he keeps a night table crammed with books he is currently reading ("I tend to read a number in parallel")." Recently, among some forty-five books squeezed into the table, with its four sturdy legs and gilded Bombay front, were the following examples of widely scattered interests:

The Rise and Splendor of the Chinese Empire by Rene Grousset; *Burn After Reading* (World War II espionage) by Ladislas Farago; *Anatomy of Britain* by Anthony Sampson; *The View from a Distant Star* by Harlow Shapley; *Napoleon* by André Maurois; *Business Decisions that Changed our Lives* by Sidney Furst and Milton Sherman; *Power in Washington* by Douglass Cater; *The American Revolution* by George Otto Trevelyan; *Confessions of an Advertising Man* by David Ogilvy; *The Board of Directors in Small Corporations* by Miles L. Mace; *The Living Sea* by Captain J. Y. Costeau; *Life*'s Science volume on mathematics; *Hitler, A Study in Tyranny* by Alan Bullock; *The First Five Years of Life* by Arnold Gessel; *The Making of the President—1964,* by Theodore H. White; and *Decision Making in the White House* by Theodore C. Sorensen.

A problem that consistently bothers Diebold is that as consultants he and his associates must accumulate information on many clients in order to tackle their problems to begin with, yet much of the information must be held confidential. "We're constantly privy to highly sensitive information. Leakage could affect certain stock prices, or touch on anti-trust matters. Our relationship with clients is similar to that of a lawyer—we have the strictest ethical and moral obligations."

Another element he stresses is detail. "We must be meticulous in our work with clients, paying perhaps even more attention to the details than we would in running our own business. It is the little things that count," says Diebold, adding a piece of advice he like to quote frequently from Michelangelo, *"Trifles make perfection, but perfection is no trifle."*

He emphasizes to his staff that the entire relationship with a company may depend upon the impression the client gets of the staff members he meets for the first time: their dress, decorum, manner of speaking and other personal factors. This is communication, just as much as the vital function of getting a client to understand what a consultant does, or can do.

So, too, is listening. "To *listen,*" Diebold asserts again and again, "is one of the capabilities one has to learn to develop. Sometimes it takes months of listening to determine what a client really needs. Things that would be trivial in many companies may be vital to this particular one. We must determine the relationships, the values of the small things."

As one of his associates added, "Knowing when not to talk is essential. Clients are not interested in our problems. We have to learn to keep those to ourselves. It's like taking your illness, your problem, to a doctor. You want him to listen to you and then come up with a remedy. You don't want him to say, "Just a tummy ache. That's nothing. Let me tell you about the aches *I* have."

In his dealings with staff members, Diebold tends to be a good communicator. He observes. He listens well. He expresses himself with enthusiasm and interest. He is forthright, too. At a recent meeting for young executives who had recently joined the Group, he said, after briefing them on communications, "Every one is not attuned to consulting. Our British firm expresses the opinion that only about 20 per cent of the staff members remain in consulting. If you find that you don't like consulting, I can understand this point of view. Talk it over with us. We are in a good position, because of client relationships and other exposures, to help people into other positions. Whatever happens, take an open approach. There have been only a few times when a client has come in and spirited off a staff member. But when it's done behind our backs, it never seems to work out. The men get into wildly incompatible situations.

"Think in terms, not of what you are doing today, but what you want to be doing five years from now, or in the future." (This is a typical Diebold outlook on everything, from people to business to personal matters.)

Diebold finds himself constantly looking for new talent, a search made more difficult by the fact that his is a new profession, with few precedents to use as guides. When it comes to a showdown between the quantitative and the qualitative, Diebold will invariably choose the latter. Stated more precisely, his ingrained perfectionism will not let him do otherwise. Yet there is a constant inner conflict. For Diebold is a man who is on the one hand dedicated to achieving perfection and on the other hand motivated by boundless enthusiasms to pull out all the stops.

9

Pandora's box

"Long before there was enough automation to
make even a dent on the economy as a whole,
the general public looked on automation and
unemployment as Siamese twins. Whether or
not the fears are justified, we do not know. They
may be. They may not be. But the fear itself is
real, and it is the single most important fact surrounding automation. If automation is to be positively pursued, it is essential that we deal openly
and honestly with this fact of fear and that we
examine the reasons underlying it. Then proper
steps can be taken to eliminate its cause."

JOHN DIEBOLD, ADDRESS BEFORE GOVERNOR'S CON-
FERENCE ON AUTOMATION, JUNE, 1960, "THE BASIC
ECONOMIC CONSEQUENCES OF AUTOMATION FOR
THE STATE OF NEW YORK."

IN A HEATED MOMENT a labor leader once accused John Diebold
of deliberately ignoring, or at least having no interest in, the
problem of unemployment. "You have indicated," said the
man, "that unemployment caused by automation will be of no
consequence, that automation is here to stay and there is nothing
we can do about workers who get displaced."

As Diebold quickly and earnestly pointed out, he does not—
and never will—undervalue the unemployment factor or the
fears that surround it. He even wrote a major magazine article

evaluating jobs that were on the ascendency and ones that were on the decline, and what people could do to avoid making themselves obsolete. What he emphasizes is the fact that unemployment (as well as re-employment) is only one of many, many consequences of automation that must be taken into consideration, and that focusing on the too narrow viewpoint will result in far greater problems than the displacement of workers alone.

He is concerned with the real things, the situations and the measurable actions. But he is also acutely concerned with the intangibles, the fears that cannot be charted or regarded on data sheets. Here, for example, are six very real fears which people have expressed—four of them entirely unrelated to unemployment or jobs:

• "Automation took away my husband's job, along with the jobs of about fifty other people in the plant. By the end of the year, they tell me a hundred more will be let go, and still more after that. I tell you this place will be a ghost town. No more jobs. We'll all be on relief. And what will happen to our kids growing up? We have two boys seventeen and nineteen, ready to go to work the way their father did before them. Now there's no work. You tell me the answer."

• "Automation is a curse . . . a real threat . . . it could bring us to national catastrophe. . . . We have a great system in this country. It has brought more benefits for those who work for wages than any other on earth. But this system could go down the drain on this very one problem — and it's a problem for all the country, not just labor."

• "The current tendency of men to give up individual identity and escape from responsibility is nurtured by the computer. It takes man's output and turns out judgments without obsessive hesitation, commitments or emotional involvements. It will lead us to skip over value judgments and let machines do our moral thinking."

• "Military computer systems will react so swiftly that the Army, Navy and Air Force commanders who should be making the decisions will find them already machine made. In effect, we may suddenly go to war because of the unstoppable decision of a *machine.*"

• "I don't want this hospital automated. It's all right having a computer in the business office to keep records straight. But what is the profession thinking of if it suggests that electronic gadgets and devices can take over the individual doctor's responsibility to treat a patient as a human being and diagnose what's wrong with him?"

• "Automation is going to result in mass educational suicide. Already these 'teaching machines' have gone too far. Young people need warmth and understanding in the learning process. You can't plug them into an educational electrical outlet the way you would a light cord. I get alarmed, because I see no way of stopping the approaching hordes of mechanical tutors that are taking over the educational process."

These are *troubled* people talking—people who have a real and growing fear of automation, and for widely different reasons. The expressions of fear are not isolated nor are they uttered by crackpots or chronic worriers. The men and women who voiced these separate concerns were: an intelligent wife and mother with a college degree, one of the country's foremost labor leaders, a noted psychologist and university professor, a military staff officer, the director of a hospital and a high school principal.

As a vice president at the Bank of America, Ralph Boynton, wrote recently: "Fear arrives with the first hint of major technological change. It creeps down the halls from the management offices, stops for a moment at convenient water fountains, pauses briefly in the rest rooms, lingers at the coffee breaks, is an unwelcome guest at lunch, joins the car pool at night, and quiets the conversation at dinner. Sometimes it rests heavily on a sleeper's mind and wakes him to a rigid examination of the pressing darkness."

We are becoming increasingly familiar with these persistent fears, and especially so in connection with the worry that machines will eventually take away our jobs, leaving mankind sidelined in unemployment. To multitudes of Americans, this fear is by far the most real, the most threatening, the most recognizable because there are thousands of examples of men and women who *have* been replaced by machines, who have lost their means of income and who face a bleak future because of the inroads of this technological fifth column. One report, released by the Center for the Study of Democratic Institutions cited automation as a major factor in the considerably automated chemical production field, where jobs had dropped 3 per cent since 1956, even though output had increased 27 per cent; and that in the highly automated telephone industry, where the volume of calls had risen 50 per cent, the number of personnel had increased only 10 per cent.

In June, 1961, at a time when automation was really beginning to spread throughout American industry, *Newsweek* reported, "In agriculture, where automation has taken hold fast, more than one million workers have lost their jobs in the last decade, and food was never so plentiful. In the bituminous coal industry, productivity has increased 96 per cent through automation, but 262,-000 U.S. miners are out of work. Railroad productivity has risen 65 per cent, during the same period, while employment has fallen 540,000. . . ."

In October, 1964, the Department of Labor reported that 80 per cent of all U.S. cotton is now picked mechanically, compared with only 1 per cent at the end of World War II. In areas relating to checking and inspection, many jobs are disappearing entirely, as in the case of the long established meter reader, who will soon be replaced by an electric eye; or the assembly line inspector who is losing out to various types of electronic equipment.

Labor unions are not the only ones getting worried these days. In the spring of 1964, the *Wall Street Journal* reported that OFFICE STAFFS LAST YEAR GREW AT THIRD THE RATE OF '50's; COMPUTERS PLAY BIG ROLE. For the first time in history, the white-collar worker is beginning to cast just as frightened an eye at machines as the blue-collar worker has been doing since the dawn of the Industrial Revolution. Four months later, the *Journal* headlined an even more alarming report—alarming, that is, for the upper-bracket ranks: Wall Street was proposing to automate odd-lot trading (dealing in blocks of stock that are fewer than 100 shares).

"When automation eliminates jobs," said the *Journal*, "the people affected are most often production workers and office clerks. But now automation is threatening the livelihoods of several scores Wall Streeters earning $50,000 or so a year."

But perhaps the topper came when IBM unveiled a super-computer system that was capable of performing the work of any *four* other IBM computer systems in service. "When computers start causing unemployment among *other* computers," said one commentator, "it's time to start worrying!"

The implication was not quite so frivolous as *World Telegram* advertising columnist Charles Sievert made it out to be when he reported recently, "In the Pen & Pencil," he said of a local New York bistro, "where some of the ad boys find time to cut their meat between martinis, they were talking about office computers that are so near human they (the computers) have hired less expensive computers to do their work for them."

Unemployment is a serious problem. Yet, although hundreds of thousands of examples could be given of men who have been eased out of jobs by the relentless inroads of computers and other automated devices, the situation is not quite that easy to analyze. On the one hand, you have a man like the late Dr. Norbert Wiener, who bluntly stated that this new revolution "will produce an unemployment situation in comparison with which . . . the depression of the 1930's will seem like a pleasant joke."

On the other hand, you have an authority like Arthur J. Goldberg who, when he was Secretary of Labor, said that technological changes have "favorably affected" some occupations and that "since 1900, mechanization and new inventions have also created many new skilled and specialized occupations." Or Vannevar Bush, one of the pioneers in the new technology, who wrote:

> The thought is abroad that the inevitably increasing use of sensing mechanisms, tape-instructed machines, more and more sophisticated feedback circuits, is going to put almost everyone out of work and that the mass America will then stand about with its mouth open and nothing to do; a nation of village idiots watching a mechanized parade go by. A more nonsensical notion transcends the imagination. There will always be enough work to do in America and everywhere else, to keep every man and woman busy for as many hours a week as future societies think desirable.

Diebold says: "We have no choice between the status quo and the automation age, for change is a certainty. *We have a choice* between being led, reluctantly, into this new world—or leading in the introduction of new technology both at home and abroad. The one thing U.S. labor has to fear is not the employment situation but the fact that the worst catastrophe that could happen to the American work force would be for us to move too slowly, to fall behind. Our high standard of living comes from our being ahead in technology; and a favorable employment and wage situation comes from having a high standard of living. If we do not move rapidly, we are going to be in real trouble!"

In this viewpoint, he was well supported by the President's Advisory Committee on Labor-Management Policy, which as long as three years ago was stating, "We emphasize . . . the imperative need for and desirability of automation and technological change. . . . Failure to advance technologically and to otherwise increase the productivity of our economy would bring on much more serious unemployment and related social problems than we now face."

The situation is, to say the least, confusing, with so-called experts in all fields differing sharply with each other. Historically, what has popularly been referred to as "the Second Industrial Revolution" is somewhat similar to the real Industrial Revolution of the late eighteenth century. That phenomenon saw a sharp split between the optimistic economists who felt that machinery would forever free mankind from labor and the Luddites who went around smashing labor-saving machinery in an effort to save the world from the threat of the evil machine.

Part of the confusion comes from contradictory definitions of automation itself. People commonly think that if a factory installs a bank of automatic drill presses, each of which can do the work of three men, that automation has taken place. The impression is a mistaken one. Automation is not simply mechanization or the installation of a series of work-saving machines. As John Diebold points out, it is an entirely new method of organizing and analyzing production, sometimes even to the point of changing product design itself. It is the development of capacity, to achieve things previously impossible. Fundamentally involving management as well as labor, it is a concern with production and business organization as a system—a philosophy as much as a way of utilizing a specific technology.

"Industrial automation brings new problems as well as new solutions. To harvest all of its fruits we must, in many cases, redesign our products, our processing methods, and our machines."

One of the most appropriate definitions, expressed at an industry conference, is this: "A means of organizing, analyzing and controlling our production processes to achieve optimum use of all of our productive resources—human resources, as well as those that are material and mechanical."

No matter how you define the subject, however, you cannot escape from the fear, and the very tangible problem that many unfortunate employees are going to find themselves out on the street because of the new technological invasion. When a machine is invented (as was done recently) that can not only wrap heads of lettuce, but reject ones that are spoiled and feel out the size of the heads for sorting purposes, it is obvious that the humans who now perform this task are soon going to be eliminated from the production line.

Any one who thinks that these fears are groundless has only to consider the case of one major corporation. Automation was such a dirty word in the corporate ranks that management forbade its executives to refer to it in public, or even to speak at professional gatherings where the subject was discussed.

Realistically, though, the problem that stimulates these fears and tensions is not so much one of unemployment as it is of dislocation and change. The fiercest detractors who continue the "unemployment" alarm are often guilty of using "obituary accounting," that is, adding up jobs that have been eliminated, but taking little account of jobs that have been created by our new technologies. Testifying before the U. S. House of Representatives Committee on Education and Labor, John Diebold asserted that "it is more correct to say that sixty million jobs will change than that twenty million workers will be unemployed as a result of automation."

Former Secretary of Labor Goldberg stressed the need for retraining, estimating that the need for craftsmen would rise about 25 per cent during the next decade, "despite all the automation we can expect." A spokesman for IBM, "one of the prime movers of automation," focused on the fact that the problem is one of training rather than joblessness when he pointed out that his company, constantly changing internally because of the advances in its own technology, was spending some $60 million a year just in educational programs. Despite constant displacements, it had never had to lay off a single employee because of automation.

Speaking as Secretary of Labor in May, 1965, W. Willard Wirtz also stressed the need for education in an article "Automation and

Employment," written for the occasion of the third congress of the International Federation for Information Processing: ". . . the white-collar worker has taken over first place in occupational standings from the blue-collar industrial worker. Only 5 per cent of the entire American labor force is unskilled, and the ports of entry previously available for the unskilled newcomer to the job market are rapidly disappearing.

"Under the circumstances, it perhaps should not be surprising to anyone that one out of every three unemployed *never went beyond grade school* and that two out of every three of our jobless do not have a high school diploma."

He also stated that "the only clear job security today is in continuous education, even of an informal sort."

Clearly, if there is a real villain in the unemployment picture it is not so much automation itself as the reluctance to achieve a proper education and then to accept continuing education as a vital part of employment life.

As Diebold wrote in an article in *McCall's* magazine, "If American families are going to *fear* something about automation, it should not be unemployment, but getting into a dead-end type of job rather than one with a bright future. Are you or a member of your family, for example, a bookkeeper? . . . a machine tool operator? . . . a clerical bank worker? . . . a painter? . . . a railroad dispatcher? . . . an elevator operator?

"These jobs have rapidly narrowing futures. They will be taken over by machines.

"On the other side of the fence, there are numerous occupations which will be in multiplying demand: engineers of all kinds . . . athletic directors, and others in the recreational fields, to meet the needs of our increased leisure . . . business and management consultants . . . writers, editors and specialists in communications . . . teachers and others in the field of education, to take care of mushrooming demands for knowledge which will not be met, even by the new teaching machines and methods."

As we move toward, and into, the seventies, fewer and fewer people will work in factories, or perform monotonous routine chores that can be better performed by machines. Offices and laboratories will offer the setting for more stimulating occupations, and the work week will become considerably shortened. Some of the old trades will continue, but with more exciting activities and broader horizons. The rather uninspiring title of "plumber," for example, will soon be thought of in connection with dynamic new products, such as complex systems for atomic submarines or intricate pipelines for refineries or new types of plastics and flexible tubing that will improve our homes in a multitude of ways.

As we move forward, however, in the new technology one of the other areas of concern will probably multiply rather than diminish: "numbers neurosis," or the fear that personal identities are being lost as individuals become mere combinations of digits. During the past two or three years, great concern—amounting in some instances almost to panic—has greeted the announcements by the telephone company that exchange names were being eliminated, to be replaced by numbers. As AT&T explained it, the company regretted having to abolish such familiar names as *BUtterfield* and *PEnnypacker* and *SWiftwater,* but it was a "mathematical necessity," in order to take care of the increased load made possible by automated devices coast to coast and around the world.

No one likes to be thought of as a number, said Dr. Leo Goldberger of the Research Center for Mental Health at New York University, reporting that "long series of numbers, such as Army serial numbers, have come to connote loss of individual identity: one becomes—to add insult to injury—not only an insignificant cog in a great machine, but anonymous as well."

Taking a not-so-academic stand on the subject, a group of influential citizens on the West Coast formed an organization called the Anti-Digit-Dialing League and began taking steps—legal as well as promotional—to block the switch to all-number calling. So far, they, and similar groups around the country, have been unsuccessful in stemming the mathematical marauders. The fears become compounded when the government forces the stockholders to maintain identification numbers for all investments, when banks install computer systems that file depositors away in their complex brains as digits rather than names, and when even our post office addresses become so impersonal that a number of curious people have successfully mailed letters to themselves using nothing but numbers on the envelope.

"We are all going to become complete nonentities," said one

labor leader, echoing the sentiments of a large number of his colleagues, "with machines not only taking over, but actually *looking down* on human beings with a kind of mechanized scorn."

True or false?

It depends on the point of view. John Diebold wrote almost a decade ago, when some of today's widespread fears were germinating: "Of all the myths and fears that have sprung up about automation, there is surely none quite so absurd as the contention that automation will debase the worker." He admits that "there is certainly some truth in the frequently voiced criticism that production in many modern plants and factories seems to subordinate the worker to the machine." But he points out that "it is precisely this one great drawback of all other forms of increased mechanization that automation promises to eliminate."

There is considerable truth in this argument, since automation, properly developed, performs the kinds of routine, repetitive and monotonous chores that most intelligent people look down upon to begin with. In many areas, though, the subject is a touchy one and almost sure to breed controversy and argument. The medical profession, for example, looks upon automation with mixed emotions. The human factor is stressed by the critics as being something that should not be tampered with through the overuse of machines. "Many medical people still complain," said the producer of a device for monitoring heartbeats, "that electronics companies don't understand enough about human disease and patient care to design new medical electronic equipment properly."

Dr. Ross Adey of the Brain Research Institute in Los Angeles, expresses the blunt opinion that bio-medical engineering has a long way to go before it can receive proper acceptance. He cites the life scientist as "abnormally deficient in physics and engineering"; reports that the medical doctor "isn't much help either . . . still has a lot of evaluating to do to discover even what instrumentation he wants"; and says that most electronic engineers "haven't even discovered yet that the human body is the most complicated of chemical factories—a dynamic factory with no stationary values."

The fears that human identity will lose out are so great that controversial issues are either avoided altogether (as in the case of the company that refused to let its executives participate in any meetings where automation was to be a subject on the agenda) or else furtively aired in tense, strained discussions that are completely devoid of humor. One of the rare examples of humor, in fact, is the story about Walter Reuther, president of the United Auto Workers, when he was visiting the automated Ford plant in Cleveland some years ago.

"How are you going to collect union dues from those guys?" quipped a Ford executive, pointing to some new machines.

Replied Reuther: "In the same way you're going to get *them* to buy Fords."

Although it would have seemed absurd as recently as three or four years ago—related to far-out ideas on TV superdramas—one very real fear among American citizens is that someday machines will actually be able to outthink us and outsmart us. These fears are based on knowledge about some of the utterly fantastic accomplishments in the machine world. Did you know, for example, that right at this very moment thousands of machines are talking to each other by long distance telephone around the world? Or that by 1970, the telephone company will derive more income from business machines communicating between cities than it will from all of the calls made between people?

"Will the Computer Outwit Man?" asked *Fortune* magazine, devoting an entire six-thousand-word article to the subject in the October, 1964, issue. The editors aired the growing fear that "the computer will eventually become so intelligent and creative that it will relegate man, or most men, to a humiliating and intolerably inferior role in the world." John Diebold is aware of this fear. As he said, "Man in the not-too-distant future will be faced by the fact that creatures of his invention are able to reach solutions, not only faster than he, as is already the case, but by means which would take many lifetimes for man to understand." Yet he goes on to say, "perhaps also it does not matter, if man turns an inward look on man, competing neither with angels nor computers but only with himself to excel his past and stretch his potential, ennobling himself in the eyes of Creation."

Such concerns are based on the established fact that computers already have a capacity to learn, can show "purposeful behavior" and can even create situations that the programmers did not anticipate or expect.

It is common knowledge that machines can play games as in

the case of a computer that was "taught" by Arthur Samuel, a data processing consultant, to play checkers so well that it consistently beats him.

"The science of psychology will change," said John Diebold. "The startling fact about computers which play checkers is not how well they play, but that they improve. The current work being done on information systems, programing, and computer language has already brought us to the threshold of a breakthrough in learning theory. We can only guess what such a breakthrough would mean in all phases of education."

How far can this learning process go? Two research scientists at the Carnegie Institute of Technology, Allen Newell and Herbert Simon, have made a frightening prediction: man, they say, is technically just a kind of complex computer, "programed at birth by his genes," and thereafter responding to different situations in accordance with the input of information received during the course of a lifetime. We will see the day when programming (feeding information) will enable machines to do everything a man's brain can do.

The Perceptron, a mechanical brain developed by a Cornell psychologist, has already demonstrated—and has done so for years—that a machine can improve its own ability to recognize things (in this case, numbers and letters of the alphabet.) Machines have one tremendous advantage over man: they never forget. One amazing demonstration of memory perception is the Baseball wizard at M.I.T., a machine which can be questioned in English and which answers an almost endless number of queries about American League teams. Yet this is only the very crudest prototype of a mechanical superbrain that will one day be able to retain and instantaneously refer to any one of the billions of items of information stored in the Library of Congress.

If the input of information and the storing of facts in a central brain system has anything to do with outwitting mankind, the products of the emerging automation have it made.

Speculation could go on indefinitely. The significant factor here is that intelligent—or more accurately, *brilliant*—men are studying the situation, and that some of them are themselves greatly concerned over the future. Of more immediate concern is the fear that the development of the machine, and especially the computer, will seriously affect man's judgment and his ability, and desire, to make vital decisions. One authority, Ulric Neisser, fears that the machine's role in decision-making will be deliberately abused. "If machines really thought as men do," he said, "there would be no more reason to fear them than to fear men. But computer intelligence is not human, it does not grow, has no emotional basis, and is shallowly motivated. These defects do not matter in technical applications. . . . They become extremely important if the computer is used to make social, business, economic, military, moral and government decisions."

Recently, *Science* magazine warned of the "current tendency of men to give up individual identity and escape from responsibility," emphasizing that this unfortunate trend was being magnified by the ease with which men in responsible positions could push buttons and get answers without having to bear the burden of decision-making.

An unnerving question comes up, too: Could two or three unethical, or even criminally inclined, men in a great organization feed information into a computer system in such a way as to warp the system's brain so that it would make decisions in their favor? Just as clever and scheming bookkeepers have in the past been able to manipulate and juggle accounts in order to ease company funds into their own pockets, so it might be possible for embezzlers of the future to rig machines in their nefarious favor.

Already there have been frauds committed that would not have been possible without the event of automation. An interesting example was "the case of the digital depositor." Not long ago, a metropolitan bank converted to the numerical identification system. Each holder of a checking account was designated a number and provided with deposit slips, at the bottom of which were digits, printed in special magnetic ink, which enabled a machine to credit that particular account and no other. One clever depositor had an idea. He placed several dozen copies of his own, numbered deposit slips in trays bearing similar, but *un*numbered slips in the bank's service desks. The unsuspecting depositors who were not yet familiar with the system and who used these slips were in for a shock. Since only the numbers determined whose account received credit, you can easily guess where all the money was channeled.

The possibilities of turning automated devices into partners in crime are as great as the imaginative workings of the criminal mind. Some consolation may come, however, from the fact that automation is successfully being used to combat crime. Computers are being used to tighten inventory controls and reveal suspicious patterns whenever the using company finds its merchandise or supplies disappearing unaccountably.

The computer has also been tested for its capabilities in taking over new roles in the courtroom, "as plaintiff, defendant, expert witness, and maybe even judge." In a mock trial, the American Bar Association, constructed a fictitious anti-trust suit in which one company claimed that it had been the victim of a conspiracy. Its supplier and a competitor were deliberately freezing it out of a geographic market and fixing prices. How? By hooking up their respective computers by direct wire so that they could compute prices and markets to the disadvantage of the plaintiff.

The big question posed by the mock trial was this: Although it was evident that the plaintiff had been a victim of conspiracy, who could be held liable? The computers themselves had established prices and manufactured their own records. *And how can you crossexamine and convict a computer?*

As one attorney put it: "Computer records are going to require that judges and counsel be part electrical engineer to follow very complicated cross examination."

Perhaps the most ironic and contradictory fear that is developing as part of the new technological neurosis is a nervous concern over what to do with our ever-increasing leisure time. Two generations ago, the average work week was almost seventy hours, with only Sunday off, and most of that devoted to traditional activities that required little planning in advance. Today, the work week is about forty hours (less than half the total designated as leisure time) and predictions for the future set it as low as twenty-five hours or less. Some jobs will involve fewer work days; others will be a matter of shorter hours. In either case, "Time on My Hands" will be the theme song, and what we do with the free hours may well determine whether we find pleasure in the new trend or simply go out of our minds trying to make recreational decisions.

In 1960, Diebold voiced his concern that "the youngsters now in school are . . . going to be living in a leisure society—that is, a society where many more of their waking hours will be spent off the job than on it. As far as I know, society is doing very little to save these future consumers of leisure from chronic boredom."

In an article in the New York *Times* entitled "Using our Leisure Is No Easy Job," noted author Bruce Bliven had this to say about the trend to shorter and shorter working days: "Many students of human behavior believe that this change has led to profound frustration, and that the character as well as the amount of recreation today represent an attempt by the individual to restore his psychological balance . . . (they) fear that people simply will not know what to do with themselves if the work week is still further reduced."

Again and again, psychologists who have studied the problem have reported profound and highly damaging fears among people faced with long hours of unwanted leisure—as in the case of men about to retire. But even among average citizens a long way from retirement, but with more and more weekend and vacation time each year, there are deep-rooted feelings of guilt. It does not seem to matter that a man has worked his way into a choice job, where automation not only provides more free time for him but ends up accomplishing greater results for the man, the company and society in general. He is still likely to be tugged by pangs of guilt because he is "loafing."

It is a perplexing inconsistency that one of the major byproducts of the new age of automation—leisure—should turn out to be partially unwanted and subconsciously feared.

The pioneers in computer equipment, the top spokesmen for the development of automation, the research scientists developing the complex machines of the coming age—all of these people are familiar with the fears that the new technology has generated: the alarm over unemployment; the apprehension about becoming numerical nonentities; the misgivings about not having enough to do. They have an answer—though not a particularly comforting one—that *automation is a necessity,* that it is part of an inevitable technological process that cannot be cut off any more than we can halt the passage of the seasons.

Without automation, and its ability to make the most complicated calculations in millionths of a second, we could not have

109

missiles and rockets and satellites, or any of the other products of the Space Age. Telstar, and the breakthrough into incredible new methods of communication and weather control, would be impossible.

The spokesmen for the new era of automation have fears of their own—fears which to them are more significant than the concerns over unemployment or dehumanization or excess leisure:

From the immediate viewpoint of American trade and industry, automation is an economic necessity, if we are going to maintain our position in world affairs. "The real danger," says Francis K. McCune, an engineering vice president at General Electric, "is that by slowing our advance in technology we may end up by undergoing a very painful adjustment to the loss of our place in the world's economy—a far more painful adjustment than the one required in keeping up with new technology."

Dr. Vannevar Bush himself said that in order to compete in the world market we must "further in every way possible those features of our system which have brought us well this far. . . . It includes, in particular, encouraging in every way possible the extension in a sane manner of that old process for which we have a new name: automation."

Writing in the New York *Herald Tribune,* columnist John Crosby made this observation, taking a viewpoint from London: "It has always struck me as decidedly peculiar that Americans can get themselves so emotionally involved in minor and distant and transient crises like Viet Nam while ignoring a far more important revolution under their noses. The revolution of automation is likely to be infinitely more shattering on human life and civilization than the Industrial Revolution, and yet Americans are undergoing this convulsive transformation without paying much attention."

Since Mr. Crosby is no authority on automation, his words signify that perhaps some of the meaning of the new technology is getting through to opinion makers, general businessmen and private citizens.

John Diebold is perhaps the most outspoken of all in pinpointing the weak points and dangers. "There are indications," he says, "that America is falling behind. The factories of the Ruhr, northern Italy, France and the United Kingdom are automating to the hilt. What is more, they are becoming major producers of automation equipment. . . . We like to think of the United States as a pioneer in industrial methods, but the most modern steel plant in the world is being built in Wales; highly sophisticated computers are being built in France and West Germany; Japan and France have advanced car-building processes that rival the best in Detroit; and Japan is now the world's hottest market for computers."

In the Soviet Union, reported Diebold more than three years ago, "automation has become an important part of the whole philosophy. It is a part of the Russian's current development program. A new institute has been set up in Kiev devoted to the application of technology to industry. Everything in the current environment encourages the application of technology to business. . . . The Communists are positively embracing automation, while many Americans are hoping it will just go away."

10

". . . *And now doth time waste me. . . .*"

"Ultimately the most pressing problem is to educate individuals for a society in which leisure is the center of life rather than the fringe."

JOHN DIEBOLD, ADDRESS DELIVERED AT THE UNIVERSITY OF CHICAGO, CHICAGO, ILLINOIS, NOVEMBER, 1956.

O F ALL THE FEARS discussed in the preceding chapter, the most perplexing one of all is the fear of time—time that can be described on the one hand as a vacuum, and on the other as leisure. Few people seem really to understand what leisure is, and what it is not.

"Two hundred years ago," explains John Diebold, "when it was necessary for most people to put in sixty or seventy hours a week in miserable factories just in order to survive, the question of what to do with nonwork—with leisure—never presented itself. Today, with our forty hours of work a week, we are already facing the two-day weekend with something of a self-conscious attitude. When leisure time spills over from the weekend to Monday and Friday, when a man leaves his desk or station after six hours of work still fresh and full of energy, then, for the first time in history, we will really face the problem of what to do with leisure.

"This is a revolution, in other words, which will take us *be-*

yond the civilization of an industrial society, a revolution in which human beings will be largely freed from the bondage of machines. It will raise an entirely new set of problems: business problems, social problems, and economic problems. It will tax our ingenuity to its utmost. And it will bring about its changes—many of them, at least—within our own lifetime."

In 1883, in a work entitled "The Story of My Heart," British author and naturalist Richard Jeffries wrote plaintively, "I hope succeeding generations will be able to idle. I hope that nine-tenths of their time will be leisure time; that they may enjoy their days, and the earth, and the beauty of this beautiful world; that they may rest by the sea and dream; that they may dance and sing, and eat and drink."

The way things are progressing, it looks as though Jeffries' dream might some day come true. The not uncommon thirty-five-hour working week represents only about one-fifth of a person's total available time devoted to on the job work. And by the mid-seventies, according to some predictions, our present work week will be cut almost in half. One economist, Marion Clawson, has come up with the staggering prediction that by the year 2000, Americans will have 660 billion more hours of leisure time to burn than they had in 1950. Will this be the Nirvana the poets have been dreaming about?

Unfortunately, Jeffries' concept of a world of leisure in which the multitudes prance about happily, singing and dancing and enjoying nature does not seem at all likely to become as much a reality as the hours available for such recreation. Already large numbers of people are going out of their minds trying to fill their free time in a manner befitting their understanding of what leisure is supposed to be. To some, it is supposed to be a period of doing absolutely nothing—or as close to that attainment as possible. To others, it may mean scheduling as many recreational pursuits as can be crammed into the time allotted: golf, swimming, boating; spectator sports; indoor games such as bridge or poker; social activities such as cocktail parties or dances.

No matter which point of view is taken—absolute inaction or feverish activity—there is still something in the makeup of the American adult, no matter how progressive his thinking, that accepts leisure time only with conscious or subconscious pangs of guilt. "I wasted time, and now doth time waste me," wrote Shakespeare in lines that seem more appropriate today than they did almost four hundred years ago. Our great grandparents were brought up with the idea that too much leisure was sinful and that idleness bred mischief. Perhaps they were simply consoling themselves for the lack of free time available. In the latter part of the nineteenth century, the average work week in the U.S. was about seventy hours. By 1900, it was still some sixty hours, with only a little more than twenty hours a week available for recreation. Although wealthy families vacationed at seashore and mountain resorts, the men seldom participated to any extent. As for the middle class and the poor, they were fortunate to have two or three vacation days out of the entire year. The concept of the real summer vacation just did not exist.

It seems unbelievable in an age when we spend about $400 annually (on a per capita basis) on recreational pursuits that two generations ago our grandparents were spending less than $10 a year. Yet, as psychologists have noted, increasing leisure brings with it traces of the belief expressed by Lord Chesterfield in one of the letters to his son that "Idleness is only the refuge of weak minds." Or, as Lord Avebury expressed it in 1888, "The idle mind does not know what it is to enjoy rest. Hard work, moreover, not only tends to give us rest for the body, but, what is even more important, peace to the mind."

The feeling of guilt, as much as the desire for more income, is one factor that has nurtured the trend to moonlighting, or taking on second, even third, jobs to fill the hours not occupied by the first one. Some moonlighters work as much as eighty hours a week at their various crafts, one evidence that overwork does not seem to be as much of a problem as some union leaders would make it out to be when they demand shorter work weeks. One-third of labor union members queried in some parts of the country replied, in effect, that if they had shorter hours, they would sign up for additional jobs, to bring in more income. It would seem that a great many citizens just plain cannot afford the leisure hours they already have.

Automation is making it possible, not only to increase leisure time, but to space it out, with no regard for the seasons, or even the days of the week. "Vacation" has long since ceased to be inalienably connected with summer. Then, too, it has been convincingly demonstrated that certain types of business can be carried on as successfully in leisure-time settings and circumstances as in offices. Restaurants and golf courses and resorts evoke fewer and fewer snickers in sophisticated executive circles when mentioned as places for conducting business.

"I have developed more income and profit for my company with a golf club or martini glass in hand," said one sales manager recently, "than I ever did behind a desk with a pencil and telephone in my fingers."

Automation is bringing our generation the opportunity of making choices. Which do we want—more goods, services and comforts, or more leisure? In most instances, we shall select some of both. We want new and better products and improved services, but we are largely willing to sacrifice some of the great abundance we could have, in order to enjoy more non-working hours. What too many people overlook, in the great pressure for that wonderful Nirvana known as leisure is that there is a considerable difference between time that can be turned into fun and time that hangs heavy.

Diebold looks at the situation objectively. "Many observers," he says, "believe that machines will soon provide a choice between added products and comforts and added leisure. If leisure becomes the choice, it is entirely possible that the three-day weekend, or the three-month vacation, will be a reality within the next decade. While a major sociological study would be required to deal fully with the implications of added leisure, some of them can at least be suggested.

"For one thing, leisure is sure to change patterns of consumption . . . people with more time off will spend more money on sports clothes and equipment, on hobbies, on travel and its adjuncts. The already booming do-it-yourself movement is certain to boom even further. Americans have the reputation of being a nation of joiners. It seems likely that the number and size of fraternal and community organizations will grow as more free time becomes available."

Diebold adds that additional leisure "may also have more subtle and perhaps less favorable effects." He cites Erich Fromm's conviction that increasing man's leisure only tends to increase his sense of insecurity. "Too much time," says Diebold, "may isolate him psychologically, create problems which he is unprepared to face, and drive him to socially harmful actions."

David Reisman, the Harvard sociologist, says that the threat of added leisure provokes many people to look upon it as "a threat, a problem, a burden or hazard."

The problem has even been reviewed by a Congressional subcommittee, which expressed concern over the ethics of making a choice between goods and services and leisure. The subcommittee's report pointed out that there are "substantial groups of comparatively underprivileged and lower income groups who should be remembered before those in the more favored industries can conscientiously turn to a shortened work day or longer weekend."

One outcome of the new leisure is the responsibility that larger employers of all kinds are assuming in trying to help their employees find activities for their spare time. There is hardly a corporation in America today that does not have its share of bowling leagues, softball teams, theatrical groups, choirs, art and hobby clubs or organized cultural instruction of one kind or another. Some of these activities are stimulated by the employees themselves who, consciously or not, sense that group efforts are necessary to combat the spread of spare time. Others are deliberately conceived, arranged and promoted by company executives, or by some sort of committee appointed to the project. Many firms go to great expense and trouble to maintain playing fields, picnic areas or even vacation retreats for employees at all levels. Adding to the recreational impetus are the labor unions, which keep insisting on shorter and shorter work weeks, or which work longer lunch hours and regular coffee breaks into their contracts.

A few observers have tired—usually in vain—to explain that shorter working hours are not necessarily the answer to any of our problems. In the past, many jobs were satisfying ones, where individual workers could take pride in their achievement. Cabinet makers, painters and craftsmen of all kinds could see that they were accomplishing something from hour to hour as they proceeded through their long (by our standards) work day. Ironically, workers today who demand more free time and who speak disparagingly of how their fathers had to work ten hours a day, six days a week may be the very ones who are committed to dull,

117

plodding jobs and who then go home to spend hours in a basement shop *working* at the production of furniture or other things for around the home. One authority on the work habits and desires of our times, Ferdynand Zweig, says, that this desire to do-it-yourself, along with a great yearning for outdoor recreation, such as camping, hiking or touring the wilderness areas, is a direct reaction to the kind of assembly-line employment so many people are committed to, day in and day out.

Automation has not only contributed to the amount of spare time we have, but is also speeding up various processes whereby we can cover more ground during that spare time. Computers are being applied to a variety of cultural applications. One, for example, is their use in libraries, for information storing and disseminating purposes. Within a few years, it will be possible to acquire instantly all of the information that you might today spend several hours browsing around the library to accumulate. The result will be more time to devote to other pursuits. Which pursuits? That may be a problem. Automation has already become a necessary factor in certain recreational areas. One example is the electronic scoreboard used for big league baseball and football games, providing instant information as the play progresses. Another is the automatic pinsetter, which has speeded up bowling and which is now so essential to the game that few bowlers will play in lanes which are not thus automated.

Most Americans seem to want their free time to be anything but leisurely. Spectator sports have to be fast-paced to attract the big crowds. Whenever a game seems to be too slow in any respect, committees are set up to study the regulations and see if the game cannot be speeded up. Thus, we see basketball as a top spectator sport because the scoring continues with computer-like swiftness. When football seemed to be getting lethargic, the rules were changed so that platoons could be rushed in and out of play with clockwork regularity. Even when a particular game itself is not exciting, with the teams deadlocked, it *looks* as though a great deal of action were taking place. A recent musicology report stated somewhat disparagingly that "We even play Bach and Mozart 10 per cent faster than was usual in their lifetimes."

Rugby has achieved some recognition and success in the United States in recent years (although mostly for participants rather than spectators). Yet it seems unlikely that Americans could ever become interested in the leisurely paced British game of cricket—not unless some promoter Americanizes the game in such a way that the players can run around in a frenzied fashion and somehow conclude the play within two hours.

One reason why television has boomed so successfully is that it is a voracious consumer of free time. It solves the problem of how to spend leisure hours without spending much money. It also accommodates people who do not know what to do with their spare time. Significantly, many top-ranking executives find TV "relaxing," because they can almost always locate a comedy, a musical, a mystery, or a western that requires "no thinking or concentration." Another big consumer of executive time is the daily commute, a factor that increases with the growth of metropolitan areas all over the country. The time is occupied further in a number of ways: playing bridge; catching up on reading; furiously shuffling papers and working on projects that cannot be crammed into normal office hours; talking with fellow passengers; dozing; or (homeward bound) lounging in the bar car.

"Commuting is not exactly leisure time," remarked one spokesman for the New York Central, "but it is *relaxing*. No one can reach you on the phone. And no one is looking over your shoulder—unless it's kibitzing a bridge game."

What the truth really boils down to is that automation has not given us leisure time as much as it has given us a greatly changed pattern of time. In 1959, before automation had really begun to play a significant role in the matter of formal working hours, author Sloan Wilson wrote an article for *Life* magazine entitled, "Happy Idle Hours Become a Rat Race." In the text, he depicted men in all walks of life furiously devising ways for turning their spare time into production lines. He depicted leaders of business, labor and education interrupting busy schedules to make speeches and told how "exhausted physicians totter home from their hospital rounds to write articles advising everyone to take it easy."

When you toured the suburbs, said Mr. Wilson, you could see plenty of lawn furniture and hammocks of all kinds, but they would invariably be empty, "rocked only by the wind or ghosts of men who had died from overwork."

Almost every commentator or writer who discusses the subject of leisure sooner or later gets around to the "Honeydew" (or

"Honey-Do") syndrome. This is the compulsion that motivates wives to say, "Honey, do this. . . ." and "Honey do that. . . ." whenever they see the Old Man lounging around and looking too contented. At least one survey has pointed to this as a common complaint held by husbands everywhere.

The fault does not entirely lie with the wives, however, since numerous spouses give the distinct impression that inactivity is not for them. As *Life* magazine stated, "For many men a job is simply a tournament entered in order to finance another tournament. Such men try to get the highest salary at the office in order to buy the fastest boat on the lake."

Another author, Harvey Swadow, wrote in the *Saturday Review* that the billions of dollars Americans spend on hobbies each year represent, not just a feverish attempt to fill spare time, but "seeking elsewhere for the satisfactions of personal fulfillment that formerly came from the job of work itself."

"One trouble with us Americans," said the *Reader's Digest* in August, 1964, quoting the remarks of an anthropologist, "is that we carry our work habits over into our leisure hours. The American does not just go bowling when the spirit moves him. He joins a bowling league, which means that he is obligated to show up promptly at 7:45 every Tuesday night, as if punching a time clock at a factory. He reads not for fun but to improve his mind. . . . He takes a walk not to admire the beauties of nature, but to keep his cholesterol down."

"Retire young," advises a typical advertisement for an insurance company, "while you can enjoy life." Plans for retirement at sixty, and even partial retirement at fifty-five, instead of the traditional sixty-five, are not uncommon in some fields of business. Yet the whole subject of retirement has become a controversial one in recent years. Many men cannot face the idea of giving up the routine of daily jobs. Even the most optimistic ones, looking forward to escaping the old bonds and using perfectly sufficient pensions and other funds for later-life leisure, tend to go rapidly downhill after about a year of tasting their new-found freedom. Many take on new jobs. Others simply sink back into a semi-vegetable existence, letting old age overtake them as mercifully as possible. Housewives are not exempt, either. As one psychologist said "middle age often finds the once-active and long-ebullient mother retreating into a shell of neuroses. Her children have

grown old enough to move out of the home. She has become re-
lieved of the burden of car pools and ferrying young folk to endless social and educational activities. Her husband has probably
taken on extra business responsibilities that keep him at work
longer. She has nothing to do. Leisure is a big fat bore."

Thus, we have the curious contradiction of problems. On the
one hand, there seems to be no good answer for what to do with
people who have too much time on their hands. On the other
hand, there is the problem of how to prevent people from going
into sheer panic and turning leisure into a maelstrom of dis-
ordered activity.

When you get right down to it, the whole subject of leisure
may be nothing but a collection of myths. When the Twentieth
Century Fund assigned Dr. Sebastian de Grazia, to a three-year
study, "Of Time, Work and Leisure," the noted philosopher and
political scientist came up with some surprising facts. For one
thing, he noted, we tend to compare the new leisure with the
nineteenth-century work week (seventy hours) and completely
overlook other periods in history when man had far more time on
his hands. In the Greece of antiquity, it is pointed out that
people enjoyed more holidays than working days during the
course of each month. In ancient Rome, people enjoyed one
day off for every two they worked. And in medieval times, there
were 167 days a year that were Sundays, community holidays
or Church holy days.

Also, as the Twentieth Century Fund study revealed, our so-
called scientific statistics today are more than likely to be open to
question. The much discussed thirty-five-hour work week does not
take into account such factors as commuting time and overtime,
and it includes a large element of parttime workers who throw the
figures off balance.

We are going through an awkward age, partially—but not
wholly—influenced by automation. It is an age of confusion and
doubt and fear regarding the matter of time, what it is and how
to use it. The chances are that the situation will become further
muddled before it improves. But someday, when computers can
make more decisions with authority, they may convince man that
he deserves certain leisure time and should, during prescribed hours, settle down to the business of total relaxation,

without fears, without guilt and without the nagging urge to get up on his feet and do something.

"The education challenge is the greatest we must face," says Diebold, ". . . education for an age where leisure is the center of life. Today's toil is perhaps more nerve-wracking than back-breaking, but time—time to be something other than a machine is one of the great promises of automation."

11

Push-button medicine

*"Information storage and retrieval systems will
also be used in medical diagnosis and research.
A running record of each patient's history, kept
in electronic form, will enable doctors to spot
disease symptoms or tendencies long before
they could be discovered by conventional methods. If one becomes ill while traveling in any
part of the world, a physician will be able to
dial a record-storage center and in seconds have
a complete medical history."*

JOHN DIEBOLD, "LOOKING BRAVELY BACKWARD TO
1948 OR SO," PENGUIN SURVEY OF BUSINESS AND
INDUSTRY, 1965.

THERE IS A CARTOON in the growing collection of *automationa
comica* that shows a young lady lying on a couch in the office
of a psychoanalyst. Instead of the usual bearded doctor, however,
she is attended by a tall, angular computer with blinking lights
and an ear-like receiver.

One thing that fascinates John Diebold about such cartoons
is that very often, in addition to the satire, they depict situations
which will one day be sober, accepted, day-to-day occurrences.
"It is not so ridiculous as you might think," he says, "to imagine
that computers will be of tremendous assistance to psychologists,
psychiatrists and others concerned with mental health. Much of

123

what doctors are doing to try to help the mentally ill, the neurotic and the disturbed involves the application of past case histories and therapeutic methods to the patient. No matter how astute a doctor is, no matter how sharp a memory he has, he cannot possibly call to mind all of the data that are going to assist him in any particular case. Therefore, information-retrieval systems will be valuable aids in psychiatric work in the future."

It is not easy for a layman to understand how a computer, or any other machine, could assist the medical profession in the complex and intangible world of mental illness. It is, however, not too difficult to see the computer at work in the area of physiological medicine, where at least the actions and processes can be visualized. A good example is that of a young business executive, a patient at the University of Tennessee Medical Center in Memphis. The man had to be constantly under observation, for he was a cardiac-arrest patient. At any moment, as it had done several times, his heart might stop, necessitating instant action by a team of nurses trained in heart massage, administering oxygen and otherwise taking action to save his life until the doctor could take over.

In most hospitals, the patient would have required a nurse at his bedside around the clock. At each moment of crisis there would have been time-consuming steps, first to determine that there actually was stoppage, then to summon the necessary assistance. The man's chances for survival would have been poor. Fortunately, the Medical Center is one of the growing number of hospitals with a revolutionary new set-up called ICU—Intensive Care Unit. It consists of an eighteen-patient ward with a central monitoring system which actually keeps a far better check on each patient than any bedside nurse alone could accomplish. Through the use of electronic monitoring instruments, the nurse at the central desk can observe the smallest warning signs. Each patient is taped to sets of sensors that take blood pressure, temperature, pulse rate and other readings and transmit them continuously to tiny television screens, buzzers and alarm lights. Such complex information as brain wave recordings and electrocardiograms can also be hooked into the monitor.

Most patients in intensive care units are critically or seriously ill and require very little socializing. Yet each is instantly connected by intercom with the nurse if he needs to communicate, or if he requires personal attention. Moreover, a single nurse can, in just five minutes, take a series of readings (for fifteen or more patients) that would have required an hour or so of normal rounds.

"This is medical automation at its best," said a Mt. Kisco, New York, surgeon, shortly after his hospital installed a ten-bed ICU, "but more importantly we have seen that it does not take away the human element. On most hospital floors, the nurses come and go, often pressed for time. But with ICU there is always a nurse on hand, and others can be called in as needed."

Yet, as Dr. Hildegard Peplau pointed out at a clinical session of the American Nurses Association, there is one contribution that machines can never usurp from nurses, and that is T.L.C. (Tender Loving Care).

Monitoring devices are not new, but only within the past few years have they begun to receive acceptance in medical circles as instruments in regular hospital care. An important factor is that distance presents no problems. This was graphically demonstrated in June, 1961, at the annual meeting of the American Medical Association. At that time, participating doctors interested in the impressive progress being made in electronic medical instrumentation watched the image of a patient's heartbeat oscillating across a screen, and were able to judge effectively that the man was suffering from hardening of the arteries.

The significant fact was that the patient, with an instrument the size and shape of a fountain pen, connected to dime-sized transducers (tiny microphones) taped over his heart, was pacing back and forth in the office of a hospital *twenty-five hundred miles away*.

Long distance cardiograms of this type will prove useful for doctors in any part of the country to consult instantaneously with heart specialists in large hospitals. In the not too distant future, worried heart patients who would like to take vacation trips will be able to carry wallet sized transmitting devices so that, in case of trouble, they can relay their condition to their own doctors back home and receive advice. Any ICU monitoring device can be tuned into a transmitting system for consultation with specialists in other hospitals in the U.S., or even abroad. The distance over which information can be transmitted has been conclusively demonstrated in various flights made by astronauts, during which their physical condition was telemetered to earth during every second of the trip.

Some of these monitoring devices are being perfected so that they not only transmit data, but can store it indefinitely. Thus a complete record of cardiac reactions during a week or more of varying activities might be recorded for overall analysis. Instead of instructing a patient, "Take these pills and come back in ten days and we'll see how you are," doctors of the future may well say, "We'll tape this miniature recorder to your chest and see what kind of information it picks up on your heart during the next two weeks."

Automation is beginning to make a broad impact, too, in the pharmaceutical field. "The impact of electronic data processing in the drug industry has just started," says Eliot Steinberg, director of research administration for the Warner-Lambert Pharmaceutical Company. Computers, for example, are heavily involved in processing information for chemists and biologists experimenting with new formulas for drugs of the future. In recent years, information has been computerized by a number of the nation's drug manufacturers, so that scientists are able to obtain more complete and more accurate information—and with considerably greater speed than in the past.

The drug industry, spending many millions of dollars annually for research on such killers as heart disease and cancer, has enormous problems. One is that many scientists are, unknowingly, duplicating each others' work because they cannot possibly know about everything that is being done, or even everything that is being published on the subjects of mutual concern. Computers are helping to spread the word. The American Chemical Society launched an organization, Chemical Abstracts Services, just to provide such information and make it available to research staff members. In addition, the government, through the National Library of Medicine, and several private companies, have been using computer systems for centralizing information on drugs of all kings.

Automation in the medical field really began coming into its own with the start of the sixties. Early in 1961, A.M.A. President E. Vincent Askey asserted, "Judging from the work taken over by new medical machines, instruments and complex devices . . . during 1960, the future of automation in medicine looks bright."

All medical men were not in agreement, however. Many voiced the opinion that automation was a "dehumanizing process" that would never adjust to the needs of the medical profession. In June, 1961, a professional medical school journal headlined: PUSH-BUTTON MEDICINE? IT'S HERE! then asked the question, "Will it be a mixed blessing?"

The journal reported that some physicians were afraid that the future of the individual practitioner would fall into grim decline. One spokesman for this school of thought was Dr. Peter Forsham, a specialist in metabolic diseases at the University of California School of Medicine. "By the year 2000," he prophesied, "both diagnosis and treatment will be largely turned over to technicians equipped with electronic devices. The physician's job will then be essentially what it was in the nineteenth century— to serve as friend and confessor to the patient, counsel him on emotional problems, and help him adjust to disease the machines are unable to lick."

Other critics felt that the days of individual practitioner were numbered and that doctors would have to—because of the expense of new gadgetry—join forces in medical groups or else become even more hospital-oriented than they were.

Characteristic may be the attitude of one physician, a general practitioner. When his son went to medical school and announced that he was going to follow in his father's footsteps, the father reacted with alarm. "Don't go into general practice," he cautioned. "Get into medical research, where you will be able to make contributions. In twenty years or so, machines will have taken over so much of the doctor's work that a general practitioner will have nothing to do but stand by the bedside and hold the patient's hand."

These doubts are by no means unique. Their presence in the medical field parallels what has for some time been occurring in the business field.

"Automation has presented management with a major new problem," says Diebold, "As yet management has not faced up to this problem; in fact is not even grappling with it in any true sense. There is a wide gulf between the possession of the marvelous new machines and their profitable use. Management must learn to use the new technology to gain more accurate and timely information about the operation of a business, and to capitalize on such information through new decision-making techniques. This can be done in ways that were impossible before the advent of information technology. But managers will have to look afresh at each development and overcome certain stereotypes, myths and limitations. . . ."

Although Diebold was talking to management in general, he might just as well have been addressing his remarks to *hospital* management or to other areas of the medical world. Physicians and surgeons proceed with caution in studying and accepting new methods of treatment and care. Fortunately, they are not given to snap judgments in endorsing new devices. Yet automation does seem to offer new horizons in medicine that have long been obscured.

Diebold's approach to the problem is the planning of an institute to examine and evaluate the changes now taking place and that will take place in the future. More importantly, he says, the institute would not only prophecy the changes, but recommend ways in which entire communities and individuals alike could cope with these elements of change. Diebold is familiar with the problems at first hand, for, among other things, his Group undertook one of the first studies ever performed in the medical field. On behalf of the American Hospital Association, it ran a pilot study on the Baylor University Hospital in Dallas, to determine what role computers might play in hospitals. The Group has educated more than five hundred hospital administrators in the use of computers and related aspects of the new technology.

How can a computer, or any other type of mechanical or electronic machine, take over the thought functions and judgment of a doctor? The answer is that it cannot, but it can serve as a valuable complement to what professional people are doing at various levels. Take the matter of diagnosis, which is an area much talked-about in relation to computers. "When a physician arrives at a particularly brilliant diagnosis," said Dr. Gerars S. Schwarz of New York's Presbyterian Hospital, "he has employed consciously and unconsciously a vast storehouse of information, has considered hundreds of facts and combinations thereof, and has rejected perhaps a thousand others. But today, available information has increased to the point where no single human brain can retain, much less utilize, all the medical facts at its disposal."

128

The answer to the memory storing and retrieval process is the computer, into which teams of medical men feed all of the necessary information for the diagnosis of all known diseases. Thus, within seconds, a doctor who keyed all of the symptoms evidenced by a patient would receive back a listing of the possible illnesses relating to those symptoms. It has been demonstrated many times that computers can perform the diagnostic function with great accuracy. In Salt Lake City, for example, at the Latter-Day Saints Hospital, a control data computer system consistently comes up with diagnoses of congenital heart disease that are as accurate as those of an entire panel of experts. Man for man, it can outperform individual doctors with dramatic success, studying blood pressure, taking pulse rates and checking other constantly varying factors. Clinically applied, this new medical research is bringing new hope to many heart patients.

Another computer, at the Omaha Veteran's Administration Hospital helps researchers study the kinds and quantities of trace elements in organs of the body. One aim here is to evaluate theories that certain elements are lined to certain diseases— notably cancer.

The Veterans Administration has been using a computer system to store a broad range of specific diagnostic heart information in Washington. Linked with the computer system are ten VA hospitals, which are able to send the electrocardiograms of their patients directly over the telephone lines. The robot physician makes an immediate analysis which, according to Dr. Hubert Pipberger of the Veterans Administration, is not only quicker, but more detailed than any report that might have been made by an individual physician.

As an example, in cases where a patient has thickening of the walls of the ventricles, the machine analyzes the condition 94 per cent of the time. Physicians score only 24 per cent. In other types of medical cases, the computer scores 100 per cent, where doctors average only 70 per cent, or lower.

Computers can be used, too, directly with certain kinds of medical instruments and diagnostic equipment. A new device for studying brain disorders depends upon automation. The patient wears a pair of oversize eyeglasses, equipped with built-in photocells. These measure degrees of light reflected from the wearer's eyes and feed the data directly into a computer. By analyzing the light-reflection figures, the computer then comes up with comparative data that can help medical specialists pinpoint the patient's illness.

Perhaps a simple example will indicate how computers and other information-compiling machines serve as assistants to doctors. At the Texas Institute for Research and Rehabilitation, at Baylor University, doctors were faced with a common problem. No one had determined exactly how long casts should remain on patients who had undergone surgery for straightening of the spine. On the one hand, the spine tended to lapse back to its original curvature if the cast were removed too soon. On the other hand, if the casts were left on too long, other parts of the body, such as internal organs, reacted badly. So the Institute fed information into a computer—data collected from many cases. The answer came forth almost immediately: twelve to sixteen weeks.

Dr. William A. Spencer, director of the Institute, described the computer as "an extension of the human mind which offers physicians a new freedom to practice the art of medicine."

Speaking at the World's Fair in July, 1964, David Sarnoff, chairman of the board of Radio Corporation of America, which is one of the largest manufacturers of automation equipment in the world, expressed high hopes for what can be accomplished. "The computer," he said, "will emerge as a major tool of the medical fraternity as it strives to eradicate disease. . . . In the electronic future it will be possible to maintain a complete medical profile of every person in the community and in the nation." He pointed out that in the long run, the correlation of immense quantities of information would help to speed up our medical research programs, as well as help to determine the relationship of various elements, such as air pollution and cancer or nutrition and longevity.

It is quite possible that cancer and certain forms of heart disease might have been licked by now if computers had been available for this kind of medical research for the last decade or so. As it stands today, only some ten per cent of all labs engaged in medical research have any access to computers.

How computers can be effectively used in medical research has been demonstrated by Professor Walter Rosenblith, a biophysicist at M.I.T., who has been conducting studies in "brain electricity." The procedure used is to examine the nervous system by linking it electrically with a computer which then provides multiple reactions. Although scientists have been studying brain waves for many years, through such methods as attaching electrodes to various parts of the skull, or even within the brain, the results have been spotty and inaccurate. There are so many millions—even billions—of elements involved in brain electricity that research in the past has been about as successful as a study of the oceans would be by taking a bucket of water from each of them. A single recording can be thrown off by noise, or many other factors. So what the computer does is to record hundreds of thousands of effects in the brain that occur when the subject is exposed to a single phenomenon—observing a color or listening to a bell—and then present a pattern. Individual recordings will vary, but the overall pattern will be accurate and meaningful.

In May, 1965, in a telegram to the International Federation for Information Processing, at the Hilton Hotel in New York, President Johnson said:

> . . . Advanced information processing technology will be a major factor in making the results of our research programs available to those who need them, in our efforts to improve education and health services, and in improving job opportunities for all our people. We are eager to extend these services for the benefit of all mankind. The recent proposal by the United States to the World Health Organization to develop a worldwide early warning system for drugs is, for example, dependent upon your technology.

One of the greatest complaints among physicians and surgeons (as in law, engineering and other professions) is that a single practitioner, reading by day and night and never pausing to perform his medical function at all, could not possibly keep up with all of the printed material on medicine that comes out each day—magazine articles, professional papers, books, and other published works. Already, computer programmers are at work, compiling what will eventually be an enormous *Index Medicus*, available to doctors from coast to coast. Into this electronic memory system will be poured all of the material that comes along in published form—placed there by a team of communications experts on a daily continuing basis. When a doctor wants information on any particular disease, injury or other subject, the indexing system will track down all references needed and provide up-to-the-minute information—*in less than four minutes!*

To understand the implications of this on a very broad scale for the future it is worth considering what can happen today in just one hospital alone. The Massachusetts General Hospital, emphasized this kind of information system as a "new dimension to medical research," which would make available a permanent collection of records of all patients. Suppose a surgeon needs as much data as possible about the after-effects of knee-surgery on boys between fifteen and twenty who are engaged in school athletics. He could obtain the records immediately. Formerly, it would have taken staff assistants hours of work, perusing endless case histories, to come up with what at best would be a 10 per cent sample of such cases.

Even this kind of sampling would then have been filed away, overlooked or difficult to find again, when information might be needed on the same subject months later. But today, with ever-increasing case histories being fed into the information system —for use next week or two generations from now—data will be available at once, and in sufficient quantity to be significant. Machines are even being educated so that they can compensate for the inadvertent misspelling of a drug name or a biomedical term!

Multiply this kind of process in a system tying in hundreds of hospitals across the country and the results will be incredible.

As John Diebold points out, in answer to critics who say that automation is a dehumanizing process and therefore cannot be applied to medicine where the human element is all important, medical automation is not being perfected to replace doctors, but to provide them with more effective instrumentation. He refers to such advances as the use of computers to help develop new methods for diagnosing and analyzing the often conflicting evidence about the heart. In advanced experiments, the computer is used to read the heartbeat diagram made by an electrocardiograph. What happens is that the computer examines hundreds of points along each line of the electrocardiogram, the image of the heart's electrical activity. It then instantly prints a detailed analysis.

One problem that doctors have had in the past in studying patterns of heart activity is that they have had to rely on the relatively small sampling made by a patient lying prone, with electrodes taped to his arms, legs, and chest. Now, tests are being made with continuing electrocardiograms, recorded by a small device attached to the patient—an instrument that records information as the subject goes through all kinds of different activities. Formerly, it would have been physically impossible for doctors to examine and analyze the endless graphs resulting from the tests. But now machines can do the job in a matter of minutes.

In other experiments, says Diebold, computers are being used to analyze the sound of a patient's heartbeat, since rhythm and intensity can reveal abnormalities which the machine's brain can detect and classify. From an overall, long-range standpoint, computers make it possible to complete mass statistical studies of heart disease, so that the medical profession can see a pattern of millions of facts about hundreds of thousands of case histories.

Not only can the information be tracked down immediately, but automation can then be put to use to assist in the diagnosis and treatment which follows. The new tools of medicine range all the way from the large, complex computers down to devices no larger than a shirt button. There is also a growing list of gadgets, many of which are extremely valuable in examination. Among the more ingenious are miniature cameras that can be swallowed and then manipulated in the stomach so that pictures of the lining can be taken; an electronic instrument for measuring blood pressure, to replace the old pump bag and tube the doctor wraps around your arm; and a device that looks like an oversize pencil, which can be placed on a patient's chest or abdomen, where it emits ultrasonic waves that reproduce X-ray information on a tape. Even the familiar stethoscope will be replaced soon, by an electronic counterpart that will be far more sensitive and make for more accurate diagnosis.

Much of the automation that is taking place in medicine today, says Diebold, is aimed at disposing of routine chores that free doctors and laboratory technicians so that they can concentrate on more important matters. The Peter Bent Brigham Hospital in Boston, for example, has for several years been utilizing a new method for analyzing blood samples. Even the drawing of the sample has changed, through use of a disposable tube, vacuumized so that the blood is sucked into it quickly and with no exposure to outside atmosphere. The samples are sent to an instrumentation unit, where a completely automatic instrument analyzes them and enters data on a strip-chart recorder.

As a result, said Dr. Ralph Thiers, Director of the Chemical Laboratory at the hospital, "The cost of the laboratory work to the hospital has decreased. The salary of the medical technicians has been raised because the efficiency has improved so much. For example, in the space where we were doing five thousand analyses per month, we are now doing ten thousand analyses. Three years ago, that amount of space was inadequate; now it's adequate because these instruments can not only do forty determinations an hour, which is the rate at which three technicians can work, but can do them in less space. Today, a blood count can be taken in twenty-five seconds. And in a matter of less than two minutes, technicians can now analyze, with the help of computers and mathematical "models" of the human blood stream, as many as fifty-six different changes that can occur in blood.

Not long ago, an expectant mother in Baltimore announced proudly to her friends that she was going to have a baby by machine. She could not explain what it was all about, but had the impression that some kind of a computer would be taking the place of the doctor and that somehow the baby would eventually emerge untouched by human hands. The mother-to-be was somewhat misinformed, yet it was true that a machine was to contribute to the delivery. At Johns Hopkins University, Dr. Dhirendra Kumar and a medical team had perfected an electronic device that helps to induce labor. Coupled to a tiny pump, it rations out administrations of oxytocin, the drug used to stimulate uterine contractions, but which must be controlled precisely if it is to be used safely. The machine monitors childbirth labor continuously and accurately.

According to Johns Hopkins, the machine has already been used successfully with more than two hundred women, including many who had heart trouble, toxemia, or other ailments which add danger and complications to childbirth. Without this form of automation, many of the mothers would have required Caesarean operations.

Machines are being effectively used to protect the lives and health of babies as well as mothers. "On a quiet street in Philadelphia," reported science editor Earl Ubell in the New York *Herald Tribune* "the clickety-clack of a Univac turns out statistics to stop the medical mistakes that kill in obstetrics. Each number, each percentage tells hospitals what is going wrong;

too much anaesthesia, improper surgery or inadequate nursing—any of which the doctors may, in good conscience, believe to be all right. But the numbers tell the truth."

Established with a $46,000 grant from the American Medical Association as an experiment, the computer was first demonstrated in June, 1961. At the time, Dr. Sydney H. Kane, the pediatrician and mathematician who was directing the project for ninety-one hospitals, said that the objective was to include the entire nation —some forty million births. "If we can change the infant death rate by less than 1 per cent," he said, "we can save thirteen thousand babies a year."

Working with the computer, one hospital cut the death rate in half, from thirty-four deaths for each thousand live births, to only fifteen, or ten below the national average.

Since that time, steady gains have been made in the field. The method is relatively simple. Each doctor fills out a single report sheet on each obstetrical case. He enters data about the mother's condition, complications, procedures used, timing and other factors. The sheet then goes to the central processing system where data are entered on punched cards and fed into the computer. If, over a period of time, certain hospitals seem to have more breech deaths than others, their methods are carefully analyzed and corrected. If the administration of a certain drug turns up as a factor, the drug is eliminated or dosages changed. In the long run, the computer absorbs millions of facts without ever forgetting them.

Computers can be used, too, to create and study the functions and diseases of specific organs, through the creation of theoretical models. It is possible, to take all the variables of kidney function, for example, and create a hypothetical kidney. By tabulating functions and malfunctions, doctors can then get new insight and determine more effective methods for treating ailments of this organ.

There seems to be no limit to what machines can do when carefully researched and developed. Often, however, we do not realize how extremely complex the human system is and how difficult it is to simulate it by machine. Take the act of eating, so routine that we think little of taking fork in hand and transferring food from the plate to the mouth. At the International Conference of Physical Medicine and Rehabilitation in Paris, in September,

1964, a group of Cleveland researchers described a mechanical device they had designed to help paralyzed patients. "And," reported *Time* magazine, "their report made it clear that mechanizing the human body's functions is an awesome engineering feat."

The "aim-aid" turned out to be "an intricate melding of computer parts, photocells, electrical wiring and metal" that took scientists at Case Institute of Technology and at Highland View Hospital in Cleveland some three years to complete. The device consists of a splint-like section attached to the forearm, which moves the patient's arm, and the use of a photo-cell and infrared light beams to give directions. The patient selects a special program for eating, by focusing the beam in the proper place. He then activates his hand through a series of photoelectric commands, moving the hand from the plate to his mouth and back again as he desires. According to the report, it requires some thirty minutes to eat a computerized meal.

From such crude beginnings, the medical world is looking out towards far horizons that will change the entire perspective of mankind. "Man's form, physical and psychological," says Diebold, "has been freed from the imperceptible course decreed by natural evolution. The undirected or misdirected application of technology is threatening not only man's environment but the quality of future generations. At the same time, man's knowledge, his technology, can vastly accelerate—even bypass—the evolutionary process. Even now the creation of cyborgs—men with artificial organs—has begun. This, extended by the incipient ability to alter the blueprint of future generations through the manipulation of DNA (deoxyribonucleic acid), the basic genetic material, gives man the power to participate in and largely control the act of his own continual creation. But he has decided neither if he should do so, nor to what end he should do so."

Through the cyborgs, the automated organs of which Diebold speaks, a whole new world of medical conquest is opening up. Perhaps the most dramatic progress thus far has been in providing assistance for the heart through the use of tiny pacemakers, no larger than half-dollars, inserted right in the bodies of patients.

Maimonides Hospital, in Brooklyn, N. Y., working with scientists at General Electric has produced a workable model which thus far has been implanted in more than six hundred patients suffering from heart trouble. Using tiny batteries, pacemakers can last up to five years without replacement, taking the workload off hearts that beat irregularly. Thus far, the model has failed only fifteen times.

Six staff doctors at Maimonides and two electronic engineers are researching new ways for making paralyzed or diseased muscles obey the electronic commands of new devices. Another development is the bladder stimulator which will eventually help some two hundred thousand paraplegics in the United States, patients who cannot empty their urinary bladder because of paralysis of their lower bodies. A tiny disk (much like the heart pacemaker), is implanted under the skin, powered by a minute battery cell. The disk releases an electric charge whenever the patient flashes a radio signal from a portable unit, thus taking the place of paralyzed muscles. Already tried successfully with seven paraplegics, it will eventually save thousands of lives, since more than half the deaths among paraplegics can be attributed to complications of the urinary tract resulting from large amounts of residual urine in the bladder and the subsequent infection of the kidneys.

Despite the remarkable advances made in the whole field of medical automation, there are numerous frustrations. Many doctors balk at the idea of "machines taking over." Others feel that automation is still much too new to be reliable, and that if used at all it should be regarded with considerable suspicion. Reporting on the frustrating stages of trying to marry the medical profession to the electronic industry, *Business Week* reported the plea of the research director of a large medical institute: "The need as well as the possibilities are there, just crying to get together. There have been formidable barriers holding them apart, but now a few big cracks in the wall have started to appear."

According to the editors, "the decisive point in acceptance of electronic medical devices will be reached when more medical doctors are trained in electronics and physics and more engineers get training in medicine. Then the gap between doctor's needs and the devices that are available will begin to close." Yet today, there are probably not a dozen trained Ph.D.'s in biomedical engineering.

"Medical electronics has come a long way in the past few years," says the head of the bioelectronics division of a large psychiatric institute, "Ten years ago a doctor who was interested in electronics was suspect at best and often considered an outright nut." Today, his position may be controversial, but at least it is gaining acceptance.

From now on, we are likely to see an astonishing increase in applications in the entire field of medical automation. According to one industry estimate, biomedical engineering is well on its way to becoming a billion dollar a year industry by the early 1970's.

12

A Diebold day

"Some people think of me as a 'young man in a hurry.' Perhaps that is true, but although I may do a lot of hurrying, I do a good deal more pausing—pausing to reflect where I have been, where I am and where I am trying to go."

JOHN DIEBOLD, COMMENT TO A WRITER DURING AN INTERVIEW, 1964.

MANY PEOPLE WONDER, upon hearing about dramatic achieve-ments brought about through automation, why there are not far more applications of computers and other inventions of our exploding technology to combat illnesses and save lives. One answer is that it takes several years to plan, develop and install complex data gathering systems. Another answer is that, while there are engineers and scientists who can steadily perfect the necessary hardware, there are far too few consultants who are qualified to advise business, industry and the professions on the uses and applications of information technology.

The field is so new, and the precedents so few, that it is ex-tremely difficult for a sophisticated businessman—let alone prac-titioners and administrators in the highly complex areas of the medical sciences—to select an adviser and then have faith in his judgments. How, and why, is a man like John Diebold quali-fied to give advice in many fields? People are always asking, "How does he do it?" Achieving such success at age thirty-nine is unusual, to say the least, and explaining it is not an easy task, although many have tried.

Editor Clay Felker of *Esquire*, after spending some ten days with him abroad for an article that appeared in the magazine in March, 1962, describes him as "far from the popular image of a dynamic, table-pounding young entrepreneur whose fast talk and fast footwork sweep all obstacles before him. . . . Neither does casual conversation reveal the secret of his success, for he makes conversational small talk in a soft voice graced by an old-fashioned politesse, accompanied by a shy but friendly smile. . . . But great corporate leaders . . . have sought him out and listened with fascination as he spoke. Behind his words is the power of an idea—an idea which captures the future and is a method for exploiting its vast opportunities."

The *London Times Review of Industry and Technology* described him in June, 1964, as "Mr. Automation," a "tall, fair-haired young man," whose "hands moved in awkward, diffident gestures" and whose voice was "soft and hesitant." He is further profiled as having an energy and drive concealed by an abstracted, rather shy, manner, "with eyes that are mournful, brightening only when he speaks of the challenges ahead."

The New York *Times* in an article about him on March 28, 1965, commented: "His standing in the hierarchy of the modern technology has been attested to by the fact that he was the initial witness at the first joint Congressional hearing on the problem of automation."

These are impressions, good impressions, and they are reflective. But what is much more difficult to grasp, to come solidly to grips with, is the inner drive—call it almost compulsion—which motivates him, which makes reporters and writers refer to him as a man who "never seems to stop hustling," and which suggests the epitome of "a young man in a hurry."

One way to see realistically how Diebold "does it" is to take a close-focus look at him in day-to-day action. The picture will not, of course, be entirely accurate, for although it is easy to get an *impression*, it is not possible to pick any day that is completely typical.

When an experienced reporter and competent Midwestern writer, Ted J. Rakstis, who had never met the young entrepreneur before, was assigned to follow him around Chicago during the course of a business day, he had this to say:

"Spending a day with John Diebold is like following a small cyclone for nine or ten non-stop hours. By the time it's over, your legs ache from trying to keep up with this marathon pace and your brain reels from the mass of technological facts that you've accumulated. By nightfall, you're glad to get a rest."

Later on, he described him as "leaping down the hall like an Olympic sprinter," and sprinting eight blocks on foot to an appointment because he did not have time to take a cab. It is not unusual for observers to come away with this supercharged physical image of the man. Even in summing up the day's activities, journalist Rakstis could not help marveling at the energy output displayed. During a single working day, he reported, "Mr. Diebold personally conducted seven business conferences of a top-level nature involving crucial decisions by some of the nation's major corporations. For him the day was termed 'fairly easy' and more or less typical." Rakstis goes on to recount how his constantly moving subject seemed equally at ease in a wide variety of situations: helping a newspaper publisher make decisions on automating communications procedures; discussing how an oil company could consolidate its computer systems; proposing methods whereby a major book publisher could develop one of the most important information outlets in the United States; and leading an electronics firm into new areas of production.

"A different type of challenge arose in each case," wrote Rakstis, "Yet it took Diebold only a matter of minutes to grasp the kernel of each problem, thinking the matter through spontaneously, yet comprehensively. For most out-of-town consultants, the Chicago trip would have been important and worthwhile to hold a discussion with any *one* of these seven clients. But Diebold made the entire round in what I gathered was for him a routine, if productive, business day."

This physical, on-the-surface impression, however, is only one facet of a personality whose roots go extremely deep. If a day with John Diebold in Chicago seems, to a perceptive journalist (but one who has really not had enough time to know him) like a kind of ebullient executive tennis match, it is easy to see how certain superficial evaluations of him were made during his early years in the field. "He goes off half-cocked," was the remark of a disgruntled competitor a number of years ago, who figured that any man who could cover so many bases must be touching them pretty lightly in an effort to make an impression.

"He is a bull in a china shop," commented another, viewing Diebold as an alarming business opponent, who might start picking off his own clients one by one as he charged about, or perhaps stir them up with all kinds of new ideas, spreading his own philosophies with increasing impact.

The Diebold whom such detractors did not see, or perhaps did not want to see, was a deeply reflective man who could spend many hours on end in contemplation of a problem, developing answers, yet never satisfied that they were good enough. He was a man who could concentrate so deliberately and intensely on a subject that over a weekend he could master by himself an unfamiliar subject that would have required most executives several weeks of seminars and reading to absorb.

The years, bulwarked by John Diebold's accomplishments in his field, have seen the "bull-in-a-china-shop" criticism slow to a trickle. If some people still do consider him to be over-enthusiastic, it is largely because they do not know him well enough to realize that behind the open, physical expression of interest there lies a solid and meaningful absorption in the subject at hand. He admits that he lets himself get carried away at times, yet only because he becomes genuinely involved in a subject and intends to pursue the matter at considerable length.

In the business world, John Diebold would certainly be labelled conservative rather than promotional in the methods he uses to approach prospective clients or to deal with existing ones. Planned presentations are rare, and even charts and other visual tools are used in moderation and with restraint.

He has not infrequently been referred to as a perfectionist, a term which in his case is far more the embodiment of a strength than a weakness. From the negative viewpoint, it could be said that perfectionism makes him demanding to work with. He says that he cannot abide seeing a job done imperfectly, whether it entails a vital assignment for a client or a personal project. When he was at King's Point, he admired a series of albums maintained by Admiral Steadman, the Superintendent of the Academy, a man who urged cadets to start scrapbooks. Diebold decided that he would follow his superior's advice. Each volume, complete with snapshots, letters, clippings, and other personal material, would cover a different period in his life, from childhood through school, college, the war and the various phases of his later career.

After much planning, during which he drew upon his knowledge of and love for bookmaking, he designed a suitable type of album, which he then made himself, page by page, and later had sewn and bound in leather.

In the process he went to the New York Public Library, to the Rare Book Room and asked what type of glue was used to repair the ancient and very valuable books on hand. After a certain type was specified, he made a personal visit to the glue factory. "I was in uniform," he recalls, "They must have thought that I was a government purchasing agent, ready to order tank cars of the stuff. The smallest quantity I then could reasonably buy was a whole gallon!"

In another instance, he wrote to the British Museum, which he considered to be the outstanding authority in the field, for advice on leather dressing to protect the albums and also the many rare, leather-bound volumes which he owns. After the museum had sent him full specifications, he ordered the recommended dressing and commenced using it. Later, to his infinite distress, he learned that perhaps he had not conducted his research thoroughly enough. "After using the British Museum leather dressing for some time," he said, "I discovered that it was somewhat acid. The formula may be proper for the English climate, but I'm not at all sure it's good with American central heating."

He spends long hours establishing office procedures. Every detail in the office is worked over a dozen times—to achieve absolute efficiency and simplicity. "Details are important. I've always felt this way."

He is also a perfectionist when it comes to intangibles, and especially to areas where he believes that certain knowledge he should have is too limited. "One thing worries me a great deal," he confided not long ago, "and that is that I am always with older people. I don't really know enough people who are *young*. So I am consciously trying to meet younger people all the time. A college student mentioned the Watusi to me one time. I knew it was an African tribe, but I didn't realize until then that it was a current dance fad." He was honestly disturbed at this oversight.

Because Diebold enjoys a full life, he used to be open to the criticism that he was too much the connoisseur. People who know him, however, soon learn that he has a real and fundamental interest in the pursuit of excellence in all he touches. His fascination with the architecture and running of great houses and estates, for example, started at an early age. In Pennsylvania, and later in Cambridge, during college and business school years, he would, as he wrote in a letter, "drive into the entrances to innumerable estates around Philadelphia's Main Line and later around Boston —to get some feelings of the house and grounds—often leading to amusing situations."

Once on Long Island, he and some friends drove into an estate, only to sight the hostess coming down a tremendous flight of steps to greet them. Hastily turning off on what seemed like a side roadway, they inadvertently circled around and came up smack against the woman again, at the bottom of the steps, in the midst of an enormous formal reception.

Some observers are perplexed on occasion by a whimsical, playful part of Diebold's nature that clashes with the traditional concept of the sedate, London-bound chairman of the board, dressed in Chesterfield and Homburg. His sometimes disarming activities reflect a unique way in which he obtains relief from business pressures or intense intellectual strain. Relief may come through a joke, absorbed interest in a child's puzzle or game, or by some totally unexpected action.

"I love banisters," he says with a puckish grin, "If I see a good banister, I always slide down it!" And he does, occasionally to the consternation of onlookers.

No matter what the reaction may be, it is constantly apparent that Diebold is not an easy subject to characterize. Like the intricate, often intangible field of automation which he represents, his own nature embodies many complexities and subtleties that can be evaluated only through long, sustained contact with the man himself, in the widest imaginable circumstances. It is not the purpose of this book to weave a psychological, analytical study of a personality. Rather, the objective is to present a realistic, understandable picture of a man thoroughly immersed in his work—creating the world of the future, the world of automation —in such a way that his outlooks, approaches and objectives will make that subject itself more meaningful to the reader.

To the extent that any event can be typical, the European trip depicted in the photos on the following 16 pages are thoroughly typical of one of John Diebold's trips to Europe, which occur three or four times per year. These photographs, taken by Marvin Newman for a profile that originally appeared in Esquire Magazine, cover a trip that began with arrival at the Dorchester Hotel in London on November 14, 1961, and ended on November 22 with departure from Paris.

Whenever he can, John Diebold fits his route to a mixture of familiar landmarks such as St. James Palace *(above)* and exploration of new locations with which he gains first-hand familiarity—e.g. *(right)*, the latest computer installations.

Dining with friends at a London club *(below)*—Denis Greensmith *(left)*, of Boots Pure Drug Co., and Robert Simpson, a British computer pioneer.

Visiting with old friend and British automation leader, Sir Leon Bagrit, Chairman of Elliott Automation, Ltd. *(above)* in the superb Adams town house that serves as his headquarters.

After breakfast at the Frankfurterhof, flight by private plane with German colleagues for a tour of an enormous open pit coal mine in the Ruhr. A conference with directors of the company follows for review of a planning assignment that Diebold Deutschland GmbH has been undertaking for this major German company. The mine is operated continuously by a group of what are probably the largest automatic machines in the world, mounted on enormous caterpillar tractors, each using the electric power required by a city of 30,000.

Early morning walk along snow swept quay across from the Royal Palace.

Visit to the soon to be dedicated Axel Wenner-Gren Center in Stockholm.

(above) A quiet walk through the grounds of Häringe Castle outside of Stockholm with Mme. Brita Procope. Photograph was taken while visiting Marguerite Wenner-Gren a few days before the death of Diebold's friend, Axel Leonard Wenner-Gren.

(below) Inspection of a Swedish telephone equipment and computer plant outside of Stockholm.

(right) Happy always when in the quiet of nature, here on the shore of the Baltic near the guest cottage at Häringe Castle in which he sometimes stays.

Typical late evening arrival at Michelangelo Airport in Rome, followed, as often, by a long exploratory walk through the city.

With Italian colleagues Vittorio Vaccari, Director of UCID (the Catholic employers federation), and Pietro Vaccari, then President of RCA-Italy, as they pass the Trevi Fountain, returning to Diebold's Rome office after lunch.

With Giuseppi Foddis, the President of the Telephone Company of Rome.

Leaving the Vatican after a visit to the administrative offices with his Italian colleague, Massimo Brighi, the Protestant Diebold furthers by first-hand investigation a long-standing interest in the organization of the Catholic Church.

Inspecting a model of the new campus of INSEAD (European Institute of Business Administration) with Jean Tarbé de Saint-Hardouin, a French colleague of Diebold's, and Olivier Giscard d'Estaing, Director of the Institute. Diebold serves on the U.S. Advisory Committee of this school.

Factory inspection at Compagnie des Machines Bull, the French computer manufacturer, with their senior executives. Diebold maintains first-hand familiarity with the present and future of the computer industry by frequent on-the-spot investigations. He directs endless questions at scientists and engineers who are making the future in the countries he visits.

Addressing the Council, or governing body, of the International Chamber of Commerce, Paris.

The control system at the jet engine test facility in the S.N.E.C.M.A. plant at Villaroche, France, a client of Diebold France, S.A.

Dining at a private club with friends, including Claude Janssen, a Parisian banker and member of the Board of Diebold France, and Olivier Giscard d'Estaing.

(Right) Computers work around the clock at this bank in Strasbourg, France, a long-time client of Diebold France.

Graduate students follow him from Fontainebleau Chateau where he lectures whenever time permits during visits to France. A popular lecturer, crowds of students typically follow him with questions every moment that he is able to spend at the school.

Reviewing the mammoth computer installation of Nouvelles Messageries de la Presse Parisiennes, a unique distributor of newspapers and magazines in France who have made what Diebold feels to be imaginative and progressive use of a computer control system.

A long, quiet walk with his friend, Olivier Giscard d'Estaing, through the park at Fontainebleau Chateau provides the opportunity for what John Diebold feels to be the true work of a future maker—planning the education of future generations of European and U.S. managers.

One vehicle helpful in bringing the reader on scene is that of making a visit to Diebold's Park Avenue office in New York City. The date, selected at random, was a characteristic Monday, on a hot day in mid-August.

His day had begun, as is usual for him, at about 6:00 A.M. Hot chocolate and fruit taken in his library, overlooking and almost a part of the East River, and the summer greenery of the upper stretches of Welfare Island permitted an undisturbed hour of serious reading and study. After shaving, dressing and eating a characteristically light breakfast he left for the office, usually by car, but today by cab.

By 8:15 that morning, John Diebold had already been at his desk for some thirty minutes, going through letters, memoranda, clippings and other papers in the quiet of the hour. He was thoughtfully sipping tea which he had brewed in a pantry which adjoins the conference room connected to his personal office suite. He drinks his tea plain, poured from a delicate, pure-white Limoges pot, six inches tall, into a thin straight-sided cup decorated with gold and blue bands at the top, in a pattern that is repeated on the saucer, and carried through in all of the office china—giving very much the flavor of restrained good taste of china in a senior flag officer's service.

His tall (six-foot-two) frame was clad in a dark gray suit, with the ever-present vest, a striped blue shirt, French cuffs, a dark blue four-in-hand tie, with double gray stripes and black socks and shoes. His breast pocket blossomed neatly with a blue handkerchief designed with small, conservative polka dots. On a shelf in his clothes closet lay the straw boater with wide black silk band which he prefers in the summer.

Diebold's worktable—being a purist as a member of the clear desk school, he believes in having no drawers in which papers might accumulate and consequently does not use a desk at all—is situated at the north end of Group's fourteenth floor office. His table, which he designed, is six feet long, severely simple in design, with thin brushed steel legs. The top is a husky slab of finely grained walnut, two inches thick, decorated only by a four-inch-wide band of wood that borders it all around. The chair is a swivel type, designed by Saarinen and upholstered graciously in black leather.

Diebold's office is anything but pretentious. It was designed in

145

good taste, the proper environment for hard work. It is perhaps fifteen feet wide and twenty feet long, with the east side, overlooking Park Avenue, completely glassed, softened by simple floor-to-ceiling beige drapes in a net-like weave. The walls at either end are eggshell white; the west, or inner, wall is composed of seven vertical walnut panels, set flush so that the presence of a door, near the desk—at the seventh panel—is almost totally concealed. The ceiling is fashioned in acoustical tile with fluorescent and incandescent fixtures embedded flush within it. The carpeting is a stippled brown and beige, which blends with walls, draperies and furniture. A beige upholstered chair, in modern style, sits in front of the desk; while the southwest corner of the room contains a thirty-inch-square block of walnut which serves as a coffee table and two Barcelona chairs designed by Mies van der Rohe, with backs and a flat seat, in black leather with brushed steel legs. On the table sits a telephone, alongside an ashtray and a trophy—a sculpture depicting two hands reaching upward and downward, toward each other. The latter was awarded by the United States Junior Chamber of Commerce to John Diebold as one of the "ten outstanding young men of the year," in January, 1962, along with such other young notables as Theodore Sorensen, Captain Virgil I. Grissom and Newton G. Minow.

When The Diebold Group, Inc. moved back to 430 Park Avenue, after five years at 40 Wall Street, they rented the entire fourteenth floor running a full Park Avenue block—in marked contrast to the single room the firm originally occupied in this very same building.

Determined to provide the finest professional facilities for his firm, and deeply interested in design and architecture, John Diebold retained Skidmore Owings and Merrill and together with his wife Doris worked closely with the architects for over a year. They completely gutted the entire floor, down to the concrete slab, and rebuilt everything.

Since Diebold has long been intrigued with art in practically every form, considerable attention has been given throughout the offices to works of art which are in many cases linked to the firm's professional practice. For example, the office of each consulant contains original prints of fine photographs by such photographers as Marvin Newman, Magda Vasillov and Henri Cartier-Bresson. The photos depict the consultants themselves in action in the field, the operations of client firms, and location shots of important assignments Group has undertaken over the years. Among them, there is a photo of the King of Nepal, a Griffenhagen-Kroeger client, sitting atop one of his elephants.

In preparation for the move to a new headquarters office, Diebold began collecting ancient maps of the cities throughout the world in which Group maintains offices. The art in his own office is by two leading Roman abstract expressionists. The north wall of his room is dominated by an abstract painting, some five feet in length, by Toti Scialoja—"Metamorfus"—and the south wall by a large, framed oil by Count Capagrossi. A superb bronze of a mythical animal, a "chimera" executed on commission by another Roman, the sculptor Mirko, guards the reception room to Diebold's area.

Behind Diebold's desk chair, against the north wall is another chair and a small cabinet on which stands a telephone and onto which he plunks his extra-thick black dispatch case and his ever-handy tape recorder. The latter accompanies him on his longer trips, for use in dictating communiques of all kinds. Its batteries are constantly being drained and recharged, whether he is seated at his desk, reclining on his bed, jolting about in a taxi, spanning the seas on a jet or driving from place to place by private car.

It was in use then, at 8:15 A.M., as he shuffled papers, examined the mail and contemplated a few dozen matters that had to be attended to: ideas that could be explored, people who should be communicated with, or information that he would like to obtain.

By 9:15, he had gone through the pile on his desk in somewhat the manner of an automated reaper harvesting corn. It was not quite evident whether he pushed a hidden button or whether timing played its part, but at precisely 8.30 Liosa Bing entered the office. Liesa is a petite young lady, to whom nine out of ten writers would immediately apply the adjectives alert and attractive. The tenth would say she is pretty, but the adjective applies more to her manner and graciousness than to purely physical attributes. In a calm, but purposeful way, she is as closely attuned to Diebold's professional needs as any associate could be, relieving him of many of the details that might tend to interfere with his compulsive business pace. She first arrived on the Diebold scene in 1958, when the firm was on Wall Street, as an executive secretary, quickly graduating to a position that might be described as a girl Friday, but with considerably more stature.

"I remember Mr. Diebold so clearly from the first time I went in to apply for a position as secretary," said Miss Bing. "He stood up when I came in, and was pleasant and charming. Very few men in business are so considerate, especially with a job applicant. It was a great deal of fun in those days because the firm was small and we all knew everything that was going on and what every other person was doing. Today it is still fun, but it is not always possible to keep up with everything.

"We had a Chicago office by then, and the Griffenhagen branch; and the European company was just being formed. But the firm was small in comparison with what it is today. Even in those days, Mr. Diebold was already being referred to as the elder statesman of automation. Yet no matter how hard he worked, he was always talking about opportunities that were missed because he just couldn't get to them, or because he had to make a choice between one course of action and another. He has one observation he likes to make, 'You rarely regret the things you do—only the things you do not do.' He would have been successful no matter what field he had gotten into. He has a great sensitivity for other people. And a memory for things. He is not always good at remembering names, but he remembers who people are and what their interests are, even after many years have elapsed since he last saw them."

At 8:30, Liesa Bing briefly discussed the day's schedules, to alert her boss to any changes or additions to it and to make certain that there were no conflicts in timing. Diebold was also concerned about the format for a report with illustrations describing the nature of its professional practice that the Group was preparing. He has an experienced eye for layout and is a perfectionist about the positioning of photographs, type, white space and other elements. Not fully satisfied with what had been arrived at, he decided to consider the project at greater length later.

The next half-hour was devoted to a careful examination and frequent editing of a series of tests that had been prepared for the Group, for the purpose of evaluating staff members. "We have never used personnel testing before," he said, "and I really do not like this kind of testing. But we have to get into it sooner or later, to help to prevent obvious errors when selecting candidates for various executive positions. My plan is to test the tests, as it were, on our own people, to see how accurate they really are."

Despite a continuing pattern of activity during the day, such as going through papers or discussing plans with staff members, Diebold is endlessly involved with an inner creative process. Mary Stephens-Caldwell Henderson, the thoughtful student of automation at George Washington University, who devoted the 170-page master's thesis to the study of John Diebold's innovations, concluded that:

> John Diebold has been an innovator both as a man who organizes reality into new relationships and as a man who communicates ideas which are new to the people who hear of them. That he has been so outstanding in either of these roles is rare. But that he has been outstanding in both is extraordinary and is the key to his having left his mark on our times. John Diebold's life and works make him a symbol of our age.

Miss Henderson listed twelve Diebold innovations, global in impact, which have affected in the most basic way the development of the new technology. With such sweeping innovations and concepts behind him, and ahead of him, John Diebold must constantly look beyond the confines of his desk, his business and even the total managerial world as it is known today.

13

The ever-continuing process

"I never want to stop at perfection. . . ."
JOHN DIEBOLD TO A BOOK PUBLISHER AT LUNCH.

B Y 9:20, JOHN DIEBOLD was on the phone, taking the first of
what might to some executives have been a maddeningly
persistent string of calls from across the country and overseas. On
the phone, however, he is equally as relaxed and communicative
as he is in direct conversation. He listens well, but always alert to
an opportunity to develop an idea.

By 9:25, he was turning over a collection of recording tapes to
one of his secretaries to transcribe. He normally has two full
tapes each weekday, and three or four over a weekend. These
contain memos, letters, references to the innumerable articles
he tears from magazines and newspapers which are filed or sent
out to various people, speech material, or ideas that he wants to
think about and develop. Each tape requires about a full day's
work for a secretary to transcribe, organize and follow through
on the instructions contained in it.

At 9:30, more tea was brought in, along with a pot of coffee
for a guest. It was followed shortly thereafter by a huge pile of
mail that had already been opened and pre-sorted, in order of
priority. At the bottom, was a formidable collection of magazines
and newspapers, which Diebold would absorb at some point
during the day. The tape recorder began to see action again, as he

dictated immediate answers to correspondence, memos for the staff, or notes to publishers regarding material read in passing. Diebold's dictating is highly informal, interspersed with "umms," coughs, occasional instructions and frequent apologies. ("I'm sorry, what I meant to say was. . . .") "I try," said Diebold, "to keep my mornings clear for correspondence, writing and creative matters; and I usually have a session with my general manager, to go over matters of import."

Many things caught his eye in the periodicals. Some items he tore out for later reference; others he noted in his tape recorder for further action by some one in the Group. On that particular Monday, there was an article on electronic data processing in *Business Week*, and another on executive secretaries, including one male secretary. ("We toyed with the idea of having a male secretary, but so far have not hired one.") A few items were marked for clipping from the *Wall Street Journal*. Into his brief-case went an issue of *The Economist*, which he prefers to read quietly at home, and a number of out-of-town newspapers, which he had perused, but was in the habit of re-reading later. "We tend," he suggested, "to become far too much New York-oriented. So I make it a practice to read many outside newspapers. Basically, though, I prefer the New York *Times*—even when it is two days old—to any other newspaper in the country. Sometimes, when I've been out of town, I'll have a collection of issues from Wednesday through Sunday at home and not get around to them until Sunday."

He does not like clipping services, except for routine filing. "I like to read through everything myself."

Correspondence on this particular Monday was typical. It included, among many other items: a letter from a company seeking a consultant; a Group schedule showing where each staff member would be on each day of the week, in New York, across the country, or abroad; business reports on company assignments in progress; data regarding the Diebold Research Program; the "Weekly Desk Sheet of Business Indicators," from the National Industrial Conference Board, of which the Group is a member, and many letters from clients.

Numbered among the collection were several letters indicating John Diebold's catholic interest in events and activities considerably apart from business—many of them related to civic and governmental problems. "John," said a close associate, "feels a profound public responsibility. In the history of our country, we have been most fortunate in the *ad hoc* availability of private talents for public purposes in times or areas of critical need. I would say, however, that few, if any of our private-enterprise figures consciously planned for such duty at a stage of life as early as John's. Perhaps in this, as in other fields, he is a forerunner of a new type of national servant. This outlook is encouraging, for the increasing complexities of our national destiny will demand private enterprise ability with the desire for public service."

Diebold has, since the very beginning in the mid-1950's, been concerned with public policy and has time and again stressed the international implications of technological change in his field. Testifying recently before the United States Senate, he said, "Only the application of the most advanced technology within the United States will assure our proper role and prestige internationally as well as our strength and leadership of the Free World itself. . . . Without such application, our role in international trade and investment will deteriorate and significant unemployment will directly result—as other exporting nations with the most modern productive facilities and plants, with lower labor costs and with national resource advantages, squeeze and erode our overseas export and investment position."

He tells a story that is disturbing in its implications. Not long ago, he had occasion to attend, within the span of a few days, conferences in London, Paris, and at Georgetown University in Washington, D. C. At the first meeting, he was told by participants that automation was what was going to save Britain, and that all concerned were pushing its development as hard as they could. At the meeting in Paris, a member of the Central Committee of the Polish Communist Party told him that automation was what was going to make the Communist system work. But when he arrived at Georgetown, he found that the American outlook was one of gloom, that those in attendance there thought that automation was going to destroy the country and that steps should be taken to slow it down.

The case would be less alarming were it an isolated event. Unfortunately, Diebold encounters the same attitude in the United States again and again.

The dim view in America is particularly characteristic of labor groups, echoing the warning that massive unemployment will result. This contrasts with a British viewpoint expressed by Sir Leon Bagrit, chairman of England's Elliott-Automation, Ltd., who does not foresee great unemployment in his country as a result of technological change. "The unions," he says, "recognize that we are coming into a new era. Instead of being satisfied with the old slice of cake, they realize that they should help bake a new cake and get a new slice."

Diebold talks too about the need for leadership in the shaping of public policy in this changing world. "The technological revolution confronting society today," he wrote in a recent book, "varies in form, and its consequences—human, business, and managerial—exceed in dimension those which are commonly perceived. The new technology is viewed as creating net changes in manpower. But this is only one aspect of the challenge, and viewed in historical retrospect some years hence, it may appear as a comparatively minor one. Machines that give the mind of man entirely new dimensions will have a far greater impact. Major social and economic innovation to adjust to fundamental technological change has become a prime responsibility of today's industrial and political leaders." *

It was natural that a man with Diebold's outlook on public obligations should have been a great admirer of the late President Kennedy, whom he knew and had occasion to advise on the new technology. "The President," said Diebold, "knew exactly what I was talking about when I spoke about the long-range concepts of automation. He could put his finger on situations with great clarity. One of the most significant statements he made was before the National Academy of Sciences in the spring of 1961 when he said, 'One of the problems of a free society is that all of the questions we must now decide are extremely sophisticated questions.'

"He knew the complexity of it all, and he knew how to shoulder the responsibilities of office. 'Those of us who are not expert must turn,' he added, 'in the last resort, to objective, disinterested scientists who bring a strong sense of public responsibility and public obligation.' I have the strongest conviction that we who are busi-

* *Beyond Automation: Managerial Problems of an Exploding Technology*, McGraw-Hill Book Company, New York, 1964.

ness leaders, as well as those who are political leaders, must assume strong roles in specific areas of public service."

Diebold has himself served on various governmental committees, such as the Secretary of Labor's advisory committee, concerned with the long-term study of the effects of the new technology on employment and related matters. And he was one of the "ten distinguished Americans" named by Secretary of State Dean Rusk to head the hundred-man U.S. delegation to the United Nations Conference on Science and Technology, for the benefit of less developed areas, which was held in Geneva, Switzerland, in 1963.

He is a director of the International Cybernetics Association, and of a Swiss Foundation, International Foundation for the Technical Advancement of Modern Man (for education in developing countries), a member of the advisory council of the Society for the History of Technology, a member of innumerable professional societies in this country and abroad such as the Systems and Procedures Association in New York, and the Office Management Association in London, a committeeman of the National Planning Association, and a member of the advisory committee of the Institute for the Crippled and Disabled, in New York, and has been active in the United Epilepsy Campaign.

Unlike many business executives, who are inveterate joiners or who associate themselves passively with philanthropic and civic organizations for prestige, Diebold participates in the work of broad-range organizations because he is drawn to them just as intensely as he is to matters of business at hand. "I can't help becoming involved, if it is an activity of significance that interests me," he has explained on occasions when asked why he has plunged into still a new field of activity.

At 10:15, with most of the correspondence out of the way, there was a further discussion with Miss Bing regarding plans for the staff luncheon, which would be held in the office dining room, and to determine the business relationship between two vice presidents from two large corporations who were about to arrive to discuss a project that their companies were mutually considering.

The discussion also covered plans for a small business dinner to be held in his apartment that evening. The arrangements approved, Diebold then brought up the matter of other luncheons, to be scheduled during the rest of the month, with subjects to be covered at each and lists of participants to be invited. "It is not easy," he said, "to avoid conflicts by having certain people together at the same time. You have to plan carefully. We try to bring together people whose interests are mutual, yet far enough apart so that they profit by provocative discussion, rather than simply holding a pleasant reunion."

Such sessions are important to Diebold. He is acutely aware of time, of the continual ticking away of life, and he finds that he can cover a lot of ground, as much for his own education as anything else, by bringing together at private luncheons and dinners creative people, leaders in public life and in business and the professions. The conversation at these sessions is lively and invariably of an inside nature, since the participants are in the center of the mainstream of current events.

Whenever John Diebold leaves his desk, he moves in dashes —even within the confines of his office. He is on his feet easily and, often as not, bounds up out of his chair to retrieve something out of the briefcase, although he can easily reach it by swivelling around. If he has occasion to go out of the office, to look up something in the firm's library, for example, he races down the hall with the speed of a commuter trying to catch a train in motion.

"Did you ever run into any one charging along like this?" he was asked.

"Only once. I knocked someone down only once."

Apparently, staff members sense him coming and get out of the way.

It is an intriguing experience to watch Diebold at his desk, disposing of the papers that have been put before him. He starts out in a chatty mood, then becomes more and more wrapped up in the work at hand until he is entirely oblivious of people in the room, or comings and goings. He laughs and smiles easily during the process, occasionally bursting into an uninhibited guffaw when something strikes him as amusing. The sound starts deep down in his throat, almost as though it were out of control, and ends up in a husky snort. When he smiles, it is often with his tongue pressed against his teeth, a kind of long, reflective smile. But occasionally, the eyes darken and the brow creases as he contemplates something that spells out "problem."

At 11:00 he rang for his secretary. "I think I'd like a little broth now," he said, half apologetically, as though perhaps he would not really get it. But the broth was ready, and brought in almost immediately, in the same pure white Limoges pitcher used for the tea, with extra cups for anyone else who might want to join.

He accepted a telephone call from his brother, William Diebold, Jr., to whom he turns frequently for advice. William, whom John still calls by the boyhood name of Billy and greets with a bear hug even on the most sedate of occasions, has in recent years been a director of Group. His first-hand knowledge of world events and of the men who make them—being himself one of this country's leading international economists—coupled with his first-class intellect and encyclopedic store of information, make him the ideal individual for John Diebold to sound out on ideas. It is rather like the way Sherlock Holmes went to his older brother when he needed to talk out a problem but could not communicate with outsiders. Despite the fact that the Council on Foreign Relations is only twelve blocks further up Park Avenue, it has been the monthly Board of Directors meetings and the many non-business activities stemming from these frequent contacts that have really served to draw their lives more closely together again.

Fifteen minutes later the door opened and the Group's executive vice president walked in. Diebold started talking almost immediately, in a kind of undertone, yet with a slight trace of what might be described as a British briskness of speech. He gave a rundown on various activities, pausing at appropriate moments to get comments or suggestions. At one point—for the first time during the morning—his voice rose. The matter of business development had been under discussion, and it had been suggested that Group should undertake a certain project, even though it would mean revising established company practices.

"I don't think we should take on an assignment and have to compromise. It's not right! We cannot change our policies and beliefs, just to assure business in hand."

Throughout the discussions, Diebold freely offered opinions, made decisions when asked for them, and left no doubt where he stood. Uniquely, however, he also gave the impression that he was willing to let others make counter-decisions and have free reign if they could present good reason for doing so.

He covered such matters as international projects; keeping the foreign log under lock and key and reprimanding a staff member in another office whose capabilities had not been fully extended in the conduct of a particular assignment. At 11:40 the discussion was concluded and the executive vice president took his leave.

Some five minutes later, he was interviewing and evaluating one of a number of potential candidates for a staff position. Diebold is highly perceptive in this field, and could undoubtedly have enjoyed a considerable success in the field of executive recruiting. He tended to be somewhat brusque during the process, his eyes darkened, his features somber as he studied the man's resume and tossed out disarming, but highly challenging questions.

"What do *you* expect to get out of this job?" he asked, constantly exploring the candidate's reasons for approaching the Group.

At 11:55, with the job-seeker barely out the door, two men from two communications companies were brought in and introduced. This was not a client meeting, but a discussion involving one of the many special project areas with which Diebold is constantly involved. Diebold had fallen a few minutes behind schedule, and he managed, without really seeming to, to compress about half an hour's worth of talk into fifteen minutes.

It was now time for the weekly Group staff luncheon.

Shortly after 12:30, guests gathered in Diebold's office. He conducted them through the short hall and private library that form part of his suite, via a connecting door into that section of the firm's large conference room that is convertible into a dining room. The appearance was that of being a candlelit, walnut panelled, private dining room, with a table set for twelve with fine crystal and flowers. Only if it had been demonstrated to them would the guests have known that the room had sliding panels along the sides, which could remain solid, or reveal a rear projection or chart, a motion picture screen, or any number of other things.

Diebold is a great believer in visual aids (used with restraint, however), and the conference rooms have been constructed with excruciating care to his detailed specifications, to provide great flexibility, but insure that they serve with perfection each of their several functions. Thus, while this same dining room could in a few moments become one end of a conference room seating seventy or a small briefing room for review of statistical projections, for the purpose of today's luncheon, a chandelier hung overhead, its muted light bringing out the texture of the walnut paneling.

He warmly shook hands all around with the other eleven people assembled there, introducing people to each other rapidly, but sometimes haltingly. "I'm not good at remembering names," he said, flipping a typed card on which had been entered the names and seating positions of all present.

Five or six guests are normally invited to these regular Monday management luncheons. In this instance, along with the two communications executives, there was a vice president from a Diebold client, General Electric, as well as a banker, an editor and an educator. Diebold said a few brief words of welcome, explained that the luncheon was simply an informal get-together for the exchange of ideas, and indicated that there was no set topic that had to be covered.

Turning slightly, he slid a concealed panel in the wall, revealing an array of switches and buttons. "Now," he said with a laugh, "I'll just push this button and we'll have lunch. If I push the wrong button, we'll have a movie film."

The menu, which had been described by Diebold as "very simple," started with a thin, clear soup ("I love soup of all kinds. I could easily get along on nothing but soup."), and proceeded to a cold platter, a generous assortment of rare roast beef, turkey, ham and stuffed avocado. It was accompanied by a vintage wine, and concluded with coffee, mints and halved ripe papaya, marinated in fresh lime juice. During the course of consumption, the discussion ranged, in a remarkably easy manner, from some corporate planning at GE to industrial research, a problem of internal and external company communications, community relations, and research and development. Automation per se, was not the fundamental subject at hand, but it was evident that problems and solutions talked about were all concerned with certain elements of automation—methods of establishing greater, more effective communication.

When luncheon was over, Diebold and three of his staff members convened in his office with the two communications men, to pursue their discussion and arrive at a course of action. The three-part approach here was characteristically Diebold: the brief personal meeting before lunch to learn the nature of the project;

the informal lunch, during which Diebold has a chance to get to know his visitors on a broader basis; and the wind-up session, with three specialists from Group, carefully selected because of their ability to come up with concrete recommendations and proposals.

John Diebold's desk was by this time completely cleared off, except for a large leather folder in the center, into which he crammed, from time to time during the day, various papers that required action. By 2:55, with the meeting over, and about a dozen rapid-stride side trips to the offices of various staffers to hold two- or three-minute conferences, he was back at his desk, ready to receive another mountain of paper brought in by his secretary. Facing this task, he requested his little white Limoges pitcher again, this time filled with hot chocolate. "I like a clear desk. If I take care of paperwork as it comes in, during specified periods of the day," he said, "I can then reserve large blocks of time for creative work. I can think better with routine matters out of the way. Ideally, I try to finish each day's work before going home. I certainly do that each week—I do whatever is necessary to be clear of back work by each Monday morning. It's not always easy, of course, especially if I have been away on a trip and the papers have piled up in my absence. Liesa helps me a great deal in handling matters that do not really require my attention, but can be attended to by someone else."

He is not a "shirtsleeves" worker, one who takes off his coat and tie, closes the door and digs into assignments. At all times, he maintains the same formal air that he would while sitting around a board table. The vest is always worn, the suit jacket on and neatly buttoned, the pocket handkerchief in place and unruffled. From time to time, he unconsciously sits more erect and squares his shoulders.

Midafternoon was a time for dictating alternately into the recorder and to teams of secretaries, and receiving or placing successions of phone calls. Diebold switched from recorder to secretary, to telephone to face-to-face discussion to reading in quick order, without once breaking stride. No matter what form of communication he uses, it is characteristic that more than 50 per cent of the sentences are questions (or instructions to ask questions): "*What* is your inclination on this?" "*What* would you do?" "*Who* makes the research decisions at Blank Company?" "*How* is the corporate policy formulated in this case?" "*Ask around* to see what type of equipment is planned for. . . ."

By 3:30, the three staff members who had attended the earlier communications meeting were back. They had studied the problems and circumstances further, and now had specific recommendations to make regarding the extent to which the Group should participate and the policies it should have in certain functions. Diebold nodded approval on most of the points, or gave quick decisions in instances where there had been disagreement among his staffers and it was necessary for him to arbitrate. In one case, he suddenly interrupted a recommendation. "I think that this is courting disaster. If we must proceed, by all means go ahead rather than sit back and do nothing. But the danger signal is up. I see red flags all over that aspect of the project."

When John Diebold is pessimistic, his brows furrow deeply. His eyes narrow and take on a brooding look. He stares down at the desk top, in silent contemplation. Then he will suddenly look up, his eyes bulging. He uses his long-fingered hands frequently in speaking, in the French manner. Sometimes he writes in the air with a pencil when trying to describe something more graphically. To indicate that he is finished, he may slip his right hand inside his jacket in a restful way. His hands, accustomed since his earliest years to making things, to fashioning tiny and intricate models, to accomplishing sleight-of-hand tricks to building model stage sets are extremely flexible and expressive. The long, slender fingers give emphasis to the words which he sometimes feels he does not express adequately. If he is impatient, the fingers drum the desk top lightly. If he is thoughtful, he rubs the surface slowly with his forefinger. When satisfied with the proceedings, he may clasp his hands behind his head and lean back.

At other times, he sits quietly, listening and contemplating, his head cocked, mouth slightly open. He usually has an expectant look, as though something is about to happen, or as though a challenge will be thrown his way and he can tune himself in, with batteries fully charged.

The meeting lasted until 3:47, with a rapid-fire windup, after which Diebold led his staff members out the door, and, with one of them in tow, raced for the conference room where there was an administrative committee meeting. For the next hour and eight minutes, he and six of his key executives discussed training and indoctrination, their strengths and weaknesses; professional development; the need for a program to develop better, more concise writing, and various internal problems that need solving. "Some of our people don't know how to *listen*," said Diebold to the committee holding up both hands behind his ears. "They are extremely good talkers, but they just can't seem to learn to listen."

At 5:00, there was another session in the conference room, this time a private showing, for this author, of the motion picture films Diebold took on his trip to Europe in 1937, including the forbidden shots of the Nazi storm-troopers marching in Munich. There was also some footage, taken by his older brother, showing the young boy, curious as always, exploring Piazza San Marco in Venice and scrambling up along a half-ruined wall at Pompeii. Diebold still has the camera, and recently used it to make films of a business meeting.

"The camera cost $37.50 at Macy's. I remember it precisely because at the time it was such an enormous sum."

14

Where other executives leave off

". . . *it is easy to recognize him as a man whose*
vision has the deadly accuracy of a guided mis-
sile . . ."

Esquire, PROFILE OF JOHN DIEBOLD BY CLAY
FELKER, MARCH, 1962.

A<small>T</small> 5:15, J<small>OHN</small> D<small>IEBOLD</small> shifted from his boardroom which had
been serving as a motion picture screening theatre, into a
large conference room. There, eighteen executives of the Group,
from New York and Washington were in the midst of a weekly
staff professional development meeting, devoted in this case to
learning about new data processing equipment and methodology
being developed by a client, a manufacturer of computers. The
program leader was using charts to explain technology, and few
eyes shifted from the diagrams as Diebold slipped into a chair
reserved for him at the front table. The head of the Group was
there as an observer, not as a participant. He began taking copious
notes using large, quick scribbles, on a yellow lined pad. He
noted highlights in the talk, scrawled an occasional diagram and
listed questions to ask later.

The meeting was highly technical, but well within the understanding of the Group executives. They gave the impression of
being on the youngish side and not at all impatient that it was the
hour at which most New York businessmen were already on

homeward-bound commuter trains, or that they would be in the meeting until after 7:00 P.M. John Diebold expects almost as much from his executives as he does from himself. Group's professional development program is a good example. It insures that each man attends the equivalent of at least an hour and a half of lecture each week, devoted in part to keeping up in his specialty, in part to consultancy and in part to expose him to world developments of importance—each man is expected to be well rounded and *au courant*.

The terminology at the meeting was confusing to an outsider, but this is the new language of the age of automation: "MSTL technology," "integrated circuits," "mil spec" (military specification), "cryolectric memories," and "commercial fallout from military programs."

"A lot of gobbledeygook is unnecessary," explains Diebold, "just invented by technicians to add mystery to the whole business when they talk to each other. People in all industries, but this one in particular, protect themselves by building walls of technical jargon. Yet, no matter how unnecessary some of the terms are, in our field we have to be familiar with this new language."

Diebold has long been fascinated with the potential in this commercial fallout, the carry-over from military projects. He points out that electrostatic printing and reproduction, as it was developed around 1956, was a result of a type of high-speed reconnaissance photography perfected some three years earlier; that Polaris missiles of the late fifties incorporated equipment that led to certain master control systems of the early sixties; or that current tests with the controls of space craft will provide breakthroughs for ulta-high-speed computers of the seventies.

"The problem with commercial fallout," says Diebold, "is that it happens all too infrequently. Much of our professional work is concerned with the identification of commercial *needs*—as distinct from conscious *wants*—and then the direction of military marketing in a way planned to yield maximum usable fallout within the economic constraints of commercial markets."

During the two hours that Diebold was in attendance, he was constantly being called out by typed notes handed him by secretaries asking him to take long distance phone calls, especially from the West Coast, where it was only shortly after the lunch hour and things were highly active. At the end, however, he settled in place long enough to run through the list of ten or a dozen questions he had jotted down. Although the meeting was strictly on "hardware" (technical equipment), and although Diebold constantly describes himself as "non-technical," it was apparent that he had a firm grasp of this new technology, as the question-and-answer session ran to its logical conclusion.

It was now 7:10, but Diebold's day at the office was not yet over. He returned to the desk to clean up a newly deposited pile of mail; to place several telephone calls; to discuss some clerical matters, and to hold a final conference with his executive vice president, to tie together the loose ends of the day. There was no change in pace, no slowing down, no lessening of interest. If asked why he does not take time off for rest or relaxation, Diebold replies that the kind of work he is doing is to him as much recreation as sports activities might be for other businessmen. He has periods during the day which he devotes to certain types of work, but he does not suffer from ups and downs of energy. He is constantly plugged into a full voltage.

Often, he himself is not aware of the total time to which he has, sometimes unwittingly, committed himself. Not long ago, he gave a routine request to one of his assistants to collect and bind copies of the speeches he had made during his career. It turned out to be no small order. By the time the collection was finished, he had a total of fourteen fat volumes. "When these came back from the binder," said Diebold, "I was so floored that I literally stopped accepting any more speech invitations, other than meeting commitments which had been scheduled a long time in advance."

In the annotated bibiliography of "The Managerial Innovations of John Diebold," scholar Mary Henderson identified 203 separate works—articles, speeches and books—written by Diebold. In addition, she estimated that, in one year, 1963, Diebold had been heard first-hand by at least 10,750 business executives, and possibly double that number during his major speeches alone. Taking another kind of count, she further estimated that from 1950 through the final month of her research, May, 1965, more than 2,100 articles had appeared that were either about John Diebold and his work or that had given him significant mention.

"At least," said Diebold, when confronted with the facts about his overall participation in speechmaking, not to mention his considerable article writing, "I have something on paper to show for it." In the autumn of 1964 McGraw-Hill published a collection of his speeches. No sooner has this gone to press, than Diebold began editing a second volume of later speeches as a companion work.

The one thing that can upset Diebold above all others is wasted time. "I do not want to be involved in that meeting," he said to his executive vice president, who in one last request of the day, asked to schedule a client session. "It can be handled perfectly well by Joe—as well without my presence as with it. I only want to be in meetings where I can contribute something or learn something. Otherwise, it is a waste of manpower and the time would be better devoted to some other, more creative, process. I'd just be trying to concoct ways of filling up time. Furthermore, I don't know what I could possibly add to a conversation with Mr. ————. His total attention time is about one and one half minutes. After that, all he wants to talk about is the weather. And I certainly can't contribute much to that."

When he mentions "waste of time" he almost always prefaces it with "stupid," blurting out the word as though he had just bitten into a rotten nut and were spitting it out.

Whenever one of his secretaries sets up a train or plane schedule, she takes infinite pains to see that the one selected has the best possible connections all around, so there is no delay at either end. "One of the worst blunders we could commit," said an assistant, "would be to leave Mr. Diebold sitting in a waiting room with nothing to do!" In a way, this is slightly ironic, for Diebold never finds himself with nothing to do. Even in a waiting room, he races through masses of papers, culls information from newspapers, or amuses himself by observing what is going on around him and mentally redesigning the whole transportation system.

By 8:10, John Diebold was finally on his way home, the last one out, locking the main office door behind him. But his working day was not yet over. He still had a three-hour business dinner at his apartment. Briefcase in hand, straw boater perched firmly on head, he bolted out of the building and dashed across the busy thoroughfare, to hail a cab on the other side of the street.

It is a frightening experience to walk a few blocks with Diebold. His long legs propel him at a pace just short of a run. When he comes to a cross street, he heads across it, regardless of the color of the light or the nature of the traffic. Cars jam on brakes and drivers swear as he weaves between them, usually at a speed greater than theirs anyway.

His Manhattan apartment sits high up, overlooking the East River. With a heavily beamed and panelled drawing room which a previous owner had imported from an Early Elizabethan house in Sussex, England, and filled tastefully with fine antiques, it well reflects Diebold's taste. He is completely at home in his apartment and as different as it is from the superb modern design and art of his office, it reflects the same concern for detail and quality. The previous owner almost missed getting the apartment. A Texan had put in a bid for it, and the owner was seriously considering the offer. The building superintendent was showing the prospective buyer around when the Texan turned to him and said, "I like this place. But," he added, slapping the venerable antique panelling with his palm, "we'll sure have to get rid of all this old wood."

Hearing about this remark, the owner said, "Tell that man his offer is considerably too low. The panelling stays!"

Diebold has a deep tie to this apartment. He moved here from the house in which he was born, and while he looks forward to a country place, he has expressed the hope that he would never move out of his present apartment. In addition to being what he considers an almost perfect fit to his desires, it was for some years the home of a close friend, Paul Smith, president of Crowell-Collier and former editor of the San Francisco *Chronicle,* and was the meeting place of numerous writers and editors during the years. Looking out the window, he says, "This is where part of Teddy White's book *The View From the Fortieth Floor* is set. Much of the drama of which White wrote in the book actually took place in this drawing room—the dramatic last years and death of *Collier's* magazine, the *American* and the *Woman's Home Companion.*" Since one of Diebold's first assignments was with the publisher, he lived through many of the experiences himself, in that very room.

The drawing room windows on the east look across the river; the ones on the south down the river; and the ones on the west toward the lower tip of East End Avenue. In between the windows are fine paintings, including a Joshua Reynolds and a Gilbert Stuart, and bookcases crammed with volumes, many of them rare. The fireplace is distinctive, with a broad cast-iron fire-back plaque set on the hearth floor. The house in which the room had originated came from the part of England where the invading forces of the Spanish Armada would have landed had the fleet not met disaster. The fire-back was made to commemorate the defeat of the Armada in 1588.

In a fashion characteristic of Diebold's childhood, he wrote to the Elizabethan historian, A. L. Rowse, to learn the meaning of some initials that appeared on this plaque. Not only did he get an answer, but he and Rowse are now firm friends exchanging dinners to meet each other's friends at Oxford and East End Avenue.

The rooms reflect Diebold's interest, not only in antique furnishings, fine art, and great books, but in good music and the theatre. He has a large collection of recordings, which frequently furnish background music over a hi-fi system. As for the theatre, he has collected books on it since the days when he was first interested in creating stage sets and producing amateur plays in Weehawken. It is a delightful experience to accompany him to the theatre, for he enjoys every minute of a production, and frequently likes to discuss plays that he has seen.

He is fascinated by the theatre in all of its ramifications, from popular comedy to classic tragedy and Grand Opera. One production that could not help but intrigue him was *Laterna Magika,* a new theatre form from Czechoslovakia, which he saw in Munich. Lunching with two friends one day in a sedate French restaurant, he described the show with the liveliest enthusiasm, waving his arms, manipulating his fingers to trace images in the air and all but acting out some of the parts right at the table. What fascinated him was the intricate way in which the producer had blended motion pictures, opera, stereophonic sound, choreography, actors and other live performers. *Laterna* was so elaborate that when the production came to New York, the entire stage at Carnegie Hall had to be rebuilt, extended and modified, and various projection booths and other structures added throughout the auditorium to meet the specifications of the script. It was, to quote one New York theatre reviewer, "hybridization on a grand scale." Diebold had enjoyed every minute of it.

The apartment was immaculate. Diebold, characteristically had prepared several copies of a bound volume entitled, *Household Procedures.* Required reading, in either its English or German versions, for all his household help, it contained thoroughly detailed information and instructions on everything imaginable:

cleaning and dusting; the care of clothing; the proper way to polish silver; security measures; how to set the table; avoiding damage to a valuable ship's model on the wall; arranging flowers; cooperating with the building staff; emergency procedures in case of fire, theft or accident; serving wine; welcoming guests; and even what to do in the unlikely event that legal papers should be served.

The meeting was to be a small one: Diebold, Liesa Bing, a journalist and Herb Blitz, director of research for The Diebold Group, an economist who had formerly been the assistant to Diebold's friend, Senator Jacob Javits of New York. Diebold's wife (who, under her maiden name serves as treasurer of the Group) was out of town with their two-year-old daughter, Joan, on vacation. It is not Diebold's practice to take time off.

"As far as I can remember," says Walter Taradash, a close friend and director of the company, "John has taken only one vacation in the last seven years. That was for two weeks and he managed to combine it with a good deal of business. Mostly his 'vacations' consist of two or three days at some quiet retreat, when he is thinking through some kind of problem relating to a business assignment. He travels an enormous amount, but always with business in mind. His trips to Europe consist of two- to three-day jaunts. And he frequently may go abroad for less than twenty-four hours, with no real sleep during that time."

At 9:00 P.M., after a brief cocktail hour (Diebold himself drinks little but wine, or an occasional brandy), dinner was served on the magnificent Sheraton dining room table that was presented to Diebold by Mrs. Wenner-Gren after her husband's death. The conversation started off with the usual social talk, which Diebold managed to channel deftly into subjects of some significance. A mention was made of the ages at which people got into various activities and Diebold could not refrain from telling a story of himself. "I keep trying to dress or act so that I won't look too youthful all the time. But apparently, it seldom works. New clients, or others who don't know the firm, meet me and we have a discussion. When they leave they politely say, 'It was nice to see you, John. Next time, I hope I'll meet your father.'"

The bit about the father then reminded him of a story he occasionally uses to illustrate his ideas and theories. It concerns, he said, a Harvard classmate from business school days, the son of a

169

very successful merchant. On graduation day, the father of the boy asked him, "Well, son, what has Harvard taught you about business?"

The new graduate reflected for a moment, then brightened and said, "Buy low and sell high."

He explained that the wine which had been specially selected for the evening from his wine cellar (a rather formidable one) was a Lafite Rothschild. This led him naturally into revealing some news: The House of Rothschild, which incidental to its banking and industrial interests, controls the Lafite vineyards, had suggested partnership to Diebold—at the height of French anti-Americanism—and had bought an interest in Diebold-France. Henceforth the Group would be associated with one of the most famous names in business history.

"A good partner is always desirable," said Diebold, adding that tapping these deep roots in the French financial world would provide the basis not only for a substantial expansion of operations, but for more effective professional services. While already agreed upon, the deal was yet to be released publicly and it was not until some two months later that Baron Rothschild, in a formal meeting in the Rothschild bank, on Rue Lafitte, made the announcement.

"There was indeed much poetic justice in this whole move," said Diebold. "General Doriot used to use in his classes as an example of credit the story of a man who applied to Rothschild for a large loan. He was turned down, but Baron Rothschild said he would walk arm in arm with the man across the floor of the Exchange. 'That, gentlemen,' General Doriot used to say, 'was *credit.*' When he heard that we were completing the deal in France, General Doriot said, 'I knew that when you took a partner in Europe, it would have to be the Rothschilds.' "

John Diebold's purpose in holding the dinner meeting was to explore with his most intimate personal staff questions relating to future developments. "Not planning of the business," said Diebold, "that is something we are doing all the time. Rather, to explore the role we should be playing in education and in public policy. These are questions apt to get lost in the press of current work, but they are important determinants of whether we will be doing the things five years from now that we should."

Blitz provided sound advice, based on his own experience in the political world. The remarkable unselfish personal devotion which marks those closest to John Diebold seems to be a real comfort for him in situations like this, for he knows the advice he is getting does not have to be weighed for possible motive of personal advancement. No conclusions were arrived at during dinner, but Diebold was satisfied that he had made some progress in the matter.

As the dinner concluded and the meeting moved into the living room, other topics were brought up in succession. One was the setting up of a foundation and of an institute to study automation and its implications. Diebold had already completed the legal steps necessary to incorporating a private foundation, but he wanted to think through the programs to tackle in the initial years of operation.

Distinct from the private foundation—which Diebold expects to distinguish itself through small but imaginative and thoughtful programs—is the concept of a university institute. This has been an idea of his for some years. He feels that a distinct weakness exists in our academic community from lack of at least one center devoted to research and information exchange in the field of management and automation. "The Soviet Union has formed a whole group of institutes, concerned with the application of automation to specific industries as well as to the exploration of the basic problems. Our own firm helps to support such a center in Holland. Yet we in this country do not have nearly as much activity of this kind as we should and the great strength we could bring would be on the management side. I would like to do something about this situation."

One facet of this project—incorporating two pet interests of Diebold's—had long been the thought that he could establish such an institute affiliated with the U. S. Merchant Marine Academy at Kings Point to develop methods to strengthen the U. S. Merchant Marine. (Subsequent to this dinner, a long step forward was taken when Diebold, Admiral McClintock, superintendent of Kings Point, and heads of the major shipping levels began a series of meetings to explore the future of the shipping industry, the direction in which it would be heading and ways of getting there).

"The shipping industry," he says, "has long been married to old-fashioned concepts and methods. There are imaginative people in it today who are heading in the right direction. But you cannot change something overnight without a great deal of help."

Several colleges were mentioned as being potentially interesting in terms of an institute for the improvement of management understanding of the field of automation and related technology. "One problem you run into though," said Diebold, "is that these colleges become so enamored of *hardware*. They fall into the same trap as everyone else—just when you think they would know better."

This led naturally into a discussion of the real meanings and implications of automation. "You have to educate people for change," said Diebold, "the central problem is that of providing education on every level, not just technical, but managerial and general. It is of course, imperative that we achieve maximum utilization of the tools provided by science and technology, but the training must not be confined to the limited area of specific machine applications. It must be broad in scope. It must be imaginative. The task of any institution, any university, any educational program is not so much to train technicians in this instance as it is to educate managers. And the educated manager will be the manager who has been schooled so that he can adapt to change."

A year earlier, testifying before a committee of the U. S. House of Representatives, he had expressed the critical need for adjustment to sweeping social changes by warning, "If the steam engine, the cotton gin, the railroads and the power loom could create previously inconceivable shifts in society, think of the social change that will result from electronic computers, translating machines and electronic libraries, all linked by worldwide communications networks."

Even though the session took the form of casual conversation over coffee and cordials, it was as well conceived, planned and carried out as a successful business meeting in the board room. Diebold had a small notebook, carefully organized, like a seminar outline, to guide him in covering the points he had placed on the evening's agenda. Into this went frequent notations, as the points were covered. Occasionally, he would turn to Liesa Bing and remark, "Make a note of that point," or "Be sure to remind me to get out a memo about this to the administrative staff." Or he would suggest that Blitz follow through by getting information, contacting knowledgeable people, or arranging a series of black-tie dinners. The latter are important, not only for social interchange, but "to help us bridge different worlds by bringing people from different fields together," and playing ideas off against varying back-boards.

Being the entrepreneur that he is, and taking advantage of the stature that he enjoys, John Diebold is well able to attract a significant representation from the mainstream of our times to his dinner table. Guests range from the members of the Pulitzer Prize jury (for whom a Diebold dinner is now an annual event) to people of such diversified interests as chairmen and presidents of the great corporations, top journalists and publishers, scientists, presidents and deans of colleges, U. S. Senators and labor leaders. These people represent the normal flow of dinner guests at the address.

By 11:55, the meeting was over, and the three guests were waiting at the elevator. As they entered it, Diebold expressed real appreciation over their presence. After shaking hands all around, he gave a slight bow from the waist, a Continental gesture from the old world—almost eighteenth-century Europe—which he has instinctively, though certainly not deliberately, adopted, and which he practices even when saying goodbye to a business associate he has chanced to meet on a busy street corner.

Diebold turned, ran his hand through his hair and reentered the apartment. His day was over—but not quite. He usually reads for an hour or so in bed before going to sleep, selecting from the bedside stand whichever one of the volumes strikes his fancy at the moment.

"It gets to be a habit," he says.

15

Retooling the abc's

"Education is both the core of the problem and the seed of the revolution."

JOHN DIEBOLD, ADDRESS, "TECHNOLOGY'S CHAL-LENCE TO MANAGEMENT," AT THE EUROPEAN COMMUNITY CONFERENCE, BRUSSELS, DECEMBER, 1960.

O F ALL OF THE PROBLEMS connected with automation, one of the most serious, according to John Diebold, is that of education and re-education. In 1955, testifying before Congress in hearings on the public issues of automation and technological change, Diebold gave this warning:

"The issue of education has taken on major proportions with respect to business needs: greater need for professional college-trained scientists, engineers and technicians; less need for un-skilled workers. New applied sciences have developed in the last few years which have centered about the concepts of automation, and these sciences have synthesized the worlds of mathematics, electronics and business. As business grows more sophisticated in its applications of automation, the demand for management personnel trained in these sciences will grow. Now is the time when these people should be trained. I feel quite strongly that this task of training management personnel who can make the fullest use of automation concepts and techniques is not being carried out. . . .

We have few examples of institutions of higher learning in business which fully integrate the concepts of automation into the entire course of study."

A decade later, he was voicing the same concern.

In the 1964 keynote address before the Society for Educational and Training Technology, he spoke of "the unprecedented demands today made on our educational system. The irresistible nature of these pressures and of the forces underlying them takes out of our hands the option of whether or not we wish to make basic changes in our educational structure and methods. They leave only the question of what form the change will take. The longer we wait to respond, the less the range of our choice and the greater the problem."

Although some advance has been made in our educational system, both in the matter of using automated equipment and methods and in anticipating the future needs, the progress has been spotty. The situation applies to business and industry, as well as to specific educational institutions. Where automation has been put to good use, the results have been dramatic. The computer, more than perhaps any other instrument of the new information technology, has figured heavily in such progress.

How much is a computer worth?

To the officials of the Junior College District of St. Louis County, Mo., it is worth about $3,000,000 or 100,000 square feet of instruction space, at $20 per square foot, plus a $1,000,000 worth of corridors and access area. That amount is approximately what the educators managed to save in the design of the first of three junior colleges planned for the county within the next five years—by borrowing the use of a computer.

In the course of planning the new college campus and physical facilities, the officials in charge had consulted with educational administrators across the country to determine how to make more efficient use of space, which in the typical college received only about 50 per cent utilization. In all, they had planned on providing for ninety-two rooms to take care of the forty-five hundred fulltime day students who would attend. It was strongly pointed out by critics of the plans, however, that one junior college survey had indicated that at least 142 rooms would be required for that size enrollment. They immediately proclaimed that at least 50 per cent more space would have to be made available to avoid overcrowding and turmoil. The group reconsidered.

Then Dr. John E. Tirrell, who had been appointed vice president in charge of instruction, took the unlikely step of calling on the McDonnell Aircraft Corporation in St. Louis and asking for assistance from industry. His purpose? To enlist the aid of the company's automation center, by simulating the entire problem in the computer. He knew where to go because the center had previously been effective in solving problems relating to course scheduling and grading. Dr. Tirrell had two other valuable tools at his disposal: a $15,000 grant from Educational Facilities Laboratories of the Ford Foundation and an applicable computer program which had been completed by a scientist at M.I.T.

The next step was to indoctrinate the computer, by feeding it information about the division of courses for the forty-five hundred students, the number of faculty members who would participate, and the estimated numbers and sizes of classrooms and other facilities. In addition, the machine was provided with 191 different time patterns possible for the 45-hour, round-the-calendar schedule of classes. It took less than half an hour for the computer to analyze all of the thousands of combinations that were possible and print up a hundred-page report. More than two dozen further variations were fed into the computer, resulting in a master plan that would save $3 million and effect an 80 per cent utilization of educational facilities, compared with the 50 per cent originally projected.

Computers are finding greater and greater use, too, in helping to schedule class time, to eliminate what has been described as "two of the biggest headaches of registration: class conflicts and over-subscribed courses." Students turn in lists of desired subjects, without trying to determine schedules and hours. When all have stated their preferences, the computer then determines the room assignments and the time schedules that best suit all of the people concerned. On one computer run, simulating the setup that would be used in St. Louis, only 2 per cent of the total number of students were left to be manually scheduled because of unresolved course conflicts.

Experiments are being conducted for another vital educational service: measuring the progress of students. In the large and progressive parochial school system of Buffalo, New York, for example, records covering the progress of pupils in the elementary schools are now being compiled at the local Univac data processing center. The problem with computing median grades, failures and progress through nonautomated processes has always been that there have been so many factors involved that even the most exhaustive manual comparisons of records have failed to indicate the relative values of certain teaching methods or facilities. A median score of 85 may be excellent for one group, verifying certain procedures as beneficial. But it may be poor for another. Properly programed computers can weigh the subtle variables and analyze fractional degrees of difference that no amount of manual tabulation would ever uncover.

Starting in the 1964-1965 academic year, twenty-one Chicago schools initiated use of a computer system for keeping personal and scholastic information on some twenty-five thousand pupils. The information is quickly channeled at the Board of Education headquarters, where teachers and counselors can obtain information about individual pupils, or groups, at once, instead of having to check through the manual files of perhaps several different school offices. This pilot project, which eventually will extend to all of Chicago's 525 schools and 550,000 students, has already proved to be of great value to educational researchers studying some of the same problems and meanings as those under investigation in Buffalo.

In the Midwest and the West, five cities are jointly, and separately, pioneering in an effort to apply computers to research problems related to education, along with other subject areas, such as land use and reclamation. When the three-year projects are completed, the cities of Denver, Fort Worth, Little Rock, Tulsa and Wichita will pool their findings and determine better methods of planning for the future. This concept of *group effort* (now being applied in a number of industries) is what makes automation's potential many times greater than it was originally understood to be in the field of education. By introducing all of the necessary factors into the programing, no matter what the locality, climate, population or other factors may be, results can ultimately be pooled to determine causes and effects in the overall learning process.

In the specific process of teaching, instruments of the new technology help to improve and increase the capabilities of teachers. While a certain amount of fear has been expressed that automation will diminish the role of the teacher and make education too much of a mechanical process, the evidence does not support this viewpoint. By delegating certain repetitive, and often *non*-teaching, tasks to machines, administrators will be able to free educators for more creative and inspirational functions.

A great deal has been said about the teaching machine, which has become more and more in evidence in all forms of education. Properly utilized, computerized teaching machines can assist students with routine learning, drilling or boning up for examinations. Yet they are also of immense benefit in certain subject areas, in streamlining courses without reducing the quality or quantity of material learned. One educator estimated that some university courses, through such programing, "have been reduced to as little as one-quarter of the time previously required."

Consider, for a moment, the PLATO program of the University of Illinois, which required more than three years to develop. PLATO, which stands for Programed Logic for Automatic Teaching Operation, is the most sophisticated computer system of its kind ever perfected and installed. During a typical session in the curriculum, some one thousand students may be taped into the central data processing system, studying as many as a dozen different lessons. Each student controls his progress individually. As he follows his course, he uses two sets of electronic keys, one set to answer questions and the other to interrupt the program. With the latter, the student can instruct the machine system to go into reverse, for a review; continue, but at a different rate of speed; or provide judgment on his answer to any specific question. The user watches his progress on an individual television screen, which transmits picture slides, formulas and diagrams that are traced by the machine itself on a built-in electronic blackboard.

Automated education can be exciting and dramatic. It can be so completely absorbing that normally restless students apply themselves to the process without the usual temptations of being diverted. It can also betray an occasional element of humor. A companion system to PLATO has been nicknamed GASP (General Academic Simulation Programs), and is in use at Massachusetts Institute of Technology to make up course schedules for colleges and high schools. Not quite so humorous, perhaps, is the data processing system recently installed in California, for the counties of Ventura, Santa Barbara and San Luis Obispo. An automated report card, it furnishes parents with current marks and past grades, and tells instantly and accurately where Johnny and Jane rank in their respective classes.

Another interesting new educational communications system is GENESYS (Graduate Engineering Educational System), set up in Florida as a talk-back television network. GENESYS links the University of Florida, at Gainesville with such points as Cape Kennedy, Daytona Beach and Melbourne. Used mainly by young engineers taking graduate courses, the system enables participants —some as much as two hundred miles from the classroom—not only to look in on live and recorded educational programs, but to interrupt and ask questions at the flip of a TV switch. Other educational television programs are being taped into computerized networks so that students can quiz themselves and try multiple choice questions, simply by pushing the desired buttons.

"A computer network, properly applied in the future to the educational systems," says Dr. Simon Ramo, president of the Bunker-Ramo Corporation, "can remember the progress of millions of students, comparing their tested learning with anticipated results, measuring and reporting deviations in progress from what was expected. Yet, remarkably, that same electronic system can be designed to immediately recognize an individual student, examine his record automatically, and provide him with an accelerated or other special presentation or test. . . ."

For the educational process, as well as for the formidable needs of business and industry, there is a critical need for programers. The 200,000 programers available by the mid-1960's will nowhere near meet the needs of the start of the 1970's, when at least 500,-000—perhaps as high as 750,000—will be sought.

The new educational instruments are especially valuable as a means—and an ever more important means—of helping professional people continue the learning process. Today, doctors, engineers, scientists, lawyers and others are hard-pressed to stay informed, and to keep abreast of the floods of new developments in their respective fields. Only some form of automation can help with the process that Neil W. Chamberlain, professor of economics at Yale, has referred to as "retooling the mind." As he explained it, the continuing explosion of new knowledge is so basic to our economic life today that entire educational concepts must be revised. "The fundamental change which has taken place in our culture is a speeding up of the rate of accumulation of knowledge, an acceleration so much in excess of what we have been accustomed to that it is imposing unexpected strains." Automation provides one answer to the problem.

As Diebold points out, society must think in terms of some sixty million jobs changing in character within the next generation. "Six-year-olds now starting school," he said, "can expect their vocations to change three times during their lifetime. One shot of formal education may have sufficed for most of us, but our children will need some form of education all during life."

The retraining process has brought about a critical situation in industry today. A *Life* editorial described the problem this way: "a manager of a General Electric plant found that, without retraining, a third of his fifty-seven hundred skilled workers would have to be replaced in ten years because of obsolescent skills."

Yale University, which established a computer center for studying the use of automation in the ever-accelerating educational process, has set up seminars and conferences to examine the relationship between machines and the humanities. One such conference, "Computers for the Humanities," was described as being "designed to introduce the computer to all manner of humanists— to historians, to linguists, and to critics and theoreticians of art and architecture, of music and of literature."

Many humanists are inclined to be skeptical, however, as was illustrated by one subject area of the conference, reported by the *Yale Alumni Magazine*. Referring to the matter of translation, as an example, the magazine cited the opinion of Jacques Barzun, professor of history and provost of Columbia University. Professor Barzun was quoted as saying, "I think it could be demonstrated that since there is no such thing as a one-to-one relation between languages, or the parts of languages, machine translation is forever impossible."

"He's probably wrong," editorialized the magazine, citing the opposing opinion held by Yale's Robert P. Abelson, professor of psychology and a "man who knows the computers well," who felt that translation was possible, even though extremely difficult.

"Computers can solve *any* intellectual problem or perform any schematic process which is well ordered—that is, well specified as a predictable sequence of steps."

How computers and other machines will improve and speed up the learning process in the field of higher education largely remains to be seen.

Automated teaching systems, however, are not merely better ways of learning more things at a faster rate, in some instances they provide the *only* feasible means of accomplishing educational objectives. In Mississippi, The Diebold Group recently launched Project Literacy under the sponsorship of the state's Tugaloo College, financed by an anonymous grant of $80,000 from a private foundation and conducted under the auspices of the National Council of Churches. Its initial objective is to help wipe out illiteracy among Negroes and thus increase the registration of Negro voters. However, because of its initial success and the development of the methods used, Project Literacy may have international applications, particularly in the underdeveloped countries of the world.

The basic problem was that conventional teaching machines could not be utilized because the participants could not read them to begin with. A method had to be devised so that illiterates could teach themselves to read through their own *speaking* knowledge of words. Another major problem in Mississippi (and one that will have to be faced elsewhere in the world) is that there are really two languages used by adult Negroes: one for communicating with whites; the other, greatly changed through the use of many local and racial idioms, understood only by Mississippi Negroes themselves.

Tackling the problems, The Diebold Group in developing the program for Project Literacy, conducted research and experimentation. During one period of a little over half a year, Diebold specialists rewrote the entire program material five times. They developed what they called a dual-track approach, preparing one heavily illustrated set of material for the illiterates who would be participating, and another for the helper who would be assigned to each student for the first twelve hours. Helpers themselves were literate, but without educational training or any real qualifications as teachers. During the remainder of the sixty-hour course, the students would complete the program, using each acquired skill to move on to the next step. This form of bootstrap operation was designed to eliminate the need for highly trained teachers (not available in the first place) and for costly classroom facilities (also not available).

"This is how the program works," explained a Diebold specialist, "using a teaching technique of visual association." He showed the method:

This is a picture of a *man*
This is the word *man*
Draw a line under the picture *man*
Draw a line under the word *man.*

Students progress by using association of form—the word "mat" as a rectangle, for example, and the almost similar word "man" as a rectangle with a square on top of it. Although the system will require extensive testing and perfecting before it is ready for international use on any broad scale, there is strong evidence that this kind of computerized teaching can accomplish wonders among the almost 50 per cent of the world's three billion population now unable to read or write.

On a considerably higher plane, automation figures strongly in the manufacture of multitudes of "simulators," used for training purposes in technological fields, where part of the educational process is to simulate in the classroom conditions that will pertain in the field. Common applications are in the military profession, where crews are taught the complex operations of artillery fire, aviation, sonar and radar operation or submarine control. Most people are familiar with simple simulated driving tests (often found in amusement parks) where the operator can use the steering wheel, brakes and gearshift and try to follow a make-believe highway on a moving screen, replete with curves, intersections, stop lights and a variety of hazards.

In a larger, far more complex way, crews being trained to operate, say, a submarine, stand before a maze of wheels, dials, and other instruments and follow commands to take an imaginary submarine below the surface and along a prescribed course. This kind of simulation requires the use of automation to introduce the thousands of interrelated factors that might in any one moment of time determine the course and action of the submarine, and, in critical moments, whether the vessel and its crew would even survive.

One vital advantage of simulators is that they can be used to train personnel in the operation of vehicles, vessels, aircraft, spacecraft or other transportation media even before the actual equipment is built. It is not unusual for crews of our new jet planes to be thoroughly indoctrinated in the use of their new craft by the time the very first model comes off the assembly line. The automated training devices will have been put to use months in advance of the proposed delivery date of the jets.

Although it may be difficult on the surface to believe that there is anything in common between the simple, pictorial teaching machine that is educating the illiterate Negro in the South and the multimillion-dollar trainers, used to instruct technologically minded engineers in the operation of the most complicated craft, there definitely is a strong relationship. Simulators, trainers, teaching machines and other new devices for education depend fundamentally on some form of programed automation to prepare them for their assignments.

It is an interesting twist that, while automation is evolving as one of the most revolutionary and important innovations in the history of learning, automation itself has placed a tremendous burden on the whole educational process.

John Diebold has thus found himself continuously working with educators and with groups striving to improve the educational process. He is a member and vice chairman of the visiting committee of Harvard College, along with distinguished men like David Rockefeller and Neil McElroy. As such, he has pioneered in the founding of an economic research institute as a means of coping with the problem the department faces in attracting and maintaining a sufficiently high flow of top post-doctoral students. He is also chairman of the Business School visiting committee of Clarkson College. In this capacity, he has been instrumental in recommending basic changes in the curriculum and objectives of the school, in attracting more students, and in projecting the growth and requirements of the faculty.

Many public-minded men give voluntarily of their time and effort to further the cause of education, yet find themselves continually trying, and failing, to cope with intangibles. Diebold, however, has an inherent capacity for transforming the intangible into the specific and putting his finger on areas that need correction or development. He is an able innovator, and is particularly adept at foreseeing the immediate and the long-range impact of *change*—change in technological capabilities and change in social mores. Thus, he is able to look at a broad picture, define the elements, and then innovate methods for taking positive action.

Speaking at Dartmouth College recently, he said: "The great issues of the world can often be narrowed to a single point. I think this is the case with automation. The machines, the problems they pose for management, are enormously complex. But if we look about us at the changes that are taking place, I think we will find that one problem emerges as basic.

"That problem is education.

"The task of putting this new technology to work requires enormous human change. Change in replacing the traditional foundation of our business organization, division of labor, with the concept of the integrated system. Change in supplanting intuitive problem solving with scientific problem solving. Change of this magnitude is not going to be brought by leasing a machine and then sending ten or twenty people to programing school to learn how to operate it. . . ."

Diebold has long stressed education as one of the most overlooked factors in the whole development of automation.

He has an inherent talent for teaching. The noted Dr. Lillian M. Gilbreth told a pertinent anecdote in this respect in her introduction to Mary Henderson's thesis on his managerial innovations. "Those who know John Diebold," she wrote, "will appreciate his creativity, his disciplined research, his care in stating problems and in utilizing every available resource in solving them. He is a learner and he is a teacher. . . .

"At a CIOS Congress in Paris, where he spoke, a delegate from a small 'developing' country said, during discussion, 'You in the U.S.A. have so much and have gone so far. If we ever catch up with you, you will be way ahead of us. What can we do?'

"John replied, 'We hope that you will start where we are now—and that we can go ahead together.' There was a teacher speaking!"

While scientists bend their efforts to improving data processing machines and other devices, and while equipment manufacturers happily turn out more and more hardware day after day, too few people pay attention to the learning factor which plays—and will play—such a critical part in determining whether automation is applied as it should be. The whole technology of automation has not been nearly realized as one of this decade's greatest national resources. Time and again, the *fear* element throws its weight around, causing great confusion, yet doing little to generate positive studies of the human and economic consequences, or fostering proper educational programs to deal with the situation.

"New York should study educational and training requirements of automation," said Diebold at the Governor's conference on automation at Cooperstown, N. Y., in 1960 "and adopt a comprehensive program that ensures full attention to meeting both long- and short-term needs." Although he has urged the same educational programs in Massachusetts and other states, and among groups of many types, the entire concept of training is far behind the development and production of equipment and systems. "The businessman," he says, with considerable disappointment, "is seldom told that the machine is the least important aspect of automation, however big and fancy it may be, that it is nothing more than a tool, just as surely as a hammer or a wrench or a typewriter or an adding machine is a tool . . . such educational programs as have accompanied automation hardly even begin to reflect [an understanding of machines as merely the outward manifestations of automation] because businessmen who understand this themselves are as rare as whooping cranes."

The educational problem is the "most challenging one that we shall have to face as the age of automation advances."

What makes it a more acute problem is that the concept of education is lopsided, as it relates to automation. Proper training is conceived of a scientific and technological, rather than economic and sociological, whereas in actual practice it should be a combination of approaches, developed in breadth as well as in depth. Automation education is far removed from, say, education in handling computers. There is, for example, a small computer, no larger than a teacher's desk that has been designed by Digital Electronics, Inc., specifically to teach the programing, operation and maintenance of computers. While this is an outstanding machine for teaching computer use, or even doing some comparatively slow computing on its own, solving problems outside the classroom, it is not necessarily of great value in teaching the *over-all* concepts of automation.

Ironically, automation, with such great potential for the class-room, is not yet its own best method for teaching about itself.

16

Automation in the world that makes things

"It is not that the new technology is unimportant. . . . But the importance of the machines does not lie in their ability to perform mechanical tricks. They are important because, for the first time, they enable us to organize many different kinds of business operations, in the office and in the plant, into systems, and to control these systems far more precisely than ever before. More than this, they enable us to do new things, as well as to perform old tasks better."

JOHN DIEBOLD, ADDRESS BEFORE THE XI INTERNATIONAL MANAGEMENT CONGRESS, PARIS, JUNE 26, 1957.

HOW CLOSELY AUTOMATION is affecting our lives was very simply demonstrated one day when John Diebold was having lunch with a young college student who readily admitted that he knew absolutely nothing about the subject because it was far removed from his own experience and interests.

Diebold held up a glass of water. "Did you ever wonder," he said, "when you are in a restaurant why very often the ice cubes have holes in them?"

The student replied that he had noticed the holes, but had

merely thought that the cubes had not been frozen solidly through. Diebold then went on to explain that even the ice cube is becoming automated these days, purposely frozen in this manner so that it has a larger cooling surface and can be rapidly processed by an automatic ice-making machine.

Another commonplace example, he pointed out, is the ballpoint pen. Anyone walking into a stationery store around 1949 or 1950 and asking for a ballpoint pen would have been lucky to leave without plunking down at least a ten-dollar bill. Today, that ballpoint pen, short perhaps of some of its fancier trimmings, can be bought for less than one-tenth of that price. A purchaser can even pick up three perfectly utilitarian ballpoints for a quarter—simple products indeed, but with better writing characteristics by far than the expensive prototype which was so highly publicized as being able to write under water, even if it could do little else.

One of the factors influencing this price revolution is automation, and the use of control processes in the manufacturing steps, all of which result in a far cheaper and certainly much more effective product. As long ago as 1952, in his original book on automation, John Diebold laid down the concepts underlying the developments. He wrote: "The concept of manufacturing is a continuous process, rather than a series of separate steps, is useful as a basis of analysis for any manufacturing procedure. Thinking about production in these terms has not only led to the modern oil refinery, it has also resulted in the assembly line. And although a workpiece cannot move *slowly* through a lathe, it *is* possible to design parts of the factory other than the assembly line in terms of a continuous and automatic flow of material."

Thousands of products made by hundreds of different industries across the United States and around the world—whether writing instruments, watches, small appliances, automobile tires or egg crates—are produced or handled in whole or in part by these processes. Sugar is moved and processed automatically in many plants, flowing easily at the rate of perhaps twenty-five tons an hour through a series of steps that would previously have seen half that amount go through in three or four hours, and with a good deal of extra manpower necessary to see it on its way. You might wonder how it is possible to produce such an enormous variety of breakfast cereals, so uniformly, and with constant flavor box after box. Again, the answer is automation, complex machine supervision that measures the ingredients, controls the flow of materials, regulates cooking temperatures, fills, folds and seals boxes, arranges cartons and in all other respects does the work of many hands, eyes and minds. The same is true in the manufacture of, say, business and industrial equipment that requires close control from one step to the next, and whose tolerances are so tight that the human senses cannot make the exact judgments which are easily taken care of by a machine.

The impact and potential of the new technology are such that major conferences of an international nature are becoming commonplace, to serve as meeting grounds for discussing the information explosion and how it affects individual industries and companies. One such was the IFIP (International Federation for Information Processing) Congress held in May, 1965, at the New York Hilton. The largest such event in the history of the information processing field, it attracted more than five thousand delegates from fifty nations, and displayed exhibits of hundreds of the latest machines and processes to some twenty thousand people.

Isaac L. Auerbach, president of the IFIP, at the time cited a prediction that he had made at an earlier, and somewhat smaller, Congress three years earlier, that the computer and its application to information processing "will have a far greater constructive impact on mankind during the remainder of the twentieth century than any other technological development of the past two decades."

To this statement, he added, "I now think that this was a rather conservative forecast. The impact will be felt for many centuries. . . . The computer-based information revolution now directly affects almost every aspect of life: manufacturing, banking, insurance, accounting, transportation, communications, economics, government, traffic control, weather forecasting, physical and behavioral scientific inquiry, space exploration, medicine, education."

With every passing day, it seems that there is something new that information technology has succeeded in accomplishing.

BLUE-COLLAR COMPUTERS RUN PLANTS, ROLL STEEL, GRIND PULP AND MIX CAKE.

So ran a recent headline in the Sunday edition of the New York *Times*. It is the kind of news story that a few years ago would have been hidden in the back pages of business periodicals, or, if given any kind of feature billing, would have been featured only in technical journals. More and more you can expect to see articles on automation in consumer magazines and other general periodicals and books. Television producers are already considering plans for a series in which a computer might be the main character—the hero (or villain) of imaginative episodes in which man works with machine, man fights machine, machine competes with machine, and perhaps even where one computer seems to show some sort of electronic affection for another.

Business stories are not generally of interest to consumers, yet some of the current industrial applications have elements that are fascinating, appealing and often exciting in their nature and implications. Consider, as a case in point, the semiannual Joint Computer Conference held in San Francisco's Civic Auditorium. Most of the five thousand or so in attendance were scientists, engineers, programers and others so involved in the world of automation that they toss around as household words terms like digital, servomechanism, economic analogs, synthetic training situation, fixed sequential format, and straight cut control system. Nevertheless, many of the exhibits would have fascinated an out-and-out layman.

There was, for one thing, a machine with an intriguing keyboard, which attracted the curious. Whenever some one fiddled with the board, the machine would respond with a startlingly human protest, "Oh, that tickles!" In another exhibit was a computer which challenged participants to step up and play blackjack. All who did so lost miserably, for the machine had already demonstrated in a test that it could break the bank at a gambling casino.

The San Francisco conference also unveiled another surprise, which may soon have an effect on millions of people, for better or for worse: computers are ready to help engineers design automobiles. General Motors demonstrated how one of its computers, a model developed by I.B.M., can serve as a qualified designer. The operator (usually a design engineer) feeds the machine some basic information, and also provides it with a few handy sketches, perhaps preliminary drawings of various standard elements that comprise any passenger car. As the inner workings of the computer digest all of this information and think about it leisurely (leisurely for a computer that is—a matter of split seconds), line drawings appear on a console which is dominated by a TV-like screen. The engineer, armed with an electric pencil, marks up the drawing as he requests the machine to show him different versions of any particular element or as he deletes components that he may not want—at least for the moment.

Deletion does not automatically eliminate any element, for the machine retains everything and anything in its memory. If the operator says, "Ooops, I'd like to see that wheel design again!" the machine obligingly brings it back.

Why should a machine be commandeered to perform the kind of creative assignment that would seem to be a purely human function? "The creative talents of the designer will never be replaced," said one General Motors official, explaining that the real responsibility of the computer was not so much to display its artistic talents as to unload some of the time-consuming detail from the engineers and to streamline the whole operation. As it was pointed out, the need for speed in making design changes has become increasingly urgent as competition has intensified. The auto maker who requires two or three years for design development (as has been the case in the past) will be left far behind by the progressive manufacturer who can whittle his time down to a few months. Thus, he could quickly alter the lines of an unsuccessful model, or whip out a new job to meet a competitor's unexpected best seller.

Another automated step in automotive designing is the application of a system that not only helps with the styling but simulates a road test for the proposed model—before any physical model has been built—to indicate such factors as reaction to bumps, handling on curves and resistance to wind.

While some electronic marvels of the automation age are relentlessly and tirelessly turning out industrial designs of all kinds like these, others are being experimentally nudged into the creative fields. Every year *Computers and Automation,* a sober and highly technical journal that uses such phrases as "Modified successive overrelaxation method" as though they were everyday household terms, holds an art contest for computers.

"We invite entries from anyone interested," says the editor, adding that "The art winning the contest will become the front cover for our August issue."

One winning entry resembled a giant sunburst. Another was

like a black raven in downward flight, almost delicately Oriental in its dramatic symmetry.

Machines were creating so-called optical art long before humans ever knew there was such a thing.

The petroleum industry was one of the first to take advantage of automation on a large scale, partly because of its progressive nature to begin with and partly because petroleum products lend themselves well to many systems of automation. Speaking before the American Petroleum Institute in November, 1963, Diebold said, "Because of the nature of your operations and the traditional technical orientation of your management, you have been among the first American industries to use information technology fruitfully; your record of early installation of computers, use of operations research techniques, and computer communications devices, is unsurpassed."

One petroleum company alone operates some thirty computers, using a worldwide network to communicate directly from the corporate headquarters producing and processing centers, to keep a constant check on sources and supplies at all times. Many oil refineries are under complete automatic control. Machines keep vigil over every phase of the processing; checking and adjusting temperatures, measuring viscosity, controlling the speed of flow and sounding warning signals if anything goes wrong that cannot be instantly and completely corrected by the robots on twenty-four-hour, seven-day-a-week duty. At one characteristic plant, the only human being on regular operational duty is the engineer who sits at a complex, multi-lighted console. By pushing buttons, he can instantly obtain readings from any, or all, of several hundred instruments built into the automation system. Usually information is typed out by the machine in a matter of seconds. In some systems, however, the machines type out the message only when specially requested to do so. Otherwise, they just speak the answer.

Distance is no problem. Take the case of the fourteen-station pipeline from Ohio to Texas. It stretches for about a thousand miles, yet the entire operation is controlled by one man sitting at a machine console at Longview, Texas.

Although the petroleum industry was a pioneer in accepting automation, it is not as fully automated as the electric utilities industry, which was cited recently as "the largest user of computer-control systems, with about 36 per cent of all process computers installed." The industry lends itself perfectly to the use of computers, since it has long relied heavily on instrumentation for its normal operations. Consolidated Edison, as an example, has been developing a $1,300,000 system for its Manhattan Energy Control Center, to help provide the New York metropolitan area with more economic and efficient dispatching of power during peak-load periods.

Metal processing is a big user of automation, currently accounting for more than 11 per cent of the control-computer systems now installed. One good example, in this industry, is the Westinghouse Prodac 580 computer system installed at the Steubenville, Ohio, plant of Wheeling Steel. The robot brain monitors and controls the production of strip steel to extremely close tolerances, whether the specifications call for rolling slabs ten inches thick and seventy-five inches wide or sheets with a thickness of less than .0478 inch. Special sensing devices feed back information constantly so that the slightest deviation brings about an immediate adjustment in the processing. So sensitive is automated equipment that, although customers demand tolerances down to about .004 inch, control systems can maintain tolerances of .001 inch regularly.

One of the outstanding examples of automation in industry today is Western Electric's new electronic equipment plant located near Kansas City. "It comes as close to a total system of data-processing," reported a recent editorial in *Business Week*, "as it may be possible to achieve economically with present computer technology." The plant produces more than 450 different products for the Bell Telephone System—most of which determine the efficiency and economy of the telephone service you now have, or will have in the future. Unlike most manufacturers who standardize products and introduce relatively few changes over long periods of time, Western Electric must cope with "a constantly changing mix of equipment, to meet the ever variable needs. This is where the computers' brains step in, to try to keep the human minds from going off their rockers. They keep track of orders, billing, inventories and other listings; they plan and control production, issuing appropriate orders and allocations; they requisition materials, determine when to take inventory, and provide investment and accounting data; they control production and scheduling of metalworking operations, handling peak loads and all but eliminating down-time between short-run jobs; and they never hesitate to speak up and complain if something goes wrong anywhere throughout the whole fantastic system."

"One of the reasons we have enjoyed a long period of prosperity is that we've been able to avoid a glut of inventories," said Elmer Engstrom, president of Radio Corporation of America. Computers help industry to control inventories as no other system has been able to do in the past. General Electric used to get operating and inventory reports from the various departments about one week after the end of each month. Now, automation easily makes possible such reports two days after the end of each week.

Because machines never forget, they are extremely useful in numerous functions requiring careful steps and procedures. A case in point is the use of a computer to start up a turbine generator, a tricky operation that could result in heavy damage to equipment if small errors are made. Among the twenty-eight initial operations performed by one computer in starting a turbine, for example, were the following: monitor preliminary conditions, open drain valves, test emergency air and seal oil systems, start fuel pumps, test turbine oil pumps, raise temperature to 500° F., roll turbine to 325 rpm, bring turbine to 3600 rpm. . . .

Once the turbine (or other equipment) is in operation, the computer continues to monitor it, making all necessary adjustments the moment it detects any variation in performance.

Although the cheapest computer systems used to cost millions of dollars to develop and install, low-cost industrial control computers are now on the market for less than $25,000. These incorporate full-fledged machines for the small-user markets—companies which do not have extensive programing and engineering staffs. Each succeeding year will see gradual lowering of costs to the point where small businesses—and even homes—will be able to afford compact computer units for specialized types of work.

Automation is attractive to industry in numerous ways. According to an article in *Automation* by the editor, Robert W. Bolz, five major reasons were established during a study of some seventeen thousand plants:

1) Reduced cost. About 94 per cent of the people who answered felt that automation would lower the cost of production.
2) Increased production. Mentioned by 77.7 per cent.

3) Improved quality. The products would be better, said 74.4 per cent of the plants.
4) Elimination of scrap losses. Tighter control through automated processes, said 36.5 per cent of the people would cut down on the amount of waste.
5) Easing labor shortage. Some 16 per cent gave a reverse twist to the usual unemployment beef, and said that automation was needed to take care of manpower shortages.

As Bolz pointed out, there were also a number of forces at work which were forcing automation, regardless of whether any manufacturer wanted it or not. Among them, he mentioned the intensity of international technological competition; the demand for higher living standards; the pressures of the population increase; and our expanding horizons of scientific knowledge.

Because of the advantages and the economic and competitive factors, automation has begun to invade many an industry that, a mere five years ago, would have looked upon the possibilities as something more remote than beating the bank at Monte Carlo. The brewing industry, with its long tradition of hand production and the passing of formulas and methods from one generation to the next, seemed to be an unlikely candidate. Yet automation has finally sneaked into the brewery. At Forth Worth, Texas, Canadian Breweries, Ltd., have recently worked out the last of the bugs in an $8,000,000 fully automated plant that will brew beer through a revolutionary new process called continuous-flow brewing. Out go the old, traditional copper kettles and the great fermenting vats. In come mazes of stainless steel pipes, coils and tanks—and a computer to act as the new breed of brewmaster.

Not all manufacturers, however, feel so kindly disposed towards automation as those surveyed by Bolz's staff. Among industries, the machine tool industry, for one, has evidenced some reluctance to automate. In the spring of 1963, Diebold addressed representatives of the National Machine Tool Builder's Association with a candid speech that was designed to stimulate them to look more favorably on automation. As Diebold later ruefully admitted, "I spoke to the Association with the candor that could come only from a friend, not as a critic of the machine tool building industry. But the whole approach backfired so strongly that it practically precluded my doing anything with the industry for years to come."

Among the remarks he made at the meeting were these: "The business of supplying machine tools should be in the midst of a revolution. Unfortunately, it is a revolution that thus far has failed to take place. When revolutions affecting you and your markets do take place, you have all too often been their victim rather than their master. This need not be the case, but it will remain true until you recognize that this revolution will necessitate major innovations; entrepreneurial innovations, managerial innovations and technological innovations. . . ."

After the dust had settled, it was evident that Diebold had neither made himself popular with the industry nor stimulated its particular interest in automation.

What is difficult for many manufacturers and business executives to grasp is that automation is just as much a matter of *concept* as it is of physical equipment. Take the process of boring a hole. Any home handyman can go to the hardware store and purchase a hand-crank drill. Or, by spending more money, he can buy an electrically operated drill. A manufacturer, depending upon his needs and expenditures, can purchase a whole bank of power drills. He can install ones that are fully automatic, that drill to a precise depth, that change bits in a flash, with no human hand at the controls. To think in terms of true automation, however, the manufacturer must decide, as one technical editor described it, "to buy *holes* instead of a drilling machine." It is easily possible that the best method of ending up with the desired holes might be through some system completely different from drilling—such as blasting with a jet of sand and air, or cutting with acid. Carrying automation one step further, perhaps the product itself should be changed so that it requires no holes at all. Traditional concepts are the foes of automation.

Recently a manufacturer of turbine blades applied this philosophy with considerable success. Instead of thinking in terms of the usual machinery and methods to make it function automatically, the engineers started with the concept of the end result: what they wanted, how quickly, to what specifications, at what cost. Then they worked backward. What they ended up with was described by an industrial journal as "a pair of machines, one providing the articulation of a tape-controlled belly dancer, and the other resembling nothing so much as a small herd of elephants at the water hole."

It might well be said that automation is the application of imagination.

While this chapter has dealt largely with industry and machines and the harnessing of technology to accomplish objectives that can be charted or listed or even seen and photographed in action, it should be remembered that the physical profile of automation is actually secondary to the soul and spirit of automation. Diebold and his associates are deeply concerned, through their own business affiliations, with all of these elements and activities. They have clients who are worried about producing better ballpoint pens (or other such products), who are trying to develop formulas for better baking goods, who want to design improved automobiles, or transport oil without labor, or process metal, or warehouse and distribute parts more quickly and effectively.

In other words, neither Diebold nor any other person professionally associated with automation can escape from the mechanics and the electronics of the new technology. But the true entrepreneur, the pioneer like Diebold who applies broad perspective to the field, must cope with intangibles. He cannot be tied down to methodology and process and formula. For the incredible pipeline of today which operates miraculously with almost no human assistance will be nothing but a bizarre relic in the future; the machines that produce strip steel to extremely close tolerances will be unwieldly has-beens in the next generation; the electronic brain that monitors the giant turbine today will be far too elementary to exercise control in the power world that will soon come.

Diebold cannot—and does not—ignore *today*. "I was once present," he said, "when President Kennedy described the great realization of what was then his two years in the White House: the enormous complexity of today's world and the difficulty of making even the smallest things happen. It is with these issues—the nature of organization in today's world—that I am deeply involved."

Today, however, is for Diebold basically the launching pad for the leap into tomorrow. Like many visionaries, he is intensely— sometimes almost painfully—worried about his capabilities for contributing to the future. "I genuinely hope," he wrote to a publisher, "in my own way, to leave the world a better place than I found it. I have chosen to try to do this by concerning myself deeply with the direction and nature of the application of what I consider to be one of the most significant forces of our time—science and technology."

The objective, "leaving the world a better place than I found it," is not an easy one to define, because it involves so much more than simply developing a better mousetrap or discovering a new chemical process. Automation started with these simple aims, among others, but is already encompassing so much more that the greatest stretch of man's imagination will not touch upon all of the things that automation will accomplish in the future. The new technology is constantly invading new, sometimes surprising, fields.

One of the most fertile new fields for automation is agriculture, possibly the very last area of our human endeavor that would seem compatible with the computer. Yet the computer is no stranger to farming. "Computers," says I.B.M., "are used in soil analysis, to find missing nutrients, and prescribe fertilizers for increasing productivity. Computers have helped scientists develop new varieties of grains, such as hybrid corns that double yield per acre. Computers are even helping farmers outwit their oldest enemy, the weather. In Maine, an I.B.M. computer analyzes humidity and sunlight, then predicts the best picking time for apple growers. In the Midwest, another I.B.M. computer compares weather statistics to crop needs and gives farmers a basis for judging the best times to plant. In many states, marginal land has been reclaimed through computer-analyzed irrigation projects."

Since nothing in nature grows to exacting specifications, it has often been difficult for, and exasperating to, inventors to devise labor-saving machinery that would function properly when handling varieties of sizes and shapes. The surprising new machines of our automated world, however, make such adjustments—in infinite number—naturally and easily. So the evolution of devices like automatic fruit-pickers and lettuce-head sorters are more than mere gadgetry. Recently an agricultural exhibit displayed a tree-shaker, for loosening and catching ripe peaches, a mechanical farmhand that picks grapes from the vine and another that can distinguish between green and ripe melons, scooping only the latter from the soil.

The feeding of animals is one oldtime chore that is gradually being taken over by robots who never complain at having to go to work at 5:00 A.M. or at any other time of the day, come rain or shine, snow or sleet. In Denver, Colorado, there is an automated egg factory where a unique system of feeding takes place. Instead of using slides or chutes to funnel the feed, the designer created a climate-controlled circular building whose cages revolve slowly and continuously past conveyor-fed food and water troughs. On another farm there is an automated device that feeds some twenty-five hundred head of cattle at the push of a button.

Out in the field, automation is increasing productivity by enormous percentages. By using new types of equipment, a farmer in Iowa stated that he could plant as many as eight rows of corn, instead of the two he used to plant B.A. (before automation). "It is possible to seed about 160 acres a day," he commented, "because the machine places the exact number of seeds where they are supposed to go. At the same time, it dispenses fertilizer and if necessary, weed killer—all while the rest of the work is going on."

A new type of combine just about doubles the number of acres of corn that can be harvested in one day, as compared with ten years ago. A special harvester has been perfected that easily disposes of the tricky job of selecting and picking ripe tomatoes. However, realizing that automation is more than just machines, agricultural experimenters have been breeding new kinds of crops that are more readily adaptable to the world of automation. In the case of tomatoes, for example, the new automated breed is a strain that tends to ripen more uniformly, so that just about all of the individual fruits are ready for harvesting at the same time.

Harvesting hay has proven to be a breeze for the machine. "To harvest hay," said one agricultural report, "today's farmer swings into action a windrower that cuts, conditions by crushing the grain's stalks to permit moisture evaporation, and rakes it all into a row for later pickup—performing the three operations at a seventy-acre a day clip."

Automation is making remarkable contributions to agriculture in broad, long-range terms quite apart from the more specialized problems of feeding hogs, milking cows, picking asparagus, selecting citrus fruits or checking the ripeness of pineapples. The genius of the computer for simulating situations and coming up with answers is now being applied to what has been termed "one of the biggest simulation jobs yet attempted for social science ends."

On July 14, 1961, the late President Kennedy was visited by

President Ayub Kahn of Pakistan, who among other things indicated that it would be a wonderful thing for his country if some one could suggest a way to improve conditions in the Indus Valley, which throughout the centuries Pakistan had depended upon for crops. The entire valley had become so waterlogged and salinated by the water flowing down from the Punjab, by way of the Indus and other rivers, that about a hundred acres a day were becoming lost for agricultural use. Mr. Kennedy, immediately sympathetic, called in Dr. Jerome Wiesner of M.I.T., the chief of his science advisory committee; Dr. Harvey Brooks of Harvard, deputy chief, and a number of other experts. Brooks was familiar with the work of a team of Harvard scholars who had been using a computer to simulate rivers and to study flood control. By September, a ten-man group had been appointed to use parallel simulation studies in analyzing the Indus Valley catastrophe.

One major problem to cope with was determining how to lower the water table of the land—to eliminate the waterlogging that had taken place over many years. In the nineteenth century, the British had undertaken a huge irrigation project, building canals to nourish the Punjab, the breadbasket of India. However, accumulated leakage from these canals had so waterlogged the entire Indus Valley that the water table had risen dangerously from its once ideal location some seventy-five feet below ground surface, thus causing the roots of crops to decay, rather than grow, from over-saturation. The computer experts simulated the whole gigantic problem and situation by feeding many simulated remedies into the computer. Should the water be pumped out through wells? Should the canal system be rebuilt, or at least made non-porous? Should the river be dammed? Into the machine went a potpourri of information, on wells, dams, rainfall, water tables, crop survival, irrigation, salination, chemical action, and other related (and unrelated) subjects.

It required millions of calculations by the machine and some four months of persistent programing by the group before the best solution was evolved: locate tube wells in the Punjab at the rate of a million acres a year; develop an electric-power system using natural gas (plentiful in the Punjab); prepare certain types of fertilizers; institute a program to double farm production in each of the areas reclaimed.

Once the program was accepted by the Pakistani government,

in 1962, the computers were not finished. Now they had to get to work again to study an educational campaign for persuading local farmers to change old-fashioned methods; to work out crop programs; to investigate diets and food habits; and in short to undertake a complete social and economic revolution.

The most astonishing revelation about the Indus Valley project is not so much that computer brains were able to solve a problem that had affected an entire nation throughout most of its modern (and a great deal of its ancient) history, but that distance posed no limitations. The mighty computer functioned just as effectively in its comfortable Harvard installation on the banks of the Charles River as it would have done surveying the situation at first hand, twelve thousand miles to the East, on the watersheds of the Indus.

17

Robot housekeepers

*"Automation is not a particular group of new
machines or devices. It is a new concept . . ."*

JOHN DIEBOLD, ADDRESS AT THE XI INTERNATIONAL
MANAGEMENT CONGRESS, PARIS, 1957.

IT IS WITH considerable reluctance that John Diebold will enter
into a discussion of household appliances or other such consumer conveniences that are becoming more and more automatic
with each new model that appears. It is not that he in any way
looks down on them as mere gadgetry, but that he has to push
tirelessly and relentlessly to distract people from associating automation too closely with just the mechanical marvels that appeal to
most people.

Nevertheless, this chapter concerns itself with a number of the
fringe elements of automation, as well as with some aspects of
information retrieval that will be of enormous consequence to
people everywhere.

Starting with the gadgetry, let us investigate the remarkable experience of a woman named Mrs. Daniels. One Monday morning,
not long ago, Mrs. Daniels, a housewife in a suburb of Los Angeles backed the family car out of the driveway at 8:30 to spend a
day shopping in the city. Before she left the kitchen, she had
walked over to a multi-colored console on a counter the size of a
large desk, which was positioned in the center of the room. For a

period of not longer than two minutes, she had studied a set of instructions, then placed a series of punched cards in a slot, one at a time. With that absurdly simple action, almost a day's housework had been taken care of.

Although the house remained vacant all that day, any chance observer who might have walked in would have thought that the place was haunted. And, in fact, it was—by a family of incredible machines that had been brought to life by the punched cards.

In the wall-to-wall carpeted area downstairs, a slim, cordless vacuum cleaner with no handle was moving leisurely back and forth, skimming past furniture without ever touching it, and covering every inch of space into which it could squeeze its busily whirring frame. In the game room in the basement, a somewhat similar unit, with containers instead of a dust bag on its back, was waltzing around on the vinyl tile floor, first scrubbing the dirt off and then applying and polishing a coat of wax to remove all traces of the weekend scuffs and scrapes.

Nearby, in the laundry room, a large white appliance was also busily at work. Its job was to take each of three wire baskets in turn, feed the dirty clothes from them into a washing unit, then into a drying unit, and finally into a large basket at the other end of the line. When the last water had been flushed out, the drying process completed and the final item of clean clothing flipped into its niche, the entire machine would lapse back into silence and repose, like a tired washerwoman who has had a heavy day.

Upstairs, on the second floor, another member of the mechanical family was polishing five pairs of men's shoes, placed on an inclined chute, carefully switching from brown to black polish at the proper moment in the sequence.

By mid-afternoon, all of the scurrying and polishing and laundering ghosts had quieted down, or even departed to places of rest within the walls. Now it was time for the spirits of the kitchen to get to work. The oven was heating up, to take care of the roast that had been placed in it by Mrs. Daniels before her departure. Three packages of frozen vegetables, encased in disposable aluminum cooking jackets were propelled from a freezing compartment into a heating cell where, after about two hours of thawing, they would be cooked five, seven and eight minutes respectively, all ending up properly done at the exact moment the roast, too, would be ready.

Some forty minutes before the completion of the cycle, the dishwasher began churning happily away, timed so that it would complete the final drying at the dinner hour, its plates thoroughly heated for the helpings that would be placed upon them.

By the time Mrs. Daniels arrived home, major housework had been completed and the meal was progressing so that it would be ready for the appearance of her husband and the three children. Through some remarkable feats of automation, she was able to enjoy a day in town without experiencing guilt at neglecting housework or having to throw a makeshift dinner together for her family at the last moment.

As any housewife well knows, the experience of Mrs. Daniels was unique then—and will still be unique for some time to come. Automation in the home has progressed remarkably fast during the past few years, but not yet to the extent where women can expect to leave a platoon of little robot helpers in charge at home while they attend to other matters. Yet, what Mrs. Daniels experienced in a very costly demonstration of automation in the home will become fairly commonplace, and not too expensive, by the advent of the seventies. Cordless vacuum cleaners and waxers, operated by remote control, are in the test stages today. For the most part, these are guided by an operator who keeps a visual surveillance over the movements and controls stops and turns with push buttons. It is not a far step from this, however, to a fully automated action in which the machines are controlled by punched cards, tape or other monitoring systems. One method is for a machine to be run manually through the cycle of performance expected of it, such as vacuuming a carpet, where the unit not only goes back and forth but must skirt permanent furniture within the room. As the pattern of movement is manually established, a computer-like device records each step. Then, when these steps are played back (through the use of punched cards, for example), the machine simply imitates the original motions.

The big advantage that machines have over humans is that they can undertake and complete *specialized* jobs much better and faster than the best experts in many fields of activity. It was not so long ago that women scoffed at the idea of any kind of a machine being able to compete with her at the back-breaking task of washing clothes and really getting the dirt out. Today, with technological improvements and with new detergents and other chemicals to aid them, automatic washers find the job so easy that most of them can tackle load after load, day in and day out for a decade without a serious breakdown. In a parallel course of development, there is no reason why fully automatic machines could not do a better job than a human at vacuuming, polishing floors, washing carpets or any of a number of other physical chores. Laboratory research tests are being made, for example, with vacuums that can feel out, and go over several times if necessary, the dirtiest areas on a carpet. They are regulated by sensors that react to the amount of foreign matter sucked into the bag at any one instant of time. Other tests are being conducted to perfect self-regulating vacuums, ones that raise or lower the brushes as they move from rugs with piles of one thickness to those of another, or from worn and matted areas to the places where traffic is non-existent or light.

Automated lawn mowers are going through a similar development. Remote-control, push-button models are already available and have been for several years. The next step will be the programming process, escorting the mower on a preferred course while the movements are stored on a record or tape on punch cards so that they can be repeated at the push of a button while Dad goes off to complete other, less automated tasks.

The key to this revolution whereby machines are made to learn and memorize actions is numerical control, basically a simple process. As a new machine is instructed initially by a tutor, its computer brain records symbolic numerical notes, which in effect comprise the memory. The process is not too unlike one that no longer astonishes the average citizen: recording music on a magnetic tape. Once the music is recorded, it can be run through again and again without in any way changing the tune or the sequence. Automatic machines work in much the same manner. Each note in the memory, instead of bringing forth music says "go right," "go left," "do this," "do that."

The potentials for automated living are multiplied many times over with each new scientific development. The transistor, now familiar to most people as the replacement for the old radio vacuum tube, has made miniaturization possible, so that even the fictitious Dick Tracy's imaginative wrist radio is now a reality. Transistors, more than anything else, have brought about the development of the computer and other basic instruments of automation. Coupled with such devices as the fuel cell and the mercury battery (both of which provide cheap, efficient electricity over long periods of time and in small spaces), transistors are providing the kinds of breakthroughs that will make almost any kind of automatic product possible.

Of all the breakthroughs, however, the telephone system is providing some of the most useful and dramatic accomplishments. Westinghouse, for example, used the telephone to develop "dial-an-appliance" household equipment, which can be attached to an ordinary mouthpiece. With it, a housewife who is downtown shopping can start dinner cooking before she leaves for home. She merely telephones her regular number. Then, by dialling additional digits, she can turn on the oven, start the deep-well cooker, flick on the house lights or accomplish any of a number of actions. Motorists heading home after a weekend or vacation, can use the same procedure to turn up the heat in winter or activate the air conditioner in summer, so the house is just the right temperature by the time they pull in the driveway.

We have been building up to this remarkable revolution in the home for perhaps more years than we realize. It all goes back to the first crude machines that husbands invented and laboriously pieced together to try to eliminate the sixteen-hour day, seven-day week schedule of the nineteenth-century housewife. An early popular invention was the "automatic" wash tub. Instead of bending over it and scrubbing the clothes, the operator sat, or stood, and turned a crank, which set revolving paddles in motion, agitated the contents and supposedly accomplished the same results with half the effort. It was a dubious achievement, but one which at least lent itself to an element that was to play a vital part in honest-to-goodness automation: electric power. One of the first major milestones was the invention and later improvement of the vacuum cleaner, which began to find its way into the home during the second decade of the twentieth century. "From 1920 on," says one historian, "the floodgates were opened and electromechanical appliances poured forth."

The old icebox was well on the way out with improvements in electrical refrigeration shortly after World War I and housewives were already acclaiming a marvellous new household appliance, the electric iron, which paved the way for a parade of new, electrically heated devices: pancake grilles, waffle irons, toasters and cooking coils. But mankind was a long way still from automation. Among the first major household contributions to the coming age of automation was the Bendix automatic washing machine, which became highly popular during the middle and late thirties. For the first time, in practical application, a machine was available, within a reasonable price, that would go through a number of cycles (in this case, washing, rinsing and removing excess water) after a single setting and pushing of a button. Another step in the direction of let-machines-do-it living was the automatic record player of the thirties. At first, the exasperations outbalanced the conveniences, as the rebellious mechanisms plopped down several records at a time, scraped the needle gratingly across the surface, dropped the arm down with disc-smashing force, or simply refused to move at all.

Clever and useful though these inventions were, after the initial bugs had been removed and operating cycles perfected, they lacked some of the elements of real automation. Although automatic control is necessary for the achievement of automation, it alone is not sufficient. You might, for example, install a clock control system so that the lights in the living room all went on at 6:30 P.M. and off at 10:30. The lighting system would then be automatic, but it would not be automated. Now, however, if you added a light meter so that the lights went on as soon as a certain degree of darkness were registered (not only at night, but during the day when clouds darkened the sky), you would be approaching automation. And if you further installed a sensitive device that activated the lights *only if some one were in the room,* then you would have full automation, at least as far as the living room illumination were concerned.

According to Diebold, home heating, cooling, and climate control in general represent areas in which automation can make— and is making—important contributions. The significance lies not just in what the system can accomplish but in what it can *save.* One authority on home heating has asserted that fuel and air-conditioning bills could be "one-fourth of what they average in most homes" if properly automated systems could be perfected and installed. Such systems have already proven themselves, but only in the laboratory or in experimental homes. Solar heating has been under discussion for a good number of years now, as a means of collecting warmth from the sun, to supplement other heating systems. Yet few people are aware that solar energy can be obtained on *cloudy* days, or that it can be put to use to *cool* homes, as well as to heat them, and that it can operate refrigerators, freezers and other appliances, or even automobiles and boats.

The use of solar energy in a practical way, however, depends upon automation. The most delicate types of sensors must be employed to alert the system to changes in light, humidity and weather so that the machines will respond properly to these variations. When properly automated, any form of heating system will function more effectively, efficiently and economically with no human intervention than it would by manual control.

Automation, in the home, therefore, is more than just mechanization. It is an entire philosophy of living, dedicated to the belief that families have far more important purposes in life than simply attending to all of the little details that sustain them from day to day. Let us say you have a four-slot automatic toaster, adjustable to settings marked light, medium-light, medium, and dark. This is a big improvement over the models with no setting. But suppose four members of the family prefer four different settings? The next refinement is a toaster which can prepare four slices at once in four different degrees, and which thus cuts a housewife's toast-making actions down to 25 per cent of what they would have been. This still is not quite automation; that step would come when the push of a button feeds bread into the machine, toasts it in a manner suitable to each of the various members of the family and delivers it to individual plates. Achieving this step with current equipment would require a weird assemblage of Rube Goldberg attachments. Thus, the development of automation requires scrapping old methods and conceiving radically new ones that may have no physical resemblance at all to their forerunners.

Sometimes automation has nothing whatsoever to do with machine per se. Your electric steam iron is a well perfected product. Future steam irons will incorporate further improvements, such as a unit that automatically extracts moisture from the air so that the user never has to fill a bottle attachment. Yet no matter how clever the manufacturer may be with his gadgetry, some one gets stuck with the chore of applying the iron to fabric to eliminate wrinkles of one kind or another. The philosophy of automation is not devoted solely to the device—in this case, the iron—but to eliminating the need for it entirely, if possible. Thus, it is as much a process of automation to develop wrinkle-proof fabrics as it is to make a more efficient iron.

Along these lines, *Business Week* recently announced that "Boys and men will look neater. Girls will look sweeter. And Mom will unfold the ironing board only occasionally to touch up a few archaic garments. A technical breakthrough that can create this vision of Utopia is causing a major revolution in the textile and garment industries." The new development is that of permanent press fabrics, so far superior to former wrinkle-proof material that there is hardly any resemblance. Pleats and creases cannot even be ironed out; smooth finishes *stay* smooth for the life of the garment; and wrinkles after washing, or puckering at seams and zippers are totally eliminated.

This is part of automation in the home. But, from the manufacturing point of view, it also requires automation to develop the production processes. Only a computer brain could juggle all of the factors that must be weighed before production could successfully begin—factors such as heat, pressure, color, reactions of different dyes, basic materials and blends, threads, numbers and types of creases and pleats and smooth finishes, components like buttons, zippers and clasps.

A number of inventors and developers have been working on ideas for automating stores—supermarkets for example. They have come up with push-button racks, with chutes that bring a variety of grocery items to the purchaser as she pushes the buttons of her choice; moving belts that carry filled bags from store to parking area; battery-operated shopping carts; and quicker, more efficient checkout systems. Inhabitants of Memphis, Tennessee, may remember perhaps the most automated store of all time, but which failed because of financial reasons: the Keedoozle. Customers picked up special "keys," with rolls of tape, which they then used to insert in various machines, at the same time pressing buttons to select merchandise desired. The machine punched the tape, and printed the cost and a description of the merchandise on it. Then, after the customer presented the tape at the check-out counter and paid his bill, the tape was run through an electronic brain which immediately activated relays at the end of chutes. Merchandise dropped onto a moving belt within a matter of seconds, and was hustled to the waiting customer.

In Europe, more progress is being made with robot retailing

than in the United States. There are quite a few stores which consist of nothing but huge banks of vending machines, with automatic coin changers and no attendants at all, other than the ones who come occasionally to stock the machines or sweep the floor. Then there is the example of M. Thomasse, a family grocer in Caen, in Normandy, France. He decided that if he could eliminate bulk racks in his self-service store and simply display one sample of each product he could outdo other stores—even much larger ones—in the variety of goods he could offer. So M. Thomasse set up more than two thousand display items in such a way that beneath each one of them there was a slot with a color-coded and punched card. Each card represented one unit of the item on display. All the shopper had to do was to walk around with a wallet provided by the store and stuff cards into it as she saw items desired. One card for one item—two, three or more cards if she wanted more than one. Then she took the cards to the small checkout counter where they were fed into a tabulator. This automatically printed out her bill and notified the stock room of the purchases desired.

But, no matter how far-in-store automation is carried, the shopper still has to go through a good many motions, including the often frustrating one of trying to find a convenient place to park. So, from the housewife's point of view, real automation will come with the perfection and widespread installation of a device now in the testing stage: the television marketeer. It operates in this manner: the home is equipped with a color TV phone, from which can be dialled the numbers of supermarkets, department stores, drugstores, or any other retail establishments included in the shopping network. The purchaser selects cuts of meat, bread, brands of canned and frozen products, and many other items desired. She can instantly see the size, type and price of each item, or study groups of competitive products, as the retailer beams his portable TV transmitter at sections containing the products which the customer wants to select from.

When not used for shopping purposes, the automated television screen will be used for regular person-to-person "televoning"; for obtaining graphic weather reports at any hour of the day or night; or for studying the stock market. It will come in handy for conferences with teachers, eliminating the time and trouble of having to trek on down to P.S. 26 and climb four flights of stairs against the tide of children surging the other way between classes. Through multiple hookups, it will serve as a meeting room for as many as eight or ten others in the community, each of whom would appear in miniature in one segment of the screen.

The old TV set may soon become something of an all-purpose robot itself. Now being researched is a special attachment that would pick up facsimiles of daily newspapers on a receiving screen and reproduce them on the spot, in much the same way that an office copying machine now duplicates documents that are fed into it. Users would "channel in" on the newspaper of their selection, in any city desired, insert ten cents, or perhaps special tokens, and receive their copies immediately. Instead of putting out several editions daily, the big metropolitan newspapers would print a continuing edition, feeding the latest news, or changes, into a television transmitter. Certain columns and other basic features would remain the same over a given twenty-four-hour period, at the end of which they would change. But news stories would constantly be changing as events broke during the day and night.

Naturally, many business, civic and social activities will not be practical via TV-automation, nor will certain types of shopping. For one thing, the selection of fabrics, where *feel* or fitting is important, would largely have to be done on location. Yet even under these circumstances, automation will contribute (and already is contributing) to the spread and convenience of shopping. A good case in point is the use of electronic data processing equipment by Koret of California to keep abreast of demands for certain colors and styles of mix-and-match sportswear. Coordinated styling has "simplified the search for mix-and-match sportswear for millions of women," said company treasurer Ronald McLennan, "but it has also introduced additional complications into the normally complex task of manufacturing, order processing and distribution."

As he pointed out, however, the use of an electronic brain, analyzing the needs for styles, colors and individual items, made it possible for the company to distribute exactly the right amounts of its products, in the right styles and colors to the right places day in and day out. The ultimate beneficiary is the customer herself who can walk in and find just what she wants on hand, with no back ordering or delay—all because somewhere out there in the world of automation, machines are whirring and blinking and buzzing busily away to try to outguess her every need and demand.

Many of the benefits of automation will come unheralded, and probably without realization on the part of consumers that anything new or different has taken place. At a plant in Deerfield, Illinois, for instance, the Sara Lee company has inaugurated a program to make a Honeywell 601 computer the head baker. It will require three years to instruct the computer and train it in the nuances of the culinary art, but by that time the machine will take almost complete charge of the entire baking process. Where housewives in the kitchen, or ordinary mortals in a modern food plant, have to worry about a few dozen steps at the most in, say, the preparation and baking of a cake, the computer will be concerned with several hundred intricate variables, involving every microscopic factor man knows, or can discover, that has anything to do with the results. In addition to ingredients, timing, heat and other common factors, the computer might take into consideration the smallest variations in humidity, noise levels, vibration, barometric pressure, seasonal changes, packaging and just about everything imaginable that could influence the output.

Computers are at work elsewhere performing a wide variety of assignments that affect our living and our economy. A computer at Bell Labs uses its noggin to determine which classes of telephone service would be most economical for selected groups of customers whenever any kind of rate change goes into effect. It takes into account high, low and average numbers of calls, distances, rate zones and many other factors and in a matter of seconds comes up with answers that an entire team of mathematicians might have labored several weeks to produce. Recently, data processing machinery helped play detective for the Internal Revenue Service at the end of the tax year, combing through millions of tax returns to select almost 4,000 that did not seem quite honest. As a result, the Justice Department ended up with 1,559 convictions for tax frauds—up 26 from the previous year—this helping to make life unhealthy for those of your fellow citizens who do not care to shoulder their share of the tax burden.

In another instance, the Treasury Department used a "computer detective" to try to track down illegal gambling activities in the New York metropolitan area. Agents, over a two-year period, fed into the machines as much information as they could obtain about suspects, betting, the passing of large sums of money and other data which they uncovered or received from police informers. "If we had processed this information manually," said an agent, "the three-year statute of limitation on these charges would have expired before the vital data were even obtained." As it turned out, some thirty persons were arrested and charged with illegal gambling or bookmaking.

Another kind of computer is taking over the controversial job of the old-fashioned dowser, who used to roam the countryside with a witch hazel wand and a lot of mumbo jumbo in a hunt for wells, ostensibly to aid communities affected by drought or inadequate water supply to begin with. The machine is programed so that it can evaluate thousands of statistics about well locations, rainfall, water levels and other pertinent factors. When used with local maps, it pinpoints areas where surface water is likely to be trapped after it has run underground, or where there are likely positions for subterranean springs.

According to forecasts, automation will vitally effect our world and our way of living within the next decade and the one that follows. Already tested is a facsimile mail system set up experimentally between Washington, Chicago and Battle Creek, that provides long distance postal service within a few hours. Letters placed in a machine in one city are opened automatically and the contents scanned in less than a second. At the terminal point, the letters are reproduced photographically, sealed in new envelopes and delivered by special messenger. By sometime in the eighties, you will be able to get into the family car, push certain buttons to plot your course on a road map, and be off to your destination with no further work. An automatic control system will do the driving, while you and the rest of the family play games, take naps or simply enjoy the passing scenery. Such a vehicle would employ some form of radar impulses to measure distances and would use analog computers to serve as the brains for operating accelerator, brakes, steering and other controls. In a limited way, the automatic highway is already a reality. Michigan started building a six-lane, hundred-mile highway in 1963, to experiment with a hands-off guidance system, allocating two lanes to electronic control by signals transmitted through the pavement itself en route.

The day is not too far off when people in many communities

will find instant catering available. You are familiar already with various types of automated vending machines that dispense everything from coffee (black/regular, sugar and/or cream) to cooked meats and vegetables. The next development will be people-less, automated gourmet shops at strategic corners, ready to dispense—twenty-four hours a day—almost anything an on-the-spot hostess might want, from cheese blintzes to beef stroganoff, French pastries and cocktail dips.

Among the most significant, vital and far-reaching developments, however, is the automated library. Now being perfected as a facility of the community public library, this astonishing child of automation will one day become as integral and commonplace a part of the home as the telephone is today. When the automated library is available, you will be able to push a button, make a verbal request and within seconds receive an answer to questions that could range from "What is the capital of Idaho?" to "How do turtles hibernate?" and "How much would a 175-pound-man weigh if he were transplanted to the moon?"

Machines make the whole setup absurdly simple, through a process known as information retrieval. If you were to take a computer and program it (that is, feed into it) all of the information contained in, say, the "W" section of a standard encyclopedia, you could get that information back simply by activating certain key words, such as "Wurlitzer" or "whirlpool" or "wrench." As computers stand today, you would probably have to write this out in print or punch a key or combination of keys. But within the next two or three years, current laboratory experiments with computers and the human voice will have been carried far enough so that it will be quite common for people to retrieve information from machines merely by pronouncing clearly spoken words. From that point on, it is simple to hook this information retrieval system into a community telephone hookup. "Wallydrag?" you inquire of your Info-Phone, and the answer comes back quick as a wink: "a little-used Scottish term for a feeble, undergrown or slovenly creature; often the youngest, most immature of a brood."

If science can thus harness the "W's" in an encyclopedia, it can then do the same thing with the "S's," the "J's," the "P's," and the "Q's." It can also add encyclopedia after encyclopedia to the roster, and blend in miscellaneous facts from all over. The computer has such a gargantuan capacity that it can absorb any number of reference books, starting with Dr. Eliott's Five Foot Shelf as a mere appetizer, and ending with a series of foreign language dictionaries just for fun.

One example of what automation can do in providing information was the automated reference room, at the New York World's Fair, connected into systems in Manhattan, Washington, Garden City, Phoenix, Los Angeles, San Francisco and Denver. Gordon P. Martin, project director for the American Library Association at the Fair, said that ". . . in the not too distant future, the resources of the world's greatest libraries will be available to people in the most remote areas of the globe through the use of computers . . . transmission of information can be accomplished with astounding speed and at relatively low cost, once the system is put in operation and used by a large number of people or institutions."

The next step, and not too difficult a one according to engineers, is to tie library data retrieving machines into the telephone system, so that users can obtain desired information without ever leaving their homes.

One of the most significant facts of all about automation and the retrieval of information is that the whole learning process— for adults as well as children—will be vastly speeded up. In terms of accomplishment, each generation will become so far ahead of the preceding one in learning capacity that there will be no comparison. The results will be increasing use, right in the home, of the kind of technology now associated only with the most complex industrial operations or scientific research in laboratories at M.I.T.

As Diebold has said a number of times, "There is no reason why all of this advanced technology cannot be carried into the home, effectively and economically. Some day the housewife will be able to talk to a monitoring device, rather than have to push buttons, and set off any number of household operations: turning lights off or on, or making them dimmer, starting various appliances, opening doors, sounding an outside bell to call the children home, or asking for information on any subject under the sun."

He adds a cautionary note, however, that people must not think of automation in the home purely in terms of robots and machines. "Automated living," he says, "will be just as much a matter of concepts and philosophies and methods as it will be of equipment. Adjustments to changes brought about by technology will be serious elements and part of the makeup of the entire structure of automated living. I do not mean to underplay the importance of extraordinary inventions, but I do want to make it clear that such inventions are only one part of the great, encompassing pattern of the future."

More and more, concern over the mechanical (or, if you will, electronic) is being expressed by other leaders in the industry. Isaac L. Auerbach, whose Auerbach Corporation is directly concerned with the application of information technology in many industries, voiced this doubt when he said recently that one of three factors delaying the progress of the information revolution was "our way of falling in love with our own inventions. We do not stand in awe of the telephone. Nor should we stand in awe of the computer. We should simply put it to work."

The same applies for any of the mechanical and electronic marvels of our age and the age to come.

Diebold is not so intrigued by the machines as he is deeply and constantly concerned over the astonishing speed with which changes come about. The impact on mankind can be for the good, if man is properly prepared. But it can have tragic reactions if he is not. Diebold estimates that computer capacities, in terms of memory and speed, will increase a hundredfold by 1971, to help make possible facilities that we do not even dream about today.

Because machines have flawless memories, a computer that has been used successfully in helping educators set up class schedules and avoid conflicts may well prove to be a godsend for the home. You will be able to feed into it all of the information about dates and places—school affairs, civic meetings, bills due, social events, errands to perform, things to fix around the house, music lessons, dancing classes, luncheons, business appointments, and anything else you want to name. The machine will conscientiously keep track of every last bit of information, point out conflicts, remind you when to go, estimate time required, and even toll you if it needs attention or adjustment itself.

What if you just plain get tired of the endless round of children's activities, events, social affairs and so on? You simply walk over to the machine and pull out the plug!

18

Automated comings and goings

". . . an *important* part of the management's problem will be in knowing what questions to ask. It also involves the ability to see a pattern emerging from changing technology, so as to introduce wholly new ways of performing basic functions, of fulfilling user needs, so as to apply technology in altogether new ways to serve human needs. It is the entrepreneurial flair which looks to technology not simply to improve the way a job is performed, but rather to see whether it is not yet possible to find an altogether different job aimed at better fulfilling the same need."

JOHN DIEBOLD, OPENING ADDRESS BEFORE THE PLENARY SESSION OF THE INTERNATIONAL UNION OF RAILWAYS, PARIS, NOVEMBER, 1963.

GAZING OUT of his office window on the fourteenth floor overlooking Park Avenue, John Diebold occasionally turns away with a disturbed look on his face. "This is a remarkable view," he says, "of one of the most famous thoroughfares in the world, but I cannot help recoiling from time to time when I think of the phenomenal problems that New York has with traffic. Multiply this across the country and around the world and you get a picture that is grimly inhuman, almost diabolic. Somewhere in the concepts of automation there is an answer to all of this. In fact, where municipalities are willing to take steps forward, technology is able to come up with solutions."

Transportation, says Diebold, in all of its forms can take advantage of many of the elements of automation to serve the public need. As an example, he cites the case of Toronto, Canada, which has pioneered in one vital area of transportation. In Toronto, as in most large cities, the traffic situation had long been described in such terms as "exasperating," "impossible," "frustrating," and "murder"; and by any number of unprintable epithets. One of the fastest-growing metropolises in North America, the city had one vehicle for every twenty feet of paved road, an accident rate of about 25,000 incidents a year, and an annual death toll of 129 and an injury record of 9,000. Furthermore, it was costing the community $8 million a year in medical expenses, lost time and property damage. Drivers fumed and merchants agonized over the constant traffic congestion that cut down shopping time, increased tensions and made customers irritable when they finally did manage to reach a store and find a place to park.

Toronto, however, faced with a $40 million road construction program to handle the city's multi-directional traffic flow, decided to do something about the situation. The city's far-sighted traffic commissioner, Sam Cass, hired a local consulting firm, Traffic Research Corporation, to conduct a pilot study. TRC used a computer system to simulate existing traffic conditions and come up with decongestion solutions that would work effectively. The computer-control system reduced evening rush-hour delay by 11 per cent, and morning rush-hour congestion by 28 per cent. This result was achieved through an initial application of computerization to only seventeen critical intersections, making it evident that the overall achievement would be tremendous, as more and more traffic problem zones were added to the system.

The heart of this innovation in traffic control (now being extended to other cities) was a Univac machine known as the 1107 Thin Film Memory Computer. It functions through the use of traffic detectors, located at key points leading to trouble spots, which transmit data to the central brain and warn of potential traffic tieups. The continually changing mass of data is processed in a flash by the computer, which then sends out commands to traffic lights and other flow-control units. Bottlenecks are avoided; traffic is appropriately re-routed; and the computer can even open up lanes and routes in an emergency, to permit the passage of ambulances, police cars or fire equipment. Accidents have decreased by some 15 per cent (as compared with a general increase of about 8 per cent in other communities), and the complete system will save about $25 million annually. It also adds about 25 per cent to the capacity of the highway system—or the equivalent of adding an extra lane to every four-lane road in the city.

In Baltimore, Denver, New York and a few other large cities, experiments are now being conducted with radar screening devices affixed to traffic lights. These inform a central computer about the flow of traffic in both directions and the computer then determines which lanes of traffic should be favored and how the red and green cycles should be adjusted to meet the varying flow of vehicles.

Since automation concerns itself with more than just the narrow problem of what to do about a single network of streets and intersections, or even a method of transportation, its total application involves the overall concept of how to get individuals from here to there with the best combination of speed, comfort, economy and safety. It is not fundamentally concerned with the function of existing traffic lights. Hence, the transit expressway, which has nothing to do with automobiles, is part of the larger assignment undertaken by computers being trained as traffic experts.

Before selecting any type of vehicle for the expressway or working out factors like schedules, speeds, distances, the first consideration is to determine the kind of service required to guarantee its actual use and economic feasibility. This requires an evaluation of community needs, peak-hour demands, availability of power and communications and literally thousands of other facts that any self-respecting data processing system would need in order to make a well calculated judgment. One proposed transportation network now under development by the Westinghouse Electric Corporation consists of a form of elevated highway, on which would run rubber-tired, bus-like vehicles, joined in tandem. Each would have its own electric motor, and could be automatically steered by guide curbs at the sides. Using a computerized system, the transit expressway could be fully automated, providing economical twenty-four-hour service in such a way that passengers would never have to wait more than about one minute at any interval station at any hour of the day or night. The only difference between operation during peak rush hours and off hours would be in the number of units hooked into the tandems as they moved along. Mechanical controllers at each station, under the monitorship of a central control system, could regulate train speeds, start and stop cars, open and close doors and in general supervise the performance of each car or train within its area of jurisdiction. Typical commands given from one machine to another would be "Accelerate to maximum rate"; "Decelerate to minimum rate"; "Apply brakes"; "Open doors."

Other features of the robot-controlled system would include automatic fare collection (with variations in fares, depending upon distances traveled); recording of mileage and operating performances; alarms to alert appropriate maintenance crews (human) in the event of any form of failure; and the addition and deletion of vehicular units as passenger volume increased or lessened.

Although the general usage of transit expressways like this one cannot be expected for a number of years, automation is being put to work to try to improve existing commuter and intra-urban passenger-carrying systems. Not long ago, the Long Island Railroad was "fed" into a computer. The actual feat is almost as impressive as the visual image that may have come to mind—that of a machine doing a sword-swallowing act with a long string of railroad cars. As part of a Queens-Long Island mass transportation demonstration program, the project was jointly financed by New York City, the Transit Authority, Nassau County and the Federal Housing and Home Finance Agency.

The idea was to simulate the operations of the railroad on a computer, under the supervision of Westinghouse engineers, so that it would be possible to come up with suggestions for improving service and streamlining operations without taking the costly and time-consuming step of trying out each possibility in actual practice. Information was gathered on the volume of passenger service at points along the line, from the Pennsylvania Station in Manhattan to the Jamaica Station in Queens and other portions of the railroad that interacted with this section. This was fed into the computer, along with data on number of trains, speed limits, car seating capacity, dispatching and train signal operations. By testing thousands of variations within the computer, it was possible to see which changes would be most effective in overall passenger handling, and then to put those changes into effect as recommended by the electronic brain.

Automation is helping railroads, too, in processing seat reservations. The Japanese National Railways have for some time been using a system developed by Hitachi, Ltd., that takes about half a minute from start to finish. Listening to a traveler's request and pushing the appropriate buttons takes fifteen seconds; transmission adds two more seconds; the reading time for the centralized equipment is a mere .05 second; and printing and delivery of the ticket adds a final thirteen to fifteen seconds.

Electronic data processing equipment has helped to bring order out of chaos and simplify one of the most knotty logistics problems in the modern world: the never-ending work of trying to keep track of almost two million freight cars and their contents, scattered along hundreds of thousands of miles of track, under the jurisdiction of dozens of railroad companies. Only a computer could love the challenge of trying to commit boxcars to memory.

John Diebold points out that several railroads operate automated yards for the handling and dispatching of freight cars. "Cars are automatically switched to the proper classification tracks in these yards," he says. "After track selections are fed into the system, human action is seldom needed. Where yardsmen used to ride the tops of cars, retarding them with brake clubs as they shunted into classification tracks, now a single retarder operator in a control tower watches a control panel, intervening only in case of emergency."

As he explains, the Seaboard Air Line Railroad's automated yard at Hamlet, North Carolina, with fifty-eight tracks, can hump more cars in eight hours than a conventional yard can handle in twenty-four.

The Louisville and Nashville Railroad has enjoyed considerable success with an electronic computer that runs crewless auxiliary locomotives hauling some of its freight trains. And a Minnesota railroad has replaced human inspectors with an electronic eye that counts and identifies some ninety-five hundred cars as they rumble over automatic weighing platforms. To accomplish this, the Duluth, Missabe and Iron Range Railway uses reflective strips arranged in distinctive patterns on the sides of the cars. The scanners then sense the colors and arrangements and immediately match them into the identification system and print the data on paper tape.

The rapid transit system for the San Francisco Bay area, which will include subways in downtown areas and tracks at ground levels in open areas, will by the seventies operate faster and more efficiently because of technological innovations. A computer system will serve as engineer and conductor, dispatch trains, monitor their operations and then compare actual performance with the preprogramed schedules. In the event that schedules break down, the computer would issue corrective commands and bring the delinquent trains back into line.

A GHOSTLY TRAIN RATTLES CHICAGO, EXCITES OFFICIALS.

This recent report in the *National Observer* told how "night after night, sleepy-eyed Chicagoans have blinked in disbelief at a ghostly spectacle. Up on the famed elevated tracks rumbled what appeared to be an ordinary train. But there appeared to be no one aboard—no motorman, no conductor, no passengers."

It was all true. For weeks the Chicago Transit Authority was experimenting with a completely automated train, run by a computer. It scheduled the trips for the hours after midnight, partly because traffic was light, but also for the strange reason that it wanted to keep the whole procedure a secret. The assumption is that if the robot railway failed to behave properly the CTA would simply drop the whole matter and avoid unpleasant publicity. At last report, the train was still making its trail rounds. Doors were opening and closing, as the train started and stopped. But there was a great deal of lunging, "like a halfback trying to carry the ball a little farther." And at other times, the mechanical brain seemed to be "groping for the right place to stop." Once the lunging is corrected and other electronic wrinkles are ironed out, the CTA will consider putting automated trains into regular service.

Other ghosts are piloting other equipment elsewhere. At its farm equipment factory at La Porte, Indiana, the Allis-Chalmers Company has an entire fleet of indoor trucks that shun human operators. With no hand on the controls, they snake their way through doorways and around corners, trailing one or two small trailers with the greatest skill. They sound horns, flash warning lights and come instantly to a halt if any one gets in the way. They stop at the proper loading platforms, and if no one arrives to load them in a reasonable amount of time, they impatiently beep their horns. Battery operated, they actually steer by means of an invisible track, a magnetic cable laid in the concrete floor. At the end of the day, the foreman in charge—the only human who has anything to do with the fleet—pulls a switch. Then his robot trucks come hustling back to the battery recharging station, to feed themselves on the electricity that will see them through the following day.

In the trucking field, International Harvester is using a computer which successfully simulates driving conditions on the Ohio Turnpike. Without ever having to put an experimental truck on the road, the computer can run figures through its electronic brain and calculate what the probable life span would be for a vehicle of specific size and design, under realistic driving conditions.

Another Herculean task being undertaken by machines—as yet without widespread success—is the automation of our badly antiquated postal system. One ingenious invention, in addition to the one described in the preceding chapter, is the Intelex facer-canceller machine. As mail passes through its complex maze, electronic eyes communicate ahead the location of the stamps, thus determining which channel any one letter should move through to be cancelled and processed. Scanning heads decide whether an item is a letter or a post card, whether it has sufficient postage, and whether the stamp is on the upper right hand corner, the lower left hand corner, or somewhere else. Mail can be fed into this brainy monster at the rate of approximately seven items per second. Each piece of mail is automatically spaced three inches apart, as it whips through the machine at the rate of eight feet per second.

Semiautomatic letter sorting is another long step toward the day when the mail may go through the post office untouched by human hands. The key machine here is a letter sorter with a central memory system capable of handling eighteen thousand letters an hour. Letters, which are coded before they are fed into the sorter, are then carried along and finally dropped into boxes assigned to some three hundred different destinations.

Among all methods of transportation (whether of humans or cargo), the push-button ship stands as one of the most impressive examples of what automation can accomplish. The first American flagship built from stem to stern as an automated vessel, the *Mor-*

macargo was scheduled for delivery to Moore-McCormack Lines on August 20, 1964, on the same day that the fifth automated ship in the line, the *Mormacaltair* was to be launched at the Ingalls Shipbuilding yard in Pascagoula, Mississippi.

Although the dual ceremony was to be the first of its kind in maritime history, the event was made somewhat painful by one of automation's most common headaches: labor troubles. The dispute arose between the line and the Marine Engineers Beneficial Association over pay scales and other benefits for the engineers manning automated ships.

"Automation aboard the *Mormacargo*," said a spokesman for the line, "is so advanced that the ship can be operated with a crew of only thirty-five, compared with more than fifty needed for an unautomated ship of the same size," a ship of more than twelve thousand tons deadweight.

The issue was not so much about the number of men needed as it was over the types of duties performed by engineers in push-button engine rooms, and the salaries they would get paid for the work. The dispute was especially significant, since its outcome might well have established pay scales and work patterns for all other automated ships now under construction or planned for the near future. The issue was similar to an earlier one in which the Marine Engineers Beneficial Association delayed for more than a year the sailing of America's first nuclear-powered merchant ship, the *Savannah*. As it turned out, no settlement was reached and the sailing of the 24-knot, $10 million *Mormacargo* was postponed when the ship's engineers, acting on orders from the New York headquarters of MEBA, refused to sail the vessel.

Maritime automation received its first major setback at the moment it was poised to register its first glorious triumph. John Diebold, whose association with the maritime industry is both long and deep, going back of course to his Kings Point days, has said repeatedly that honest judgments must be made with respect to the automation of ships. The commercial aspects of America's future as a world power is inextricably dependent upon the swift modernization of her merchant fleet.

The second week in November, 1964, marked a delayed achievement, however, when the nation's newest and most automated ship, the *American Racer,* was welcomed into New York harbor on its delivery trip to the United States Lines from the Sun

Shipbuilding and Dry Dock Company's yard in Chester, Pennsylvania. The 13,300-ton cargo vessel was as fully automated as a ship could be, from propulsion equipment to hydraulically operated hatch covers, navigational aids and the first real breakthrough in shipboard refrigeration since the advent of mechanical refrigeration.

The advent of the *American Racer* focused on another dispute: How much automation does a ship need to be "fully" automated? According to the United States Lines, their vessel was the first to be automated "from the keel up." All others (including the *Mormacargo*, presumably) were originally designed as conventional ships, but then hurriedly fitted with automated equipment. The *American Racer* is the first American-built ship to have her main turbines, condenser and reduction gear installed on a single plane. According to Nicholas Bachko, manager of technical services for the line, these innovations, plus two wide-angle atomizer boilers, a brainy console on the bridge and another in the engine room, "constitute perhaps the most advanced system presently involved in a shipbuilding program."

Another shipping authority states that virtually all freighters built in the United States or in major shipyards abroad from now on will have some form of automation, at least in the place where it is most important for control and efficiency—the engine room.

A further interesting development in automation in the maritime field has been in the building of ships. Norwegian Veritas, described as a ship classification society, was the first organization of its kind in the world to set up a ship research department. Long conscious of the value of automation, Norwegian Veritas developed ways in which computers could be used to solve problems associated not only with the sailing, but with the construction of vessels. Today, it is becoming more and more common for marine engineers to rely on computers to provide such vital information as pre-calculating pressures on steel plating or simulating dynamic stresses on crankshafts.

Oceanography, and the exploration of the vast unknown reaches of "inner space," offers limitless possibilities for automation. Already, computers are being used for predicting the speed and course of icebergs in Arctic waters, so that one day their positions will be as predictable as the phases of the moon. Oceanographic survey ships are being equipped with automated

229

systems, both for engine room control and for scientific instrumentation. And submersible craft of the future, such as the Deepstar family being designed by underwater pioneer Jacques-Yves Costeau to go down to depths of twenty thousand feet, will rely on advanced technological equipment to make instant calculations and provide security for the operators under the widest range of conditions and eventualities.

Computers have already provided man with a rather unique safety feature. Dr. Alan Berman, director of the Hudson Oceanographic Laboratories of Columbia University, cites the following case. "Recently," he said, "a computer was placed aboard an oceanographic research vessel. At one point, the ship took side to side rolls of 102° in six seconds. When this happened, the oceanographers in the computing room hung onto the computer to keep from falling. Under the severe rolling and pitching the computer continued to operate and performed the service of saving the seagoing programmers from serious physical harm."

It might well be, he added with tongue in cheek, "that computers ultimately will be installed as a safety feature on board all ships."

Experienced airline passengers, who have grown up in the era of the mad scramble for bookings, never knowing for sure whether they would end up with a seat or be left on the ramp, are finding automation one of the big blessings of air travel. Not all airlines or all terminals, of course, have successfully tackled the elimination of ticket and reservation snarls. But most will soon have at least a cousin of the automated electronic reservation system that American Airlines put into operation in mid-September, 1964. Known as the Sabre, the $30.5 million project was launched by I.B.M. a full ten years before it began operations at the line's reservation center in Briarcliff Manor, New York.

"In terms of improved service to the public," said American Airlines president Marion Sadler, when announcing the Sabre to the press, "this extraordinary system is as significant in its field as was the jet to flight."

Al Williams, president of I.B.M., described Sabre at the time as "the largest and most complete teleprocessing system in existence anywhere." It accomplishes in split seconds what would normally take forty-five minutes to an hour or more to process under the old standard airline reservations procedures. Also, it eliminates mistakes and avoids the manifold passenger complaints that have plagued airlines ever since they began operating mass flights. The Briarcliff Center is capable of storing more than *six hundred million* bits of information, and has no trouble at all processing more than seventy-five hundred passenger reservations in a single hour, day and night, seven days a week.

Using some twenty-six thousand miles of leased telephone lines, American Airlines connects the center with a network of airline reservation agents, each equipped with a desksize electronic console. All the agent has to do is to query the central computer by inserting a coded card in the console. He then receives instant information about the availability of seats on any of the line's nine hundred or so daily flights, and reserves space according to desire and need. He can also feed into the system the name and address and phone number of the passenger, along with special service requests—air taxi service, automobile rental, baggage handling and the like.

Recently, a $25 million electronic reservation system, "the most extensive of its kind ever developed," was installed by Pan American Airways in the company's headquarters in the Pan Am Building in New York City. Designated Panamac, the system connects Pan Am offices in 114 cities on six continents, and also some 30 hotels of the Intercontinental Hotels Corporation chain around the world. Panamac, with no trouble at all, can handle more than seventy-five thousand *daily* requests for information—not only making plane reservations and supplying room accommodations, but scheduling air cargo shipments, recording passengers' names and addresses, and even listing such data as auto rental needs and the dietary preference of patrons.

Panamac is used also by the company to control Pan Am's world-wide message flow, handle payrolls and general accounting, control inventories, set up flight schedules, calculate crew members' flight times, and monitor the time intervals between overhauls of engines and other flight equipment.

The gigantic increase in air passenger travel has also compounded the problems of traffic control at airports. It is a certainty that the present method of using human controllers, equipped with radar and other devices, will be gradually supplanted by computers. When a man, or group of men, makes the decisions, he must take into account many factors: number of planes in the approach pattern requesting a landing; number of planes readying for takeoff; weather; visibility; types and speeds of aircraft; priorities; surface conditions; and many others. He must then do the best he can to juggle all of these considerations and decide which planes and pilots should do what. The situation is complicated, and often rendered hazardous, by the speed with which decisions must be made, and by the fact that a certain number of human errors can be expected during the course of a period of operations.

A computer, however, requires only a matter of microseconds to digest dozens of factors and issue an answer that correctly and safely evaluates all of them. "Traffic control of both air and ground vehicles has been necessary for some time," says John Diebold, "if we are to keep human lives from being subject to the danger of violent death or to hours of waiting in order to travel a short distance at supersonic speed. Information technology is today making such systems possible." He cites, too, the advances in long-range weather forecasting made possible by the use of globe-girdling satellites whose messages are hooked into computer networks to evaluate weather conditions instantly in any region on earth. "The consequences for all human activities," says Diebold, "will be enormous, for weather throughout history has been a major determinant of social organization and development."

There are numerous ways in which the new information technology can contribute to our understanding of the weather and man's ability to predict and eventually control it. The study of hurricanes affords a good example.

One normal hurricane releases an amount of energy that has been compared with that of some ten thousand hydrogen bombs. For this reason alone, it is hazardous and difficult, if not impossible, to gather at first hand all of the information necessary for detailed study—even though techniques have been developed for flying planes regularly into the eyes of hurricanes. New types of information processing machines for the first time have memory capacities so great that they can absorb complete data about such storms, including temperature fluctuations, atmospheric descriptions, pressures, ground conditions and thousands upon thousands of details from all over the world.

According to Dr. Robert Jastrow and Dr. Albert Arking, both of the Institute for Space Studies in New York, "the computer can apply the basic laws to each part of the atmosphere, calculating the new conditions which will result from the extension of the existing atmospheric motions over a small interval of time. Then, with the new conditions at the starting point, the computer program again applies the basic laws to obtain the atmospheric conditions after a second small interval of time."

Man, through his own calculations, might tackle this step-by-step process for awhile. But, say Jastrow and Arking, "a million repetitions of this process may be necessary to follow the development of weather over a long period of time. The number of additions and substractions involved can amount to *10 trillion* simple steps for one such study."

Only through the use of fantastically high-speed and gigantic memory information processing machines could scientists complete the unbelievable number of calculations required to arrive at a reasonable answer.

In flight, airlines are constantly making more use of automated equipment of all kinds. Pan American, for one, has equipped its jet aircraft with Sperry inertial navigation and guidance systems. Although this brought about a reduction from four- to three-man cockpit crews on some flights, pilots performing navigational functions were promoted to other pilot openings in the Pan Am system to meet the need for additional pilots. Inertial guidance, first used with missiles and Polaris submarines, is the most accurate method of navigation and guidance independent of ground aids yet devised.

Each automated plane is equipped with a digital computer. The crew inserts takeoff and destination directions into the machine. From then on, the electronic brain calculates directional changes and is alert to the slightest changes in speed or altitude. It continually makes its own computations, so that the pilots can tell at any second during the flight exactly where the plane is. "The device," said a spokesman for the company, "is right on the button when approaching or departing from an airport, and not more than ten miles off in the midst of the longest transatlantic flight." No human navigator could compete with this robot counterpart.

The Air Force has long made use of computerized equipment for navigational purposes, as well as for guiding weapons. In one application, a computer is used to give voice warnings to pilots if there is anything seriously wrong with the equipment. The human voice is much more effective, than, say a flashing light or a buzzer. But, just to make sure that it gets attention, some computers are equipped with female voices. "A woman's voice is a sure attention getter," said one pilot. "How often do you hear one in the cabin of a military plane?"

More and more, although certainly to a much lesser degree, other companies in the travel and transportation field are hooking into electronic data systems to keep track of the increasing numbers of reservations and service requests. Long Island's Maxson Electronics Co., for example, is developing a plan for linking more than five thousand hotels, travel bureaus and car-rental firms in a computerized reservation network.

The time may not be too far off when serious travelers will carry a computer about the size of a portable transistor radio with which they can instantly and accurately make reservations for plane seats, hotel accommodations or any other travel and transportation facilities at the push of a button. Of course, this will not be as suspenseful and exciting as the old system whereby a person did not know until the last possible moment whether he was on or off the flight, whether surface transportation would really be waiting for him at the other end—or even whether he would have a place to lay his weary head when he once arrived.

19

Electronic communication

"Communication is at the center of an information revolution for which the last ten years have
been the staging period. Business and governmental integrated information systems are becoming increasingly communications oriented
and dependent. Therefore, the communications
industry has a leading role among the advance
elements of America's economic progress."

JOHN DIEBOLD, "AUTOMATION: IMPACT AND IM-
PLICATIONS," REPORT PREPARED FOR THE COMMU-
NICATIONS WORKERS OF AMERICA, AFL-CIO, APRIL,
1965.

JOHN DIEBOLD likes to tell the story about the computer that was developed to translate from one language into another. As the tale goes, the scientist-designer of the machine had programed it to translate from English into Chinese and was demonstrating its capabilities to a group of reporters. One reporter suggested trying the phrase "out of sight, out of mind." Lights flashed, magnetic tapes whirred and almost instantly out of the printer attachment came a string of Chinese characters.

"See," said the demonstrator, "no problem at all."

"But I can't read Chinese," said the reporter, "so how do I know that the translation is accurate?"

"That's easy," came the reply, "we'll just feed these Chinese words back into the machine and have them translated back into English."

More flashing lights. More whirring tapes, and out came the result: "Invisible idiot."

Computers are still back in the Stone Age when it comes to communications, and yet they have made some remarkable accomplishments, with promises of a truly successful future. The birth and subsequent development of the United Nations provided a major stimulus for man's efforts to perfect machines that would assist with translating. The first crude inventions could do little more than provide literal word-by-word translations, with no provisions for communicating the meanings of combinations of words, or even of single words that had a variety of implications.

Christopher Rand, writing on linguistics in an article for *The New Yorker* in April, 1964, reported a discussion with an interpreter who had gone through ten pages of such translation and "could recognize its subject matter only because he spotted three key words—the rest was a sea of nonsense."

According to Rand, the problem in trying to program languages into a machine is that "one must attack and analyze them both semantically (in regard to meaning) and syntactically (in regard to structure)." Consider, he says, the frustrations of trying to teach a machine the dual meanings of such common words as "bear," "bit," "bolt," and "brace." Or the ambiguities in a sentence like "They were eating apples." Do you mean "Those men were eating apples," or "Those apples were destined for eating"?

The whole situation, complex though it evidently is, can be tremendously more complicated when a scientist tries to perfect a translator that can be used in either of two ways: from a man to a machine, or from one machine to another.

At Cambridge, Massachusetts, a group of scholars—some from Harvard, some from M.I.T.—is attacking the challenge of machine translation. Among the participants are some of the outstanding experts in the related fields of linguistics, psychology, computers and mathematics, including Victor Yngve and Noam Chomsky of M.I.T. and Anthony Oettinger and George Miller of Harvard.

"Language translation," says Diebold, "by a machine that can scan a page, translate from one language to another, abstract the translation and then store both the abstract and the full article will materially change human communications. Based on a universal machine language of concepts and ideas, rather than direct, literal interpretation, these systems are now in the development stage."

It is an interesting fact that someone programing a computer can effectively accomplish this, even though he himself may not know the subject thoroughly. Thus, a computer could be educated in, say, Greek, by feeding into it all of the principles of the language. Or it could be taught physics or chemistry by a person who did not know these subjects at first hand, but who could take all of the facts and program them into the machine. As one scientist said, "Writing a computer program is much like telling a very literal, very obedient friend every detail of how to do something."

When technology starts with the process of trying to develop a machine for a specific purpose, such as translating, it soon becomes evident that the immediate problem contains the seeds for whole families of related machines. Not only do improved computers result, but the developments may suggest new forms of commercial switching systems, control equipment or sensing devices. Sensitivity is a critical factor in perfecting intricate quality control systems or devising computers that can talk to each other or understand written words and visual images.

A second cousin to the language-translating computer is the one that translates—or tries to—political facts and fancies into election prophecies. Although a computer was used as early as 1952 to tabulate and project the vote on election day, it was not until the Presidential election of November 3, 1964, that there was a real, meaningful test of competitive systems for picking winners early and presenting a nationwide voting pattern.

In the eight months prior to that date, the three major networks, ABC, CBS and NBC, collectively spent nearly $8 million to put automation to work to report what would go on at the polls. By that time, each had rigged more than three hundred display panels to record party totals for the Presidency in all fifty states, along with those of twenty-five gubernatorial contests, thirty-five senatorial battles and the races for seats in the House. Although the actual value of the three sets of computers assembled—from

Burroughs, I.B.M. and R.C.A.—was about $20 million, the equipment was not purchased, but leased, as is customary, from the manufacturers.

COMPUTER GIANTS VIE FOR ELECTION HONORS headlined a New York City newspaper just before the election. "The Burroughs Corporation, the International Business Machines Corporation and the Radio Corporation of America are not listed on any ballots today, but nevertheless the three computer manufacturers are in a heated Election Day race," said the paper, adding that, "Unlike the Presidential election, all the spoils will not belong to the victor. Every manufacturer of data processing equipment is expected to benefit from the prolonged exposure of computers on television today."

Not satisfied with this three-way competition alone, R.C.A. put itself at what looked like a disadvantage by deliberately positioning three of its seven computers remote from the scene, in Cherry Hill, N. J.—just to prove that distance is no drawback in bringing together data from many widely separated locations. One objective was to show businessmen that communication is a natural function of data processing equipment, whether it be within four walls, between widely scattered chain stores in a designated region, across the country or even—eventually—around the world.

The reporting function was simple, something any old computer could do with its circuits tied behind its back. The real test, and something of a controversial issue, was to project the vote and analyze it. All the networks announced confidently that they intended to call their shots as early as possible—probably by nine or ten o'clock EST. The methods used were highly competitive. CBS used a Vote Profile Analysis, with some two thousand precincts that had been scientifically chosen months ahead of time, to provide the voting pattern. ABC had a similar system, based on reports from a thousand sample precincts. NBC's method was somewhat different, making use of raw vote totals as they came in and analyzing developments until the trend was so well established that a prediction could be made.

In all three cases, however, the results were continuously fed into computers, where they were analyzed electronically by being matched against such known factors as previous voting records in various precincts.

It is ironic, indeed, that the big test should have taken place at a time when the Presidential race was so lopsided that even a blind ward-heeler could have correctly prophesied the results by the time the polls closed in the East.

Computers have entered the political arena not without generating a big storm of criticism. One outcry is that computers are going to snatch votes away from humans in a number of ways. In 1960, a political scientist, Dr. Ithiel Pool, used a computer to weigh the importance of certain political issues. He selected representatives of 480 groups of Americans and questioned them about likes and dislikes. By feeding these prejudices and beliefs into a computer system, he could then test how the electorate would react if these issues were to be brought into political campaigning. In other words, no matter how strongly a candidate felt about certain issues, one way or another, he could deliberately sidestep them if the computer warned him that they were dynamite.

The late Eugene Burdick wrote a best-selling novel, *480*, around, the Pool group on the theme that the computer would take over this aspect of political influence. On October 28, 1964, participating in the ABC television program, "Polls and Computers—Calling All Winners," Burdick had this to say when asked if the machine would do away with the voter:

"I think it actually happened. We won't do away with the voter. He'll be there. The fact is that he will just be sort of an automaton manipulated by the information that comes out of computers and only a few people have access to this sacred information in the country and it changes the complete nature of American politics."

Another attack on computers strongly asserts that it is fundamentally wrong to use them in any way to help in projecting election-day results *before* all of the polls have closed. The argument is that if results on the East Coast are announced before the polls close on the West Coast, the trend may influence people who have not yet cast their ballot—either changing their opinions or perhaps discouraging them from going to vote at all. While the number of people thus influenced might not be great enough to affect the Presidential race, they could be sufficient to change the outcome of local contests in which just a few thousand, or even a few hundred, votes made the difference.

Thus, in the November, 1964, elections, it is entirely possible that some local elections were influenced on the West Coast by people who saw on television the predictions of a Democratic landslide, who had not yet voted and who decided "Why bother?" A good example might well be the state of Nevada where, a week after the elections, a goverment investigation team was still trying to decide who had won the Senate race there. Senator Howard W. Cannon, the incumbent Democrat, was leading his rival, Republican Lieutenant Governor Paul Laxalt by a mere 61 votes—67,302 to 67,241. Naturally, all 61 were being hotly contested. The question (which will never be answered) arises: Did perhaps a hundred or more Republicans, who would have swung the results the other way, fail to go to the polls at all when they saw computerized estimates that their candidate was taking a thorough beating?

In the closest race on record, Francis Altimari, a Republican, led his Democratic rival, Julius Lippman, by only forty-eight votes in the race for the district court judgeship in the Third Judicial District in Nassau County, New York. An unofficial recount narrowed the margin to eleven. When the bipartisan Board of Elections announced the final score, however, Lippman was the winner by *one* vote (53,371 to 53,370). Did the computer play a part in the outcome?

The possibilities of influence are valid enough so that Elmer W. Lower of ABC News announced, prior to the election, that "Should the outcome of the Presidential race be known before the polls in Western states close, we will remind voters in those states that there are many important state and local offices and issues still to be decided. And we will urge voters to exercise democracy's most basic franchise: the right to vote."

In an address on "The Social Impact of Computers," RCA Board Chairman David Sarnoff said, "The computer will make it possible to restore a direct dialogue between the people and their political leaders, in the tradition of an Athenian assembly or a New England town meeting. Democracy is the highest form of government ever developed but the magnitude and complexities of our society have made us poor practitioners." What Mr. Sarnoff was referring to was the pitiful truth that no more than 64 per cent of the qualified voters have cast their ballots in any Presidential election in the last four decades. He pointed to the enormous number of votes that in the past have been invalidated by incorrect marking or defacement. In the 1948 election, for example, such invalidations numbered far more than the 2,100,000 votes polled by President Truman over Thomas E. Dewey. In many elections, only a third of the population bothers to get out and vote. Automation will greatly help to change the picture and revitalize communications between the voters and the polls.

"In the future," said Mr. Sarnoff, "it will be technically feasible for voting to be done in the home, with maximum personal convenience. The balloting would be done through television, the computerized telephone, standard and high-speed phone circuits or regional and national computers. For the dwindling minority of citizens who might still lack these units in the home, special telephone polling places would be provided." Balloting, moreover, could take place within a specified time period, at the voter's convenience; and there would be built-in safeguards against voting frauds.

We already have the means for this kind of automation right in our homes, for, as Western Electric mentioned recently in an advertisement, just pick up your telephone and you have a computer three thousand miles long. "This unique computer," says W.E., "is at the command of millions of phone users across the country. It is the nationwide Bell Telephone network. Calling on the staggering amount of information stored in its memory units, it guides your voice to distant places, using thousands of interconnections for each call. It picks the best available route to the number you want, then makes the connection—all within seconds. In recent years—and especially with the advent of area code dialing—automation has also been handling the billing, keeping track of numbers called, time consumed and other information and correctly applying it to individual bills. It is easy to see how efficient an automated system can be when you consider that AT&T services more than seventy-five million telephones a year.

The telephone itself is highly versatile as a vehicle for automation, lending itself to many imaginative methods of communication. Digitronics, for example, has perfected a device for sending data over the telephone as beeps, sounding audible, coded signals into the mouthpiece. The Data-Verter, as it is called, can be used by salesmen to transmit reports to a central office, or by chain stores sending frequent routine data to the central office. In one form, the system is made up of a recorder, an electric typewriter and a transmitter. The person making out a report merely types his message on the typewriter. Electrical impulses are then automatically fed into the recorder, where they are converted into magnetic pulses and stored on magnetic recording tape. After all information has been accumulated, the tape is placed in the transmitter. The person reporting places an ordinary telephone call to the office, then positions the transmitter device against the mouthpiece and automation takes over, communicating at the rate of about 350 words a minute to a device which instantly records the data at the other end.

It is a significant trend that communications have been accounting for larger and larger percentages of the information technology developed each year, and taking greater percentages of the expenditures and the scientific thinking. The Diebold research program has uncovered this important finding: In 1955, only a negligible expense was invested in the specific area of communication in perfecting hard-core computer complexes. By 1965, the expenditure had risen to about 10 per cent, much of it in systems like the vastly expanded Bell Telephone network. Projected figures indicate that it will be 25 per cent by 1975.

Of all recent advances in the field of communications, none is more historically or technologically significant than the development of the communications satellites. In July, 1962, with the launching of Telstar from Cape Kennedy (then Cape Canaveral), a new era of communications began. Although insignificant in size, weighing a mere 170 pounds and weird-looking in design, the satellite meant that for the first time in history, the broad band of microwaves (waves which must go in a straight line and cannot follow the curvature of the earth) could be effectively bounced off an object in space, thus following two sides of a triangle to bridge the oceans or other long distances.

Fifteen hours after the successful launching, Telstar was activated by remote control from its monitoring station in Andover, Maine. The first test was a telephone message from Andover to the satellite, some three thousand miles out at sea and back to Washington, D. C. The second test was the first transmission of a television picture across an ocean. The transmission from the United States was picked up by Telstar, amplified ten billion times by the satellite and then relayed to receiving stations in France and England, which in turn transmitted the program over commercial European stations.

Computers are already beginning to play another kind of communications role, in what might seem to be an unlikely field: literature. Early in September, 1964, the University of North Carolina announced that it was programing a computer for an assault on clichés, as part of a readability study for the Associated Press. AP asked editors to send in all examples of clichés that they spotted most frequently on the wire services, the ones that were most irritating. Armed with a goodly collection of these irritants, a University programer fed them into a machine, which then calculated which clichés were the most frequent and most annoying to newspaper editors. Some of the chief offenders to abolish were: "hail" (as in CITY HAILS NEW MAYOR); "violence flared"; "flatly denied"; "Usually reliable sources"; "jampacked"; "gutted by fire"; "kickoff" (not referring to football); "strife-torn"; and "guarded optimism." As *Time* humorously reported the results: "In the wake of Univac's report, the AP had no immediate comment. But a usually reliable source hailed with guarded optimism the fact that, percentage-wise, the AP copy came out relatively clean." The number one cliché, "hail," was found only nine times among the 375,000 words.

The Univac used in the study also compared a week's run of Associated Press news copy with a formula for clear writing. Stories fed into the computer were classified by datelines and by subject: domestic news, foreign news, politics and government, science, sports, accidents and disasters, crime, war, rebellion and defense, public health and welfare, arts, religion, economics, business and travel.

The computer found that AP news was generally understandable to any one from the sixth-grade level on up, with human interest types of stories at the lower end of the scale and political and governmental subjects up near the seventh-grade level.

At about the same time, IBM's Research Center at Yorktown Heights, N. Y., announced that it had held a three-day meeting on literary date processing, to try to bridge the often-discussed gap between science and the humanities. One objective was to see how effectively computers could be taught to scan poetry, drama, novels or other forms of literature, to define themes or to make literary comparisons.

In the belief that they might as well start, qualitatively, at the very top, the participants selected Shakespeare, Milton and Shelley. Dr. Sally Sedelow of St. Louis University programed a computer to try to seek out the theme in scene 1, Act IV of *Hamlet*. She reported that the machine had actually located it to her satisfaction, the underlying theme of mental illness. There was no reason why it could not have gone on and tackled all the rest of Shakespeare.

Classical scholars might shudder at the idea of a computer trying to compare the poetry of Milton and Shelley, yet the idea is not as far-out as it might seem. Dr. Joseph Raben, professor of English at Queens College, Flushing, New York, voiced a respectful vote of confidence for the computer after seeing it swing into its literary stride at Yorktown Heights. "I could never have achieved this in my lifetime," he told a press conference, "but the way is now open to make dozens of literary comparisons, even of the whole body of a poet's work, to trace the influence of his style and meaning."

The computer, after making an estimated *two billion* comparisons of Milton's "Paradise Lost" and Shelley's "Prometheus Unbound," had in effect indicated that Shelley was more influenced by his seventeenth-century predecessor than many authorities believed. Professor Raben himself had long been interested in the connection between the two English poets, after observing that the nineteenth-century romantic had borrowed some of Milton's phraseology in translating Dante's "Inferno." The professor had spent many laborious hours studying comparative lines. Yet the farther he progressed, the more and more difficult it became to keep track of similarities, even when using massive concordances of the poetry of both men. At this point, the computer took over, under the direction of I.B.M.'s Raymond Villani, who programed both poems into the system by coding the words and lines on punched cards. He then instructed the machine to compare the poems word for word and select sentences in which combinations of words appeared in both works. The computer fed out dozens of pages of word comparisons.

The test was highly successful because, as Dr. Raben pointed out, words and combinations turned out to be the key to parallel lines or thoughts within the poetry. He cited one passage in particular, the parallel descriptions of "a bower in Eden." Seventeen unusual words were picked out by the computer as having been used by both poets. It was evident that Shelley had read Milton many times, reflected on the earlier poet's phrasing and meaning, and then developed his own interpretation of the bower sequence.

"We are now ready," said Dr. Raben, convinced that machines could assist the academician, "to tackle any poet and to trace the influence he may have had. It's an exciting possibility."

Dr. Raben is not the only scholar by any means who has become fascinated with the possibilities of what automation might accomplish in the literary field. Computers have been used to analyze Dryden, to study the writings of St. Thomas Aquinas and to explore the Federalist Papers. Experiments are being conducted on "The Iliad," to determine to what extent Homer may have had assistance in the writing, a point that has long been a controversial one among scholars.

"We used to think of computers as being only quantitatively better [than humans]," said Professor J. B. Bessinger, Jr., of New York University, who was chairman of one of the I.B.M. sessions, "but it may be that they are qualitatively better in some ways."

While many scholars are extremely dubious about the ability of a machine to exercise any kind of judgment in comparing literary works, there is general acceptance of computers as a means for compiling valuable listings of words and expressions. There is no doubt that computers can produce, far more accurately than any man might prepare, such things as alphabetical lists, word counts, and dictionary references. They will also prove to be of immense value in the exhaustive—and exhausting—chore of putting together literary concordances, alphabetical indexes of words and contexts in various works. Concordances of major writers sometimes take ordinary mortals a decade to prepare. Computers may require a year of preparation to become indoctrinated, but they can then produce the desired concordances in less than a day, perhaps only a matter of hours. Scientists have already invented a computer that can read print without human guidance. When perfected and properly programed, it will be able to prepare massive concordances and similar works almost overnight. An information processing machine could absorb all of the sentences, paragraphs and pages in this book in a matter of about five to ten seconds. Later, within a few thousandths of a second, it could pick out any letter, character or phrase in the book and feed it back on request.

The practicality of machines in this type of literary work has already been established, since computer-evolved concordances have actually been published on the works of Matthew Arnold, William Blake, Emily Dickinson and William Butler Yeats.

According to Dr. J.C.R. Licklider of I.B.M.'s Thomas J. Watson Research Center, "programed computers are entering the domain of cognition, the domain of intellect: they are demonstrating to all that no law or principle bars them from that realm." As evidence, he cites a programed computer at Harvard which can analyze the grammatical structure of English sentences. It goes about its work with Harvardian rigor, but at this stage of its development is still tediously slow, analyzing at a rate of only two or three sentences an hour.

On a far less literary plane, one computer was assigned an ingenious task, with which it whiled away several hours. It invented a dictionary for one of the leading drug companies: forty-two thousand medical-sounding names. The list started with abechamycin and ended with ywuvite. Obviously, not all of the names turned out to be usable.

There are, of course, underlying problems in leaning too heavily on computers. As science editor Earl Ubell of the New York *Herald Tribune* wrote, after seeing what has been done at Yorktown Heights: "Some literary men wonder if the new-found tool may not be a new-found toy leading critics down the road toward trivial problems that lend themselves to computing. Others say that the computer will still leave unanswered for human contemplation the basic questions: "What is poetry? How does the creative process work?" To sum it all up, he quotes a quatrain by Dr. Thomas Clayton of the University of California:

> It is doubtless wiser for the wise
> To computerize,
> But harmless, though wasteful, for fools
> To misuse their tools.

In a completely different, and somewhat more commercial, area of communications, automation will mean increasing efficiency, cutting down time lags and minimizing errors to an astonishing degree. The Census Bureau has inaugurated a new computer method which has been throwing a scare into the ranks of the public relations world—a computer method for writing press releases. According to the Bureau, the computer can type out a release at the rate of ten lines a second. The first series of releases reported on retail trade from each county in Idaho and Montana. From statistical tables, the computer simply selected data and inserted the facts in predetermined positions in a formulated release.

"Automation," said John Diebold in an address before the American Society of Newspaper Editors in Washington, D. C., in April, 1963, "spells survival for many of America's newspapers. There are few industries where the economics of automation are so starkly etched, so portentous for the community, or so long overdue.

"But automation means more than the economics of survival. It means, too, major and inexorable change in nearly every aspect of newspaper publishing—mechanical change, business change, and, most of all, editorial change."

He went on to point out that three major changes and developments would occur within the next decade in newspaper publishing, as a result of automation:

1) The tools of the trade will be vastly different. Editorial text will be fed into computer-like systems in editorial offices, whether it arrives by wire, is typed in by a reporter or is called up from the morgue, the extensive information files maintained by periodicals of all kinds. Copy will be manipulated electronically, said Diebold, displayed on television screens built right into editorial desks, which will resemble consoles. Instead of using pencils, editors will be equipped with slim tubes no larger than ballpoint which will emit thin beams of light. These will serve as writing instruments as the editors make changes and corrections on the screen before them.

These editors will not only have an easier job of editing, but they will have at their command, instantly, all of the great masses of editorial research stored electronically in automated morgues. Some data will be stored in the publications own files (old, established facts or fresh material, just written); other information will come from wire service libraries, which will operate on a commercial basis, selling their wares to all subscribers.

2) The production system that transfers editorial copy to the printing presses will be faster acting and far more responsive to revisions than it is today. "You will be much closer to your reader in both time and space," said Diebold, "Many newspapers will print simultaneously at a number of locations on light presses."

The time lapse from editorial desk to printed page will be reduced to just a few minutes, saving on costs and making edition-to-edition changes much simpler than they are today. One of the biggest revolutions of all will be that typesetting will fade into limbo. The page image set up on the screens and approved by the editors will be transmitted directly to printing plates when final approval is given by touching a button. Thus, there will be no costly resetting of type, no crucial time lag, when sudden news breaks require last minute editorial changes.

3) The entire publishing enterprise will take new form and will offer a wide range of new editorial services. "Electronic morgue services and special local and regional information will be sold by publishers," said Diebold, "over the data transmission facilities of our telephone system." Because of this innovation, among others, by 1970, the long lines of the telephone system will carry more machine-to-machine traffic than human voice conversation!

Because of the extensive, readily available material on hand, we will see more and more special editions, supplements and one-shot publications than ever before. There is already a trend to such publications, utilizing existing material or handy sources on special occasions when there seems to be a market. An outstanding example was the flood of one-shot magazines and commemorative and memorial issues turned out within days and weeks of President Kennedy's assassination. Tomorrow, special publications could be turned out overnight, and at a fraction of what it now costs, to go through the frenzy of meeting a sudden public demand.

As Diebold points out, the three major changes discussed are not blue-sky prophecies. "No new scientific breakthroughs are needed," he said, "to allow any of these changes to take place. All that is needed is the engineering of existing science to fit the needs of newspapers. What is new is the idea of engineering information technology to the needs of the editor."

The Diebold Group, at that very time, was already well along on a comprehensive research program to consider the impact of technological developments on newspapers during the coming decade. A unique aspect of the program is its international character; including such newspapers as: the New York *Times,* the *Times* of London, *The Financial Times* (London), the Chicago *Daily News,* the *Daily Telegraph* (London), International Publishing

Corporation Ltd. (United Kingdom), and the Copley Press (which serves the U.S. and Latin America).

The editor's office will not be the only area significantly and profoundly affected by automation. The layout department, coordinating with the editor, will choose electronically which stories go in which sections of the newspaper. All visual matter—photographs, sketches, charts—will be projected on the console screen at the editor's desk after sorting and captions will be written to fit.

In other sections of the editorial rooms, secondary control points and screens will be established, so that reporters, columnists, department editors and others will easily be able to feed data into the overall system, obtain the latest information of the progress of certain stories or make their own corrections and editorial changes on request, or according to the procedures established. These checkpoints, too, will be provided with pencils of light and other devices that fit into the automated scheme of things.

Down in the morgue and the news library, general information, statistics, pictures and other elements will be stored in a number of ways. News copy, for example, will be stored both optically and on magnetic tape. Facts of all kinds will be filed and indexed by computers. Photographs, art work and documents will be kept in glossy print form for mechanical use, but also classified on tape-film for reference and selection.

From the newspaper standpoint, the most important feature of automation is that it will enable editors to work with amazing speed to get the news into print. Experimentally, data can be transmitted even today at the rate of twenty million bits per second. Translated into lay terms, that means that automated equipment could process the editorial content of a five-hundred-page book in about three minutes! But this kind of automation will also lend itself well to all kinds of publication—whether daily newspapers, weeklies, trade journals, consumer magazines, technical manuals or books.

Recently, thousands of visitors to the Seibu department store in Tokyo were startled by a demonstration put on by the Mainichi Publishing Company. It was an experimental "talking newspaper," which the editors said would come out of the wall in subscribers' homes. Within a few years, said a spokesman for *Mai-*

nichi, the cost of such a receiving set would be brought down to 50,000 yen about $140). Yet already one of the Japanese newspapers is offering service through facsimile in the home.

As might be expected, automation in the newspaper field has not been totally accepted as a welcome revolution. The old controversy hits hard in the industry: "Automation will bring unemployment!" vs. "Automation means more jobs!" Recently, in a typical display of opinion about automation, all fifty printers on the force of the *Times and News* in Erie, Pennsylvania, stood up and booed loudly when a computer was brought into the composing room. There is no pat answer to the controversy, but there is something to be said for a remark by Professor Wayne Danielson, dean of the University of North Carolina School of Journalism. "If you write like a machine," he told editors and other journalists, "you can be replaced by a machine."

20

The machines that talk
to each other

"Any successful approach to the challenge of automation should . . . look to . . . the social implications of a world where machines do mental as well as manual labor, and where man will enjoy great freedom from what is known today as 'work' and vastly more knowledge and power to test the morality of his decisions."

JOHN DIEBOLD, "AUTOMATION: IMPACT AND IM-PLICATIONS," REPORT PREPARED FOR THE COMMU-NICATIONS WORKERS OF AMERICA, AFL-CIO, APRIL, 1965.

IN THE VAST COLLECTION of clippings, tear sheets and other printed matter that John Diebold has accumulated over the years on the subject of automation, there are numerous examples of the scare headline. These go something like this: COMPUTERS THAT THINK ARE THREAT TO MANKIND! or WILL THE MACHINES TAKE OVER?

All express the characteristic alarm that man is being outsmarted by machines. Few go so far as to emulate science fiction and suggest that superbrained robots will muster themselves into an electronic army. Yet many point out that man's increasing dependence upon the machine will soon make him subservient to it, or that he will no longer have a mind and will of his own.

Perhaps there is reason to be concerned. Consider, for example, the content of a recent newspaper article. The article was a report, with editorial comment on a network of new computers that could actually communicate back and forth to each other, although hundreds of miles apart. These mechanical brains were not only able to relay information, but were able to give instructions which would alter the operational procedures and make adjustments, depending upon changing situations—all without intervention by a single human being, for days and weeks on end.

By the time the astonished readers had put down their newspapers, they were suddenly aware (if they had not been already) that the concept of machines taking over man's thinking and acting processes was no longer fiction but fact. Here was an actual case where machines were not only assuming human functions, but actually talking to each other. It is neither a stretching of the truth nor a case of sensationalism to say that computers and other complex machines can talk. Not only can they speak to each other, but the most advanced computers are being taught how to talk back. They can provide answers by spoken words. They can call attention to breakdowns within the system. They can spot errors. They can even reprimand the operator for having posed a problem incorrectly to begin with.

A *Time* magazine report on cybernation stated that "computermen have even been advised to get their machines out to 'see life' . . . by setting up communications links between them and other computers in dispersed locations."

R. M. Bloch, a vice president at Honeywell, even went so far as to suggest that machines can become lonely. "The computer that lacks an ability to communicate with the outside world," he said, "is in danger of remaining an isolated marvel mumbling to itself in the air-conditioned seclusion of its company's data processing room."

As Professor Herbert Simon of Carnegie Institute of Technology said recently, computers can be programed so that they "increasingly imitate—and in some cases improve upon—human cunning."

In 1946, when the first prototypes of today's information processing machines were being developed, a computer named Eniac, the first of its kind, blew out several hundred vacuum tubes in a display of electronic tantrums. Through an error, it had been asked to divide by zero. Because it possessed a cave-man brain in comparison with today's whiz kids, it went out of its mechanical mind trying to solve a problem which no one had explained, via programing into the system, was impossible.

By 1954, however, a research group at the Rand Corporation in Santa Monica, California, had managed to program a computer so that it was able, on its own, to point out human errors, instead of blowing its technological top. Recently in a demonstration, this machine, named Johnniac, after the late mathematician John Von Neumann, was asked to divide one by zero ($1/0=?$). The machine immediately flashed back that there was an error in this question: attempting to divide by zero. Trying to outwit the machine, the programer (operator) then asked it to provide the square root of *minus 3* (-3). The machine balked immediately, explaining that attempting the square root of a negative number is impossible.

Johnniac, now practically the Methuselah of the computer world, types its answers, rather than giving them out verbally. But some of its grandchildren are well able to speak out the answers. Not only that, but they can listen, and can understand limited vocabularies well enough so that they can react differently to the accents and inflections of several different programmers.

Putting human beings in their places, the brainier machines, which make far fewer mistakes in doing millions of computations than the most learned mathematicians would in completing just a few hundred, actually correct their teachers as they work together developing a program. Time and again, after a programer has fed instructions into a system, he will find the program rejected by the computer because he has made errors (similar to asking to divide by zero or provide the square root of a minus number). The programer then has to undertake a laborious assignment, known in the trade as debugging, or finding and correcting the errors. It is like having to do your homework assignment all over again on a gargantuan scale.

It is not unusual for a program to require fifty thousand different instructions, with several hundred test runs of different sections of the program. Each run may have to be repeated a dozen or so times before the machine is satisfied and accepts the instructions of the master, and it is commonplace for a programer to have to labor for six months to a year just to set up his basic program. Nevertheless, although this may seem like a long time just to get a data processing system into operation, it must be remembered that the system will eventually save years—even decades—of time and labor to achieve results.

Dr. Ulric Neisser of Brandeis University points out that computers, with this vast capacity for work, do pose psychological problems. "The new machines," he says, "are more than magical resources available only to a few. They also have some disturbingly human characteristics. They make intelligent decisions, arrive at unexpected conclusions, engage in activities which are given such human names as 'seeing,' 'remembering,' and 'problem-solving.' One flourishing branch of the information sciences is the 'simulation' of human thought by what is called 'artificial intelligence.' There can be no doubt that these efforts are making real contributions to both psychology and information technology, but they also contribute to a growing mythology about men and machines. 'Mechanical men' already play a considerable part in the fantasies of television, science-fiction and the comic strips."

Is there actually danger that computers will some day get the upper hand over men?

When the question was asked of the late Norbert Wiener, a pioneer in high-speed communications technology, his answer was not very comforting to those who brush aside such notions as pure science fiction.

"There is, definitely," asserted Dr. Wiener, "The danger is essentially intellectual laziness. There is a worship of gadgetry. The machines are there to be used by man, and if man prefers to leave the whole matter of the mode of their employment to the machine, through over-worship of the machine or through unwillingness to make decisions, then we're in for trouble."

Computers actually do have memories, and much better ones within their limited subject areas than any man could hope for. According to Dr. Wiener, machines will at least in part approximate the functions of the human brain: "Generic memory—the memory of our genes—" he said, "is largely dependent on nucleic acids. It's pretty generally suspected that the memory of the nervous system is similar. This is indicated by the discovery of nucleic acid complexes in the brain and by the fact that they have the properties that would give a good memory. This is a very subtle sort of solid state physics, like the physics which is used in the memory of machines now.

"My hunch is—and I'm not alone in this—that the next decade or so will see this used technically."

To put it differently, the old concept of the magnetic tape or other device as a memory core will be replaced by substances similar to the genes in the human brain.

John Diebold, who knew and held great respect for Dr. Wiener, agrees that "Man could become a cog in the machine, accepting, in Norbert Wiener's words, 'the superior dexterity of the machine-made decisions without too much inquiry as to the motives and principles behind them.' "

He points out emphatically, however, that there is a way to counteract this danger of becoming subservient. To work with the new machine technology, he says, man will require "an increasing ability to think and to judge, increased understanding of mathematical and logical methods, in short, increased education in the largest sense of the term. . . . The fact that the new machines are capable of providing us with more information than we have ever had raises questions of the highest importance. Just as they can provide answers to scientific questions that could never be answered before, so machines can provide answers to questions outside the field of science that could never be answered before because no one person or group of persons could comprehend all the facts. . . . It is here that our ability to think, to judge and to understand will stand us in the best stead. For machines are only machines. It is up to men to decide how to use them."

The real danger, and the real problem, warned Diebold in a recent address, "is that science is bringing about a situation necessitating man to reconsider his role in relation to the fundamental forces of the universe.

"Man's intellect no longer sets him apart from the rest of creation. He himself has created machines which increasingly are able to think like—even outthink—him. Already in existence are 'heuristic' (goal-oriented) computers which solve problems without being told how—by trial-and-error processes which no longer can be differentiated meaningfully from what we know as human learning. Man has developed theories pointing to the almost certain existence of equal or superior intelligences elsewhere in the universe. Thus, man finds himself lacking in the self-imposed requisites for a unique place on the footstool of God. But he neither has devised new requisites which he is able to meet nor has prepared himself to abdicate his unique place."

Nobility, says Diebold is one grace which man has that cannot be built into a machine. "And nobility alone can guide man towards worthy and valid goals, as he directs his own evolution."

A certain amount of publicity has been given to an obviously dramatic use of machines: the computer that plays checkers. Some have called this a publicity stunt; others have claimed that the device was so rigged that it only *appeared* to be playing, or at the very best played a number of predetermined moves. Neither assumption is correct.

Arthur Samuel, a consultant at I.B.M., some time ago began programing a 7094 machine at the Watson Research Center in Yorktown Heights, New York, to play checkers. His objective was not to achieve publicity, but to study a program which, while it might incorporate billions of possible combinations of moves, could be defined within certain well stated rules. More importantly, while he wanted to teach the machine how to play, he also wanted to teach it *to learn to improve its game*. Sets of instructions were fed into the machine on punched cards. The computer was told to explore the board to a depth of three. Each time it selected a possible move, it was also to investigate all of the opponent's possible reactions to that move, and then consider its own counter-moves after that. "Possible move," however, might mean exploring several hundred to a depth of three before making a decision.

During the course of each game, the computer stores its moves, successes and failures in its memory, so that in the course of hundreds of games it has continually improved its ability. When it was first learning, 7094 was consistently beaten by its tutor. Soon though, it found Samuel an easy opponent to beat, and went on to tournament stuff. About three years after it started its checker career, the computer took on Robert Nealy, Connecticut State champion, for six games. It lost only one, and held Nealy to a draw in the others. Naturally, it acquired a great deal of competitive information and experience, which it is not likely to forget.

Although Samuel has not learned a great deal about checkers during his experiments, he and his associates have picked up priceless information in the art of communicating with, and teaching, data processing machines.

Through the process of indoctrinating a machine to function in a specific assignment (in this case, playing checkers), scientists see the obstacles and the opportunities in proper perspective. As more and more information is fed into a computer, says Diebold, it *"devises its own strategy in pursuit of a goal.* This is the way computers have defeated the men who taught them checkers. This is the way they can be used in business or war gaming. This is the way, eventually, that they will accomplish space explorations too dangerous for men to undertake and, even, seek out objectives men do not even know to exist."

Before computers, or any other types of machines, can reach for such far-flung, inspired objectives, however, they must prove themselves with workaday assignments of a less romantic nature. The field of banking is one practical area in which the machine can learn to read and talk and think and be helpful to man. Depositors are accustomed to walking into the local branch of their bank and asking the teller for information on their account. The usual method has been for the teller to call the central filing system and ask a clerk for the figures. Now, however, a number of banks have an automated system whereby the teller inserts the depositor's code card in a slot and punched out the customer's query on a keyboard. The computer instantly sifts out the information and answers the inquiry—verbally—from data stored in its memory system. The machine has a basic speaking vocabulary of some sixty-four words and numbers, pre-recorded by human voice and stored on a magnetic drum within the computer brain.

Electronic data processing systems are becoming increasingly useful in the brokerage field, supplying brokers across the country with much more trading data at a far faster pace, and with much greater accuracy than was possible with former methods. The system uses a central computer, armed with multitudes of facts, linked to a network of thousands of electronic desk units in brokerage firms from coast to coast. By pushing buttons or spinning a dial on the desk unit (about the size of an adding machine), a broker can immediately get split-second information on any stock coded into the system, or on the market in general. The desk-top units reveal the price quoted at that moment for the stock in question, along with data on trading volume, opening price, or number of shares in the last lot traded.

Referred to not long ago as "the insurance man's best friend," computers have for many years been vital to the insurance industry. Insurance companies, according to *Business Week*, "are probably closer to the total system than any other industry . . . taking the computer out of its glass cage and putting it as near the agent as his telephone or typewriter."

It is hardly likely that you will be dialing a computer direct to sign up for life insurance, or to determine comparable rates of automobile, fire or theft policies from one company to another. "The human element is too important," says one insurance executive, "to short circuit the personalized operation of the salesman. What the machine can do, though, is to provide immediate, accurate information to the salesman, on any subject at any time, and thus free him from a lot of routine filing and bookkeeping that he is now subjected to."

Using computers is also a sound selling point, as the John Hancock Company demonstrated in a television commercial:

Potential Buyer: Do you go into this much detail with every policy you sell?

Agent: Certainly.

Potential Buyer: How do you get the time?

Agent: Electronic computers. At John Hancock, they do most of the detail work. It gives me plenty of time to plan a program that's just right for you.

The new electronic wizards have exhibited remarkable flexibility and adaptability. At the start, scientists in the automation field hooked the systems into typewriters, teletypewriters and other keyboard devices as a means of communicating. Vocal programing started in a serious way as the decade of the sixties began. And recently, the idea of note-taking has been applied. Engineer Herbert Teager, at M.I.T., has invented a device which permits the programer to write his messages on paper on a plate about the size of a window pane. Built into the plate is a grid with very fine electric wires. Using a pen that sensitizes the charges of electricity on the grid, the operator simply writes instructions or asks questions.

One of the most remarkable features of all is the fact that the machine can be programed in such a way that it learns the writing style of each person who uses it. It can identify the letters of the alphabet, scrawled in different hands, as well as digits, mathematical signs, scientific symbols and other characters.

What has been described as a major breakthrough in the art of communicating with computers is a device known as Sketchpad, which was developed at M.I.T.'s Lincoln Laboratory by Ivan Sutherland, a brainy young man who started working on the project for his doctor's degree when he was twenty-three. It required about eighteen months to complete the basic model, which incorporates a TV-like screen on which diagrams can be drawn with a light-sensitive pen or electronic stylus, on what is known as a TX-2 computer. By using push buttons, the operator tells the machine that he is drawing a straight line or a triangle, hexagon, circle or other geometric figure. Thus, his penmanship can be sloppy and sketchy to the extreme—roughed out much, much faster than if he were trying to draft a problem on paper. The figure is then produced on the screen by the robot draftsman, which can also reduce the figure or enlarge it some two thousand times.

The operator can produce a technically accurate blueprint in a matter of seconds, and can then modify that blueprint at will, without having to go through the usual procedure of redrawing the whole thing. An important, and overwhelming time-saving factor, is the machine's ability to develop highly complex engineering calculations. For example, the operator can sketch out proposed designs for a new type of aircraft wing structure. TX-2 will then compute the stresses and strains involved under different load conditions and impart them to the operator by way of teletyped messages. If the answers indicate problems in the type of design, modifications can be made on the spot, and the diagram redrawn to incorporate the machine's suggestions. Through this procedure, known as the tennis court method, weeks—and even months—of work can be spared in arriving at certain fundamental data regarding load factors for jet planes, bridges, buildings, derricks, hydrofoils and just about any type of structure there is.

This give and take between man and machine represents a whole new outlook, both technologically and sociologically. Sometimes it gets a little alarming in the matter of relationships. Sutherland, for example, confided to a *Fortune* writer that he experienced tremendous excitement working with TX-2. "It's like flying a jet plane. . . . I spent hours with it, at night and weekends when there was no one to interrupt me, and it was a thrill to struggle with an idea and then to see it working on the screen." He also is alleged to have overheard the machine "talking to itself, recognizing loops and other operations by characteristic pulsings and squeals and whines."

With TX-2, and a few other machines now under development, there is added excitement because of the extra dimension added: the ability of the device to sit there in front of one and not only communicate with printed or verbal words, but draw pictures. TX-2's graphics are formal and mathematical; but other machines are being perfected that have sketchier techniques and may eventually be able to produce a little creative art on their own. The day is not far off when we shall see an exhibit of "art," produced entirely by machine.

Dr. J. C. R. Licklider, as a specialist in the field, speaking of the tremendous attraction that these machines have for men of science, asks, "What makes it so fascinating to work in partnership with a powerful computer?"

Answering his own question, he says that, first, the operator can "get his hands and eyes onto accurate, detailed information quickly. Second, he can turn an idea into action as soon as he has formulated the idea." Beyond that, he is able to obtain quick answers to questions he can pose in mathematics and logic, and he can share in "the constructive effort of an intellectual community in ways never before possible."

Thus far in this first generation of the computer family, most machines have been referred to by numbers of the neuter gender, simply as "it," even though a few (e.g., Johnniac) have masculine names. It is not at all unlikely, though, that the machines of the future will definitely be classified as male or female—the big, robust and obviously masculine ones handling such assignments as controlling steel mills or manufacturing operations; the smaller, more delicate ones taking over secretarial chores.

It must have been a *masculine* machine that accomplished an interesting breakthrough on Sunday, June 21, 1964. On that date, a pretty brown-haired, brown-eyed lass, Alice Ruby, a senior at Bennington College, Vermont, was crowned National College Queen.

She was chosen by a computer.

What actually happened was that the judges individually rated each of the fifty state finalists on the basis of intellectual performance in ten forums, ranging from general knowledge to specific capacities, such as table setting. The ratings were fed into the machine, where they were instantly analyzed and reported, in order of rank.

"I like to think," said the shapely (35-24-35) winner, "it was the men not the computer who chose me."

Would feminine machines tend to be more chatty and conversationally minded than masculine ones? That is a distinct possibility. Since machines are being purposely developed to communicate with each other, it is already evident that some talk more than others. In the programing and the abilities of machines to learn things and to develop their own systems of operation, some will undoubtedly find out that they are accomplishing more, or getting intended results more quickly, by developing the art of conversation.

At least one authoritative observer has expressed grave concern over what can happen when machines turn to conversation. Recently, the Center for the Study of Democratic Institutions published a paper by one of its staff members, John Wilkinson, entitled "The Quantitative Society, or What Are You To Do With Noodle?" Mr. Wilkinson stated that when information processing machines were linked together their capacities for carrying on conversations would lead to unforeseeable consequences. In effect, these computers were developing minds of their own which could establish values that endangered the well-being—even the survival—of our society.

When computers are joined together, he said, "in such a way that the decisions—or outputs—of the one become the inputs of the other, a new unitary machine is created with proporties, among others, involving feedback and secondary effects."

To put it all in a nutshell, Mr. Wilkinson wrote of computers in general, "The erstwhile servant has become or is rapidly becoming the master and displaying what very much looks like free will."

He is not alone in his pessimistic viewpoint that we are being subtly invaded by a new master race that will one day have the upper hand.

The entire picture is not darkened by technological gloom. Most of the pioneers and consultants in the field of automation look at the machine as perhaps the most valuable servant man has ever invented to propel him along the road to greater and greater achievement. Diebold is highly optimistic.

"The current technological revolution promises to have far wider effect than mere technology," he says. "This is a revolution, in other words, which will take us beyond the civilization of an industrial society—a revolution in which human beings will largely be freed from the bondage of machines. It will raise an entirely new set of problems: business problems, social problems, economic problems. It will tax our ingenuity to its utmost. And it will bring about its changes—many of them, at least—within our own lifetime.

"Like the pioneers of the Industrial Revolution of the Eighteenth Century, we face a world in which only one thing is certain: change, fundamental change.

"I think it is fair to say that this new technological revolution offers as great a challenge and reward as any which we have ever known."

Some of the rewards are already dramatically in evidence, particularly in areas of technology where man alone could not possibly have found the answers to design, research and development problems through systems of computation available a few years back. One outstanding example is the Air Force's giant new antenna system, symbolized by Haystack, a metal and glass-fiber radome, at Tyngsboro, Massachusetts, the world's most precise large steerable antenna. One hundred and twenty feet in diameter, it will be used for space communications, radio astronomy and radar research.

The significant element in this automation milestone, is the fact that the huge reflector dish and its components were designed *by a machine* in a radically new fashion. Using a computer, scientists at M.I.T.'s Lincoln Laboratory developed a highly complicated mathematical model to determine the mechanical structure that would perform according to intricate specifications. As a double check, the contractor for the project, North American Aviation, used a second, slightly different computer analysis, setting up a similar model.

The computer approach made it possible, according to the programers at M.I.T., "to design a large, complex structure on this scale a hundred times more exactly, and reliably, than was heretofore possible." In addition to the time-saving advantage—short circuiting months of tedious work previously required to make computations and then set up a prototype before constructing the actual antenna—costs were remarkably pared down, and would be even further reduced in the design of other antenna systems.

So accurate and capable is the new computer-designed Haystack that it will, according to General Bernard A. Schriever be "significant for the identification and analysis of satellites in orbit."

Computers are highly effective in making certain types of decisions where they can build those decisions on a series of current facts or statistics. A few years ago, for example, the investment trust officer of a Pittsburgh bank was talked into letting a young programer try to feed into a computer enough information on common stocks so that the machine would recommend an investment program. In one test, the computer was fed coded cards relating to possible stock purchases for the portfolio of one of the bank's clients, "a widow who had $28,000 to invest and wanted a steady income to supplement her salary as a schoolteacher."

The machine, working independently, recommended a diversified portfolio, made up of eight corporations, at 100 shares each, with an estimated dividend yield of 4.9 per cent. When the portfolio was checked against the recommendations made by the trust officer and his staff, it was found that seven of the eight companies were represented also at 100 shares each, and that the yield was exactly the same. This case is an over-simplified example of what a modern data processing system could do with an extremely complex corporate investment program, involving hundreds of thousands of shares of stocks and bonds, dozens of companies and multiple purposes.

Given certain fundamental specifications and existing data, information storing machines can work out programs such as the above and make decisions that parallel—and even surpass—those of an intelligent, thinking human being. In some instances, as in the case of confidential matters, people might well prefer to have the thinking done by an impersonal device—coldly, objectively, calculatingly, if you will. Computers are now hard at work, for example, matching job specifications and prospective candidates.

263

John Diebold

Job applicants fill out a form listing everything conceivable about
their personal and educational background, as well as their preferences in types of jobs, locations, organizations and salary range.
When personal profiles are fed into a computer system on the one
side and job specifications on the other, the selection system
matches jobs and applicants far more quickly and accurately than
any man—or an entire staff for that matter—could do. The speed
of processing can be figured in milliseconds.

Occasionally, when given a job of matching, a computer can
suffer electronic embarrassment at pulling a real boner. Once a
year, the computer at Utah's Brigham Young University is given
the romantic assignment of matchmaking for one of the college
dances, pairing boys and girls with similar interests. Not long ago,
Bonnie Mitchell, an eighteen-year-old redhead, asked for a tall
boy with blue eyes and dark hair. The date picked for her by the
computer from 15,500 students was tall, blue-eyed and dark-
haired; he met her additional requests that he be interested in
entertainment and favorably inclined towards marriage. Furthermore, Bonnie exactly matched her date's specifications, right
down to her red hair.

There was only one hitch: the date turned out to be Richard
Mitchell, nineteen—her brother.

Something that has intrigued programing pioneers far more
than routine data processing labors are the challenging questions
about what computers might be able to accomplish when given
creative assignments to fool around with. "Music is the universal
language of mankind," wrote Longfellow. If true, why not program a machine to speak in musical terms the way it can with
English or any other language?

"Art is the imposing of a pattern on experience," wrote Alfred
North Whitehead, "and our esthetic enjoyment in recognition of
the pattern." If true, why not program a machine to create art that
would be based on calculated experience and that would evoke
reaction from observers who could recognize the pattern? If a
computer could be programed to sketch geometric figures, it
could conceivably be left to its own devices to arrange patterns
that would be true art, or at the very least "artistic."

With such ideas in mind, scientists at the University of Illinois
ventured into the field of music and actually programed a computer so that it composed what is known as the *Illiac Suite*. Said

one commentator: "By common consent, the *Illiac Suite* is no great shakes; one of the moderate remarks about it is that repeated hearings tend to induce exasperation. But so, of course, does some 'modern' music composed by humans, and it is possible that one day the computer may be programed to concoct music that many regard as good."

Other programers, stimulated by requests from the advertising world, have experimented with commercials and jingles—but thus far with little success—or at least not with the kind of success that is likely to send listeners scurrying to buy the product.

It has been demonstrated that computers can write creatively (if you are willing to accept a rather loose view of the word "creatively"). R. M. Worthy at the Advanced Research Department at General Precision, Inc., in Glendale, California, and his associates have attempted to teach a beatnik type of machine to turn to poetry rather than statistics. They began by feeding it several thousand words; they divided the words into certain groupings; and they instructed the machine in the art of rhyming and using grammatical structures.

The mechanical muse turned out, among others, a poem entitled "Lament for a Mongrel," which went as follows:

"To belch yet not to boast, that is the hug,
The high lullaby's bay discreetly crushes the bug.
Your science was so minute and hilly,
Yes, I am not the jade organ's leather programmer's
    recipe.
As she is squealing above the cheroot, these obscure
    toilets shall squat,
Moreover, on account of hunger, the room was hot."

Well, Gertrude Stein and others have gotten away with it. At least the computer seems to have put the programer in his place.

No matter how you want to look at it, the evidence certainly multiplies day by day that the thinking machine is here to stay and that man has to outthink it in order to avoid being outwitted by it. It used to be that our most important machines were symbols of brawn and force, great Frankensteinian monsters that could lift hundreds of cubic yards of earth in one swoop or pound out entire molds of automobile bodies in one fierce blow or swing steel armfuls of girders ten stories up to the top framework of a building under construction. But the mental attributes are stealthily supplanting the physical in importance.

"The Scriptures were right: the meek have inherited the earth," wrote R. Buckminster Fuller recently, "But they do not know it. Though irrevocable, the will has not as yet been finally probated in the court of public comprehension. . . ."

Fuller, inventor of the geodesic dome and other mathematical marvels, estimates that there will be a quarter of a million high-capacity, information-storage, electronic computers by 1970, 250 million of them a decade later, and eight billion by 1995. At that critical moment, our entire world population will be outnumbered by thinking machines by more than two to one. If a machine *qualitatively* now has an advantage over man, think of what it will also have *quantitatively!*

Writing a paper on "The Prospect for Humanity," Fuller pointed out that "throughout the last fifteen years many philosophers have been disturbed by the claims of some cyberneticians that computers are soon to displace the human intellect. If, instead, they had confined their prediction to the effectiveness of the human brain in respect to the computer, some of their claims might in time prove valid. For a long time philosophers assumed that the computer could not ask original questions. They said that the computer can only re-ask a question man has taught to it."

Despite such wishful predictions, Fuller points out, the computer has now actually demonstrated its ability to ask an original question—one that it was not asked to give, and in fact, which was so unexpected that it astounded the programers themselves. The situation evolved in this manner. One of the computers that had been taught to play checkers was also taught to play backgammon, working on both games at the same time. Since backgammon is more complex in the matter of play and movement than checkers, the machine, playing concurrently, took slightly longer to reach decisions for moves in the former game than in the latter. For a while, everything proceeded smoothly, but eventually the unequal cycles developed so that at one precise instant the machine was called upon to make a backgammon move at the exact same time it was to work out a checker move.

No one had anticipated this conflict. It was like instructing a traffic policeman in moving vehicles across an intersection, but not telling him what to do if a police chief's car and a fire chief's car arrive from opposite directions at the same moment and want to cross. The computer, instead of being confounded and blowing out tubes or suddenly going dead, asked the classic original question, to determine which game in which to make a move and how to proceed—a question that man himself may never have asked:

"Which is more important, checkers or backgammon?"

No one has yet satisfactorily answered that question. Which *is* more important? From here it is only a step to that other currently unanswerable question: Which will be more important in our future socio-economic structure, man or the machine?

21

Beyond automation

"Our task today is wisely to use our technology, our knowledge of history and our compassion, to make the age of automation a golden Periclean age in which a society based on the work of the machine—not human chattel—rises to the full heights of which the human spirit is capable."

"AUTOMATION PERCEIVED," JOHN DIEBOLD, ADDRESS AT COLUMBIA UNIVERSITY, JUNE, 1963.

"BEYOND THE TECHNOLOGICAL and conceptual innovations of automation," says John Diebold, "lie problems and opportunities on a scale seldom encountered in human history. To meet these problems and to achieve the promise requires a perspective not often brought to bear on either public or private enterprise. . . . Social innovation is needed to match the technological innovations."

To focus for a moment, on pure technology, it is evident that better and better computers and other equipment of the automation age will be needed to keep pace with such pioneering efforts as space exploration. "Computers and experts to operate them are a vital part of teh U.S. space program," said a news release from the United States Information Service. "Without lightning-fast computers, satellites could not be built, orbited or tracked. Future space flights, such as those to Pluto, the most distant planet in the solar system, will require complex computers aboard large space ships."

In this context, the computer is to the navigation of the limitless new ocean of space what the magnetic compass was to the era of global exploration that opened some 450 years ago with the voyages of the Portuguese navigator Vasco de Gama.

Beyond the technology, however, lie the intangible moral, ideological and sociological implications that cannot be so precisely defined or charted. Dramatic examples can be seen in a study of military applications, both real and theoretical. One time, the late Dr. Norbert Wiener was asked, "Is it necessary today to use computers for military decisions?"

"Yes," he replied, "and they can be used very unwisely. How do soldiers learn their job? By war games. They have for centuries played games on the map. All right, if you have a certain formal criterion for what winning a war is, you can do this. But you'd better be sure that your criterion is what you really want. Otherwise, you can make a computer that will win the war technically and destroy everything . . . the programing of war games by artificial criteria of success is highly dangerous and likely to come out wrong."

In a *Fortune* article, "Security Is Too Important To Be Left to Computers," Colonel Francis X. Kane, U.S.A.F., made an interesting observation in regard to this war game concept. He pointed out that the Battle of Chancellorsville, during the Civil War, is "one of the best-known textbook examples of the value of initiative, skill and daring in military command." Had there been computers that May of 1863, however, things would have gone differently. General Lee would have been informed that the defense of Richmond was an impossibility for his Confederate forces.

Union General Hooker, along the same lines would have been given about a 100 per cent chance by the computer of annihilating the enemy and would have charged into battle with every confidence of overwhelming victory. "History tells us," wrote Kane, "that Lee, with forces less than half the size of Hooker's, seized the initiative, made a succession of decisions born of genius, capitalized on Hooker's mistakes in judgment, and inflicted a smashing defeat on the federal forces."

The human element simply cannot be overlooked. Significantly, too, man has to realize that the voids and vacuums in his knowledge—representing missing information that cannot be programed into any technological communications system—can trigger just as costly or tragic results as can the feed-in of false statistics. If military decision-making were left up to computers, it would be impossible to program into them individual acts of will that might change the entire course of events. It may be possible for a computer to indicate the best methods of air attack, under given circumstances, or naval defense, using specific air and sea craft. But how could a machine take into account individual acts of will that are unique and have occurred only once in history? Colonel Kane gives as examples the Japanese decision to attack Pearl Harbor, the U.S. decision to defend South Korea, and the Soviet decision to install missile bases in Communist Cuba.

Speaking of non-military uses of automation, Dr. Elmer W. Engstrom, president of Radio Corporation of America, said recently: ". . . It must be recognized that automation is not an isolated technical trend amounting simply to the design and installation of new kinds of machines. It is an evolution that fits within a larger context. As a means of increasing productivity, it can produce benefit only within a favorable economic climate determined by many factors. There would be little incentive to raise productivity if purchasing power should be diminished at the same time by other influences in the economy."

To see beyond automation, John Diebold suggests that we look back to the original Industrial Revolution, to understand how history is repeating itself. "Machines have always been important to us primarily in their role as *agents for social change*," he says. "We use the very term 'industrial revolution' not because of the revolutionary machines of James Watt and Richard Arkwright, but because they created a whole new environment for mankind—a whole new way of life. What they gave to history was much more than the steam engine and the cotton gin, the railway and the power loom. Their machines gave society a whole new tempo, a whole new outlook. . . . The very nature of today's technology, its effect on the building blocks of human society, will force us to reconsider our whole approach to work, to society and to life itself."

Looking ahead to the future, Diebold has made numerus predictions about things to come. By 1969, speech-recognition devices will be able to handle vocabularies of five thousand words in the varying accents of as many as twenty persons—thus making it possible to receive and store data without the use of paper or cards. By about the same time, fully automated newspaper publishing will be in general use; visual communication by picture phone will be commonplace; and there will be fairly broad geographic use of automatic language translation machines. By the early 1970's, automated weather equipment will be giving us regular, accurate predictions and computers will be almost as prevalent as doctors in the field of medical diagnosis.

The very structure of the machine will change, too. Today, we think of computers and other devices as being "electronic," using integrated circuits and transistors and the like. Already, however, a completely new concept is being researched and developed: *fluid control.*

In effect, this goes back to a kind of mechanical control, which is much lower in cost than the electronic type, and almost impervious to breakdown. It operates on these principles: A jet of gas or liquid flowing through a small hole is deflected from its path by another jet, thus changing the force or direction. Many such jets and holes in an integrated relationship can bring about a wide variety of actions. While much slower in action than electronics, fluid control will meet a wide need, will completely revise our thinking about machines and will bring about a revolution of its own.

Diebold and his associates have researched, developed and laid out charts for all the major fields in which automation is playing, and will play, a part. These have been grouped as an Information Technology Timetable, showing when automation will move, in each field, from "some, but not extensive, use" to "use on a broad geographic basis, but not extensive use," and finally into "general acceptance and use." The timetable serves, not as a technological guessing game, but as a necessary tool for anticipating and taking into account the sociological changes to come.

The fact that we will have picture phones in general use by 1969 is scientifically no more remarkable than is the fact that there are more radio and television sets in the United States than there are people. What is of consequence is the sociological impact that will come about through being able to see people you are talking to—to show snapshots, introduce the new baby, draw diagrams, sell products, hold business conferences, fight crime, render first aid and accomplish hundreds of other objectives not possible with verbal communication alone.

The big problem, as Diebold has seen it, is that technologically we are ready for the most astonishing advances, and scientists anticipate that almost nothing is impossible. But sociologically, we are not prepared, and we have a history of not being prepared. Man prefers to sit back and wait and see what will happen, and then suddenly, and awkwardly, try to make the adjustments he should have started anticipating a decade earlier.

Diebold describes, for example, two remarkable new developments: adaptive systems and pattern recognition: He emphasizes that it is in the way we use them to simulate, or more correctly, to perform, processes of human thought and behavior that their true significance lies.

"In one form of adaptive system," he says, "there is a computer which does not have to be programmed, in the usual sense of the word, to do a specific task. Rather, it goes through a learning period quite like that of a child. After the machine is taught the correct responses for certain sets of stimuli, it can give the correct responses when faced with these circumstances again." Among other things, the machine has been taught to distinguish between real echoes and false echoes when sonar is used to detect underwater targets, and it has been taught to evaluate data from electrocardiograms.

There are a variety of pattern recognition systems which have been programed to distinguish between symbols, letters of the alphabet, human faces, and other visible objects. They simulate the human eye mechanism in recognizing characteristics that distinguish one person from another, one object from another.

These developments are taking place within the mushrooming field known in the precise language of the scientist as "artificial intelligence." While they are technologically challenging, it is apparent that they imply some fascinating sociological challenges and rewards as well.

For example, an increasing number of medical doctors—physiologists, neurologists and others—are teaming with physical scientists and engineers in the development of systems displaying artificial intelligence. The result is not only better machines, but of greater significance, increased understanding of the fundamental nature of thought! The implications of this work are profound;

yet, as we have seen again and again, one of Diebold's greatest concerns is that society will not prepare itself adequately enough for the changes that will be brought about by the new technology. "People cannot look ahead," he says emphatically, shaking his head with a look almost of disbelief, running his hands through his blond hair, and letting his voice rise in excitement. "It is absolutely incredible that society cannot look ahead. You try to get people to think about what will happen twenty or thirty years from now, and they just cannot do it."

He likes to cite—as he did in his book *Automation*—a passage from Virginia Woolf's novel *Orlando*. Orlando, a woman who has lived for several hundred years, a personification of the spirit of England, boarded a train to travel from her country house to London, failing to comprehend that she was not going, as was customary to her, by horse-drawn carriage:

> Orlando had not yet realized the invention of the steam engine, but such was her absorption in the sufferings of the being, who, though not herself, was entirely dependent upon her, that she saw a railway train for the first time, took her seat in the railway carriage, and had the rug arranged about her knees without giving thought to "that stupendous invention, which had," the historians say, "completely changed the face of Europe in the past twenty years" (as, indeed, happens much more frequently than historians suppose).

"In historical retrospect," wrote Diebold, "what seems a world-shaking change is often accepted by the people of the day as something new that can be lived with, adjusted to, and perhaps even used with some benefit."

The person who looks ahead is more likely than not to seem out of place. "All my life," says Diebold, "people have said to me, 'You're a dreamer!'"

Sometimes the people making the comment are men who should be doing some advance dreaming themselves. Diebold tells about the head of an airline who, when the first jet aircraft were being designed, said to him bluntly, "No one will be committing themselves to these things." Less than a year later, however, he had found himself in a position where he was committing his own company to millions of dollars worth of jets. To emphasize the limited thinking of business leaders who fail to look ahead, Diebold likes to show a cartoon that effectively makes the point. It pictures a caterpillar just out of the cocoon, looking up at a moth flying overhead. The caption reads, "You'll never get me up in one of those things!"

Another problem faced by Diebold and other entrepreneurs in the field of automation is that they are hounded by critics who focus on short-range problems, which may be real enough, but which obscure the view of the long-range problems. "We address ourselves to the wrong issues," says Diebold. "We concern ourselves too much with the obvious problems. No matter whom you ask about the human consequences of the new technology—educators, government officials, businessmen—they immediately start talking about jobs. There is an obsessive concern about employment and unemployment.

"Yet there are so many other subject areas that are important—issues that are going to have to be faced in the future and should be faced right now. Think of the legal implications, for example, of one aspect of advancing technology. What happens when men are really able to control the weather? It will change man's entire concepts of property and values. The ownership concept will change. This will result in a tremendous social and economic upheaval.

"What about the field of genetics, and the changes that will come about as new discoveries are made?

"We have a lot of brilliant people who should be considering the long-range problems. But too many of them are thinking heavily about the short-range issues, such as jobs or building facilities."

John Diebold lacks no compassion for those whose employment is interrupted by automation or for those troubled by the changes in job skills. Indeed, a large part of his life is spent on precisely these problems. The federal manpower and retraining legislation grew from the advisory committee on which he served at the request of then Secretary of Labor, Arthur Goldberg, and he has testified before Congressional committees in behalf of extensions in the original legislation.

What bothers him—with his eye, typically, beyond automation is that even more severe human problems may arise from a failure to anticipate, today, the nature and extensive impact of future change. As important as are today's employment problems he feels that the truly significant human meaning of today's technological change is not yet being considered.

Diebold feels that there is too little concern, too limited an awareness at high political and governmental levels of these far-ranging problems and possibilities. "Thinking goes on in far more immediate terms than necessary. We need more agencies like the Rand Corporation to think things through, to study the socio-ethical problems and implications."

Speaking at Rollins College, when receiving his honorary Doctor of Laws degree, he further developed this earlier thinking by placing before the academic world a recommendation. "There could be created," he said, "an institute for the continual assessment of the human consequences of technological change." He saw such an institute as international—universal—in scope; one that was inclusive, not exclusive; that fostered as many attempts as possible to find answers, and did not discourage duplication of effort in the process; that was a center, not of authority, but of light; and that provided focus, but left no area of investigation dark.

"Above all, such an Institute should try to assess not only the immediate and obvious consequences of automation and related developments but the impact of accelerated change itself."

He did not at the time propose how the institute should be financed, who should staff it, or where it should be located. "It should, though," he advised, "be so structured and so financed that it can remain generally independent in its role and in its statements. This would dictate that it be at least quasi-public in nature—and I believe we should bear in mind that it is possible for an institution to be public without being an arm of the government."

The ultimate purpose of the institute, after its concepts and organization had been established through the efforts of learned men, "would be to serve man as one vehicle with which to reach Pierre Teilhard de Chardin's ideal of the 'Ultra-Human . . . by developing and embracing on earth, to the utmost extent, all the powers of common vision that are available. . . .'"

One factor that complicates the broad outlook, says Diebold, is not that man cannot find answers but that he keeps asking the same old questions, or ones that are equally unproductive. "We are not yet dealing with the right questions."

Diebold, in making a continuing study of organizations, both currently and from an historical viewpoint, feels that lessons can be learned from a knowledge of the complex formations and relations of some of the most influential organizations in history. These range, as has been mentioned, from the Roman Catholic Church to the ancient Mandarin system and even the growth and spread of underworld groups such as the Mafia. Although the structure of a centuries-old hierarchy in China may seem vastly remote from the subject of automation, it holds a sociological relationship that is pertinent. Diebold is constantly searching for patterns of relationship that will provide clues to the future. "My nature tends to see patterns in things very quickly," he says, pointing out that studying these patterns can provide an insight into immediate concerns, such as client problems, or into the future.

In an address before the International Chamber of Commerce in Paris, he explained how far automation had already gone beyond simply the programing of material to feed into machines. "Today," he said, "much work in seemingly unrelated fields is opening to us new knowledge about information systems.

"A new breed of technologists—perhaps we can call them organization scientists—have devoted themselves to the study of behavior patterns in large human organizations, such as businesses and governments. They are studying the methods managers use in making everyday decisions. They are studying business structures, situations, and behaviors in the firm conviction that the key to the very high levels of management decision-making is the understanding and ability to simulate the process of human thought itself." As he explains it, the study of human environment is directly important in evaluating the future—and even the study of "the problem-solving behavior of human beings and lower animals."

Diebold is concerned with what he considers to be a fundamental problem: He feels that "our technology is completely outracing our organizational theory. Worse yet, most of our present efforts at improving organization theory are completely 'sterile.' In universities, in business and industrial organizations, and wherever else management theory is taught, we have a tendency to look at only the 'last eyeblink of human history.' We need fresh insights, yet we continue to look at the narrowest spectrum of administrative experience."

In long-range concepts, automation is not the ultimate objective, but a step along the way in the organization and communication of mankind. The development process is not easy, yet perhaps in a unique way it will be aided by some of the instruments of automation. As Diebold points out with a touch of humor when asked about the "human elements" and the future, "Computers will be able to take care of the human element long before humans can take care of the computer element."

He constantly stresses the need for moving, working and achieving. "The process," he says, "is far more important than the achievement. This is the creative process, the striving that makes for spirit and advancement. Families, for example, need this constant striving and growth. The problems come when ease and comfort have been achieved and there is no further objective. A company should develop and look at its business completely anew every few years. Life is a continual seminar. Every businessman—every individual—needs constant honing of his mind to avoid intellectual flabbiness."

This constant striving and seeking is apparent in everything John Diebold does. It is appropriate to the field of his overall endeavor. If moments come when he sees any slackening of the pace, he is likely to look up in alarm, remind himself that he is racing against something far more all-consuming than the highest-speed computer in existence, and plunge into something beyond the confines of the possible.

"We're late in the day now," he says. *"We're late in the day."*

Summing it all up, a thoughtful observer of John Diebold—the man and the phenomenon—made a meaningful comment to him, "You had better be clear about just what it is you want out of life. You are going to get it."

The observation is a part of automation—and beyond.

Milestones in the development of automation
past . . . . . present . . . . . future

As with any major development of mankind, the roots of automation can be traced far into history. The windmills of sixteenth-century Holland contained feedback devices for keeping them always positioned into the wind. The Romans employed float control devices similar to those we use today in some of our process plants.

The tide of automation that is today moving with such enormous force has arisen in relatively recent years but it is in the highly condensed timetable of post-World-War II that we find the dates of greatest significance. A few of what are historically the most important dates are presented below as a general guide. The author appreciates all too well the limitations presented in any such compilation and is including the list in the belief that it is better to have a timetable that is clearly incomplete than to have none at all.

c. 200 B.C.	Automatic windlass—Archimedes
c. 250 A.D.	Coin-operated urn—Hero Xtebus
1680	Steam safety regulator—Denis Papin
1741	Mechanical loom—Jacques de Vaucanson
1760's	Spinning jenny—James Hargreaves
1784	Automatic flour mill—Oliver Evans
1788	Steam governor—James Watt
1801	Completely automatic loom—Joseph Marie Jacquard

1820	Difference engine—Charles Babbage
1821	First Commercial Calculator, The "Arithometer"—Thomas de Colmar
1870	Hydraulic servomechanisms—A. B. Brown
1893	Automatic elevator—E. G. Otis
1908	Electronic amplifying Tube—Lee DeForest
1915	First analog mechanical computer—Ford Instrument Company
1918	First automatic pilot—Elmer Sperry
1925	First analog computer—Vannevar Bush
1930's	Automated petroleum factory, extensively used in 1948
1935	Nylon—Dupont
1944	First digital computer (electromechanical)—Howard Aiken
1946	ENIAC-vacuum tube digital computer (all electronic)
1948	The transistor—John Bardeen, William Shockley, and Walter Brallain
1948	Definition of cybernetics—Norbert Wiener
1951	First commercial stored program computer—built for Sperry Rand
1950's	First transistorized computers
1950's	Cryogenic technology—Work sponsored by the Atomic Energy Commission
1952	*Automation: The Advent of the Automated Factory*—John Diebold
1954	Numerical control—Massachusetts Institute of Technology
1955	Bank of America, first bank to use magnetic ink character recognition for checks
1955	Optical character recognition
1955	Joint Economic Committee of the Congress Hearings on Automation
1958	U.S.S.R. Academy of Sciences—Established five institutes of cybernetics
1958	Laser—C. H. Townes and Arthur L. Shawlow (first working model 1960—T. H. Marmian)
1962	Micro-electronics—U. S. Government
1962	Telstar—Communications satellite designed by AT&T
1963	U. N. Conference on the Application of Science and Technology for the Less Developed Areas (UNCAST)

1965	COMSAT—first synchronous communications satellite
1966	Integrated communications switching under computer control
1966	Automated information services—A new form of publishing
1966	Integrated circuitry
1967	Automated weather prediction
1967	Data processing as a public utility service
1967	Automated legal research
1967	Huge low-cost file memories
1967	Information storage & retrieval—powerful indexing approaches
1968	Automated medical diagnosis
1968	Centralized medical records (large cities only)
1969	Automated computerized language translation
1969	Visual communication (picture phone)
1969	Enhanced productivity—More leisure time
1969	Automated newspaper publishing
1969	Important changes in organizational structure of business
1970	Widespread use in entrepreneurial decision-making and strategy development
1970	Automated patient monitoring in hospital beds
1972	Machine intelligence applied to system design (optimization) problems

APPENDIX 2

General books and articles on automation and related technology

The following works are listed, partly because they served as reliable reference sources in the preparation of this book, but also because they represent additional reading of significance for any one interested in pursuing the subject of automation:

1. Ackley, G. and Snyder, J. I., Jr., "Automation: Threat and Promise," *New York Times Magazine*, March 22, 1964, pp. 16ff.
2. Amber, George H. and Paul S., *Anatomy of Automation*, Englewood Cliffs, New Jersey, Prentice-Hall, 1962. (245 pp., $10.00)
3. Asbell, Bernard, *The New Improved American*, New York, Mc-Graw-Hill, 1965. ($4.95)
4. Bagrit, L., *The Age of Automation*, London, Weidenfeld Nicolson, Ltd., 1965.
5. Bell, David A., *Intelligent Machines*, New York, Blaisdell, 1962. (paperback, $1.45)
6. Berkeley, Edmund C., *The Computer Revolution*, New York, Doubleday, 1962. (249 pp., $4.50)
7. Bittel, Lester A., *Practical Automation*, New York, McGraw-Hill, 1957. ($4.95)
8. Bluemle, Andrew, *Automation*, Cleveland, The World Publishing Company, 1963. (143 pp., $3.95)
9. Buckingham, Walter S., *Automation*, New York, New American Library. (paperback, $ .60)

10. Burck, Gilbert and the Editors of *Fortune, The Computer Age,* New York, Harper & Row, 1963. (148 pp., $3.95)

11. Cubbedge, Robert E., *Who Needs People?,* Washington, D.C., Robert B. Luce, Inc., 1963. (114 pp., $3.75)

12. Dreher, Carl, *Automation: What It Is. How It Works. Who Can Use It,* New York, Norton, 1957. (128 pp., $2.95)

13. Fahnestock, James D., *Computers and How They Work,* Ziff-Davis. ($4.95)

14. *Glossary of Data Processing and Communications Terms,* published by Honeywell Electronic Data Processing, Information Services, 60 Walnut Street, Wellesley Hills, Massachusetts. ($1.00)

15. Goodman Leonard L., *Man and Automation,* London, Penguin Books, 1957.

16. Hirsch, S. Carl, *This Is Automation,* New York, Viking, 1964. ($3.75)

17. Hugh-Jones, E. M., *The Push-Button World,* Norton, Oklahoma, University of Oklahoma Press, 1956. (158 pp., $3.75)

18. Laird, Donald A. and Eleanor C., *How to Get Along With Automation,* New York, McGraw-Hill, 1964. ($6.95)

19. Lewis A., *The New World of Computers,* New York, Dodd, Mead & Company, 1965. (Juvenile)

20. Macmillan, R. H., *Automation: Friend or Foe?,* Cambridge University Press, 1956. (100 pp., $1.95)

21. Charles Markham, Editor, *Jobs, Men & Machines: Problems of Automation,* New York, Praeger, 1964. (166 pp., $4.95)

22. Silberman, C. E., "Real News About Automation," *Fortune,* January, 1965, pp. 124-6.

23. Taube, Mortimer, *Computers and Common Sense,* New York, Columbia University Press, 1961. ($3.75)

24. Thomas, Shirley, *Computers: Their History, Present Applications & Future.* New York: Holt, Rinehart & Winston, 1965. ($2.50)

25. Velie, Lester, "Automaion: Friend or Foe?" *The Reader's Digest,* October, 1962, pp. 101-106.

26. Weeks, Robert, *Machines and Man,* New York, Appleton-Century-Crofts, 1961. ($2.50)

27. White, Pauline and Percival, *Automation Age,* New York, Holiday House, 1963. ($4.50)

28. Wiener, Norbert, *The Human Use of Human Beings: Cybernetics and Society,* Boston, Houghton Mifflin, 1950.

29. Woodbury, David, *Let Erma Do It,* New York, Harcourt, 1956. ($5.75)

30. Yaukey, G. S., *Keeping Ahead of Machines.* New York, John Day & Company, 1965.

APPENDIX 3

Bibliography

Selected Writings of John Diebold

During a period of less than fourteen years, from the time of publication of his first book, John Diebold has contributed extensively to the literature on automation and information technology in general through more than 200 books, monographs, articles and speeches which have been published under his name.

A small but representative list of his writings follows, carefully selected and described by Mary Stephens-Caldwell Henderson from the collection of 201 which she included in her master's thesis on John Diebold:

1) *Automation: The Advent of the Automatic Factory.* Princeton, N. J., D. Van Nostrand Company, Inc. 1952. 181 pp.

This book is known as the definitive work on automation. Written in non-technical terms, it explains the basic concepts of automation, especially the concept of product and process redesign, or "rethinking." After explaining the impact of the new technology on the factory and office, it delves into the probable effects on employment, leisure, the Cold War, and the developing countries.

2) *Beyond Automation.* New York, McGraw-Hill Book Company, 1964. 200 pp.

This volume presents a unified statement of Diebold's views derived from addresses before various national and international gatherings and papers prepared for legislative bodies. Included in the book are discussions of the new technology on the economy in general and on management in particular. It concludes with a discussion of the public issues associated with automation both on the state and national level.

3) *Automation.* Digested by Herbert F. Klingman, New York, Controllership Foundation, Inc. Planning Pamphlet No. 106, 1954. 18 pp.

This is a helpful condensation of John Diebold's first book, Automation.

4) *Automation: Its Impact on Business and Labor.* Washington, D.C., National Planning Association, 1959. 64 pp.

This monograph points to the need for an extensive study of automation for the dual purpose of providing facts needed for intelligent national planning and to allay many of the irrational fears surrounding automation. It also includes a presentation of the currently prevalent arguments on the economic and social consequences of automation, and concludes by discussing some of the aspects of automation which he feels have been undeserving of neglect.

5) "Congressional Testimony" (reprinted from Testimony Submitted to the Sub-Committee on Automation and Energy Resources, 86th Congress, Second Session). In Morris Philipson (Ed.), *Automation. Implications for the future.* New York, Random House, Inc., Vintage Books (paper), 1962, pp. 12-76.

6) "What is Automation." *1963 Encyclopedia Yearbook,* Grolier Society, 1963, pp. 148-150.

7) "Automation." *World Book Encyclopedia,* 1965 (and previous editions), pp. 917-919.

8) "Factories Without Men: New Industrial Revolution." *The Nation,* Vol. CLXXVII, No. 12, (September 19, 1953), pp. 227-228.

Social implications and scientific principles of the new industrial revolution.

9) "Atom and Automation: Retooling for the New Era." *The Nation,* Vol. CLXXVII, No. 13, (September 26, 1953), pp. 250-252.

Technical and non-technical problems which must be solved for effective industrial use of the technology of automation.

10) "Automation and Jobs: The Effect on the Worker." *The Nation,* Vol. CLXXVII, No. 14, (October 3, 1953), pp. 271-272.

The human and social aspects of automation are discussed.

11) "Automation—Will it Steal Your Job?" *This Week,* (June 26, 1955), pp. 7-27.

An explanation of the employment implications of the new technology.

12) "What *Is* Automation?" *Collier's,* Vol. CXXXVII, (March 16, 1956), pp. 38-44.

The real questions raised by automation are concerned not with averting change, nor even with adjusting to change, so much as they are with orderly planning for that change.

13) "Automation as a Challenge to Management." *International Social Science Bulletin,* (June 1957), pp. 37-43.

Management has been misled by four stereotypes: 1) that automation is limited to companies with large dollar resources and exceptionally long production runs; 2) that the ultimate in automation is symbolized by an oil refinery or other complex instruments-controlled processing plant; 3) that automation is primarily useful as a labor-saving device; 4) that because automation is highly technical it must be left to the technician. The article points out the fallacies in each of these stereotypes.

14) "Automation, 1958: Industry at the Crossroads." *Dun's Review and Modern Industry,* (August 1958), pp. 36-96.

This article states that the profit squeeze caused by the 1958 recession resulted in a mood of pessimism in sharp contrast to the glowing expectations with which most automation programs were undertaken only a few years previously. Management has repeatedly failed to realize that automation involves basic changes in the way business is organized and staffed, and that success requires the detailed preparation that accompanies any major change.

15) "Automation needs a Human Policy." *Challenge,* May 1959.

Labor and management, working together, must show foresight, forebearance, common sense and some degree of mutual trust so that all of society can gain from the new abundance.

16) "What is Really Promised by Automation." *Chicago Sun-Times,* (June 22, 1959), p. 49.

17) "Automation—The Answer to Russia's Challenge?" *Chicago Sunday Sun-Times,* (September 6, 1959), pp. 21-22.

An explanation of the implications of automation in the productivity race between the United States and the Soviet Union.

18) "A Comparison of the Approach to Computers in Europe and America." Paper presented at the Sixth Annual International Meeting of The Institute of Management Science, Paris, France, September 7-10, 1959. (Typescript.)

Europeans stand to benefit by avoiding the mistakes made by Americans when they first began converting to automatic data processing installations. More thorough planning, clearer statement of objectives, and more concentration of data processing responsibilities could save European companies some very real and expensive pitfalls.

19) "The Challenge of Automation." Interview with John Diebold on Channel 13, New York, New York, September 25, 1960. *The Lithographers' Journal,* Vol. XLIII, No. 8, (October 1960), pp. 11-14.

20) "Life Under Automation." Interview with John Diebold. *Challenge.* (December 1960), pp. 20-25.

A series of questions and answers on automation and its effects on social change, productivity, the role of scientists in society, education, resource allocation, and leisure.

21) "Technology's Challenge to Management." Address given before the Plenary Session European Community Conference of The High Authority of the European Coal and Steel Community, The Commission of the European Economic Community, and The Commission of the European Atomic Energy Community, Brussels, Belgium, December 6, 1960. Published by John Diebold and Associates, Inc. 14 pp.

One of his best statements on the significance to management of the rate of change. Predicts its impact on the planning process, personnel management, and the process of management itself.

22) "Automation as an Historical Development." Address given before the annual meeting of the Society for the History of Technology held in conjunction with the annual meeting of the American Association for the Advancement of Science, New York, New York, December 29, 1960. (Typescript.)

An historical perspective on technological change. Examines technology as an agent for social change and predicts some of the changes in society which will be brought about by automation.

23) "Urgent Need: All-Out Automation." *Nation's Business,* (July 1961), pp. 179-132.

Reasons why America must achieve faster technological progress.

24) "Four Problems You Cannot Shirk." *Administrative Management,* (July 1963), pp. 24-69.

Management must face the problems of: a) the need for an organized discipline in the area of information systems, b) the need for educating and developing men within that discipline, c) the problem of organizing to use the technology and the problem of the organizational consequences of using it, and d) the problem of how business management reacts to the social consequences of the technology.

25) "Facing Up to Automation." *The Saturday Evening Post,* September 22, 1962.

Government, management, and labor must stop "mopping up after the damage has been done" and instead plan ahead for the tremendous upheavals being caused by the new technology.

26) "The Editor and Automation." Address given before the American Society of Newspaper Editors, Washington, D.C., April 19, 1963. Printed in the Diebold Group Professional Paper Series, New York: The Diebold Group, Inc. 12 pp.

After stating that there are few industries where the economics of automation are so starkly etched yet so long overdue, he predicts some future effects of the new technology on newspapers.

27) "When Will Your Husband Be Obsolete?" *McCall's,* (July, 1963), pp. 64-119.

This article consists primarily of a large table showing categories of jobs which are declining as employment opportunities, those which are remaining static, and those in which employment opportunities are increasing. This was based on a series of labor studies that The Diebold Group, Inc., did for the Labor Department, Office of Automation, Manpower and Training.

28) "Changing Careers in a Changing World." *Senior Scholastic,* (November 8, 1963), pp. 8-11.

29) "John Diebold's Vista of Automation." *Business,* Vol. XCIII, No. 12, (December 1963), pp. 51-81.

A summary of the progress of information technology during the preceding decade, followed by a prediction of important new developments. Among the developments which he believes will be important are advances in information search and retrieval, numerical control systems, and process communications systems. A new discipline of systems analysis is needed to utilize fully the new technology.

30) "A Short Fast Step to Tomorrow." *Printer's Ink,* Vol. CCLXXXII, No. 9, 41,408, (May 29, 1964), pp. 283-287.

In this article he amplifies his view that management must look to social change as an active element in business planning. He says that current in-

terest in new-products programs is all too often a symptom of a lack of mission or a genuine definition of direction. Such programs must instead evolve from a business plan that displays true insight into the nature of the enterprise and its environment.

31) "Automation: How Will It Change Your World?" *Glamour,* Vol. L, No. 4, (1,194,749) (June 1964) pp. 84-149. (Interview.)

32) "ADP—The Still-Sleeping Giant." *Harvard Business Review* 42(5): Vol. XLII, No. 5, (76,736) (September-October 1964), pp. 60-65.

Acknowledgments

It would have required the services of a computer to have kept track of all the people to whom the author, researchers, editor and publisher are indebted for information used in this book, and for the vast compilation of material not used, but necessary to the understanding and communicating of the subject. Therefore, this brief acknowledgment section can serve only as a means of using a few to impart to the many that we are grateful for such widespread interest and assistance.

We first acknowledge thanks to John Diebold himself, who patiently bore with us during long months of following, interrupting and interrogating while he himself was actively engaged in meeting urgent business commitments and responsibilities. Among others who were extremely helpful in the Diebold Group were Liesa Bing, Herbert Blitz and Ralph Weindling, who went out of their way many times to explain the Group's work, as well as to provide information on countless aspects of automation in general. Others closely associated now or in the past with John Diebold who provided invaluable assistance were his brother, William Diebold; his advisor at Harvard, General Georges Doriot; two outside counsels of the firm, Walter Taradash and David Mitchell; Conrad Wienk and Charles Bloom; and members of his family, including Marietta Schweitzer, a distant relative who had been close to him since childhood.

A great deal of valuable material from a source completely apart from the subject himself came from Mary Stephens-Caldwell

Henderson, who wrote a thoroughly documented and scholarly master's thesis on him and who generously permitted us to use her extensive notes and research.

Working closely with the author, as independent reporters, researchers and interviewers were Catherine Reinis, Ted Rakstis, Keith Engh, John Hinshaw, James Eysler, James A. Maxtone Graham and Joan Hansen. These people, along with correspondents in Washington, Chicago, San Francisco, St. Louis, London, Paris, Rome, Tokyo, Bonn, Belgrade, Sydney, Stockholm, Montreal, and other cities near and far, accumulated and processed what eventually amounted to some 130 pounds of papers, documents, clippings and other material—not counting bound books. To Magda Vasillov goes our appreciation for some outstanding photographs.

We are indebted to a great number of authorities in the field of automation, who gave us of their time for interview and discussion, including Dr. Martin Greensberger, consultant and associate professor of industrial management at M.I.T.; Richard E. Sprague, director of advanced business systems for Touche, Ross, Bailey and Smart; Mr. J. Carterton, of Paris, director general of S.A.C.A.; Dr. Ambros A. P. Speiser, of Zürich's Swiss Foundation for Automatic Control; Professor Fritz L. Bauer, of the Munich, Germany, Institute of Technology; Professor Borke Langefors, of the University of Stockholm; C. J. C. McOustra, of International Computers and Tabulators, London; Dr. Sergio F. Beltran, director, Electronics Computing Center, National University of Mexico; Dr. Leon Lukaszewicz, of the Instytut Maszyn Matematycznch of Poland; Dr. Sally Sedelow, of St. Louis University; George G. Heller, national education chairman of the Association for Computing Machinery; and John MacKarness, of the British Computer Society.

We greatly appreciated the time given to one of our writers by Isaac L. Auerbach, president of the International Federation for Information Processing; and to the IFIP itself for giving us full access to all seminars, discussions and exhibits during the 1965 Congress of the Federation, attended by some 5,000 delegates from all over the world and some 20,000 other outside visitors.

We cannot list all of the individual companies that furnished us information, but we would particularly like to thank representatives of the following corporations for their help—all the way from providing tear sheets, brochures and packets of information to sitting down and patiently commenting on John Diebold, on automation, or on other related subjects: American Telephone & Telegraph Company; Ametek, Inc.; Bell Telephone Laboratories, Inc.; The Bunker-Ramo Corporation; Burroughs Corporation; Computer Control Corporation; Computer Sciences, Inc.; Cutler-Hammer, Inc.; Digitronics Corporation; E. I. duPont de Nemours & Company, Inc.; Friden, Inc.; General Electric Company; General Precision Equipment Corporation; Hitachi, Ltd., of Japan; Honeywell, Inc.; International Business Machines Corporation, International Computers & Tabulators, Ltd.; International Telephone & Telegraph Corporation; Lockheed Aircraft Corporation, Olivetti Underwood Corporation; Philco Corporation; The Radio Corporation of America; Raytheon Company; Royal-McBee Corporation; Scientific Data Systems, Inc.; SCM Corporation; Standard Instruments Corporation; Sylvania Electric Products, Inc.; Thompson Ramo Woolridge, Inc.; Univac Division, Sperry Rand Corporation; Western Electric Company, Inc.; and Westinghouse Electric Corporation.

Four technical publications were particularly helpful in our coverage of the technological side of automation: *Data Processing Magazine; Datamation; Electronic News* and *Information Processing Journal.*

And, finally, we acknowledge the help of dozens of computers all over the world which unknowingly furnished us with stories, anecdotes and case histories, some deadly serious, some highly amusing. Beyond that, we cannot go.

Index

295

Reber, Hugh J., 50
Reinhold Publishing Company, 58, 59
Reisman, David, 117
"Remote position control" (RPC), 41
Reprint Series, 88
Research Center for Mental Health, 103
"Rethinking," 65
Reuther, Walter, 105
Reynolds, Joshua, 167
Rice, Ladislas, 49
Risch, Ralph, 14
Rise and Splendor of the Chinese Empire, The, 92
Robinson Crusoe, 17
Robinson, James G., 50
Rockefeller, David, 184
Rockefeller Institute, 16
Roger et Gallet, 89
van der Rohe, Mies, 146
Rollins College, 8, 49, 276
Roman Catholic Church, 277
Roosevelt Grammar School, *see* Theodore Roosevelt Grammar School
Rosenblith, Prof. Walter, 130
Rothschild, Baron, 170
Rous, Peyton, 16
Rowse, A. L., 168
Rusk, Sec. of State Dean, 3, 155

Saarinen, Eero, 145
"Sabre," 230-231
Sadler, Marion, 230
St. Gobain, 90
St. Louis University, 243
Sampson, Anthony, 92
Samuel, Arthur, 106, 256
San Francisco *Chronicle*, 167
Sara Lee, 215
Sarafian, John, 17
Sargrove, John A., 43
Sarnoff, David, 130, 240, 241
Saslow, Melvin A., 31
Saturday Review, 120
Savannah, 228
Sayre, Very Rev. Francis B., 7
Schriever, Gen. Bernard A., 263
Schwartz, Harry, 59
Schwarz, Dr. Gerars S., 128
Schweizer, Marietta, 16
Scialoja, Toti, 147
Science Magazine, 107
Scientific American, 58
Seaboard Air Line Railroad, 225
"Second Industrial Revolution," 74, 100
"Security Is Too Important To Be Left to Computers," 270
Sedelow, Dr. Sally, 243
Seibu department store, 249
Servomechanism (closed-loop systems), 41-42
Seton, Ernest Thompson, 17
Seymour, F. W., 42
Shakespeare, William, 115, 243, 244
Shangri-La, 55, 56

Shapley, Harlow, 92
Sharon Steel Company, 31
Shell, 90
Shelley, Percy, 243, 244
Sherman, Milton, 92
Shooting Star, 22
"Shrinking Computer, The," 47
Siemens & Halske, 90
Sievert, Charles, 99
"Significance of Productivity Data, The," 29, 64
Silicon-controlled rectifier (SCR), 45
Simon, Prof. Herbert, 106, 252
Simulation, 84, 254
"Simulators," 183-184
Siropolis, Nicholas C., 31
Skidmore Owings and Merrill, 146
Skill: changing definitions of, 77
Smiddy, Harold, 53
Smith, Paul, 59, 167
"Social Impact of Computers, The," 240
Society for Educational and Training Technology, 176
Society for the History of Technology, 155
Sorenson, Theodore C., 92, 146
Space Age, 110
Spanish Armada, 168
Spencer, Dr. William A., 130
Sperry inertial navigation, 233
Sperry-Rand, 86
Steadman, Admiral, 142
Stein, Gertrude, 265
Steinberg, Eliot, 126
Stevenson, Adlai E., 81, 82
"Story of My Heart, The," 114
Strid, Birger, 56
Stromberg-Carlson, 59
Stuart, Gilbert, 167
Sun Shipbuilding and Dry Dock Company, 228-229
Sutherland, Ivan, 259
Swadow, Harvey, 120
Swarthmore, 11, 21, 25, 26, 27, 28, 49: *Halcyon 1949*, 26
Swarthmore-Colby Language School, 26
Swiss Bank Corporation, 89

Taradash, Walter, 169
Tarr, Dr. Curtis, 30
Taylor, Frederick, 30
Teager, Herbert, 258
Technology: philosophy of, 43; effects of, 68-69; acceptance of, 72-77; technological revolution, 262
"Technology's Challenge to Advancement," 175
Television: automation, 213-214
Telstar, 242
Tennessee, University of, Medical Center, 124
Tennis court method, 259
Texas Institute for Research and Rehabilitation, 130

This book was designed by Laurence Lustig, and set in Caledonia type.

It was printed by letterpress on Old Forge paper, and bound at H. Wolff Book Manufacturing Co., New York, New York.